Ed Nic

TMN

OTHER McGRAW-HILL TELECOMMUNICATION BOOKS OF INTEREST

Ali   *Digital Switching Systems*
Ash   *Dynamic Routing in Telecommunications Networks*
Benner   *Fibre Channel*
Best   *Phase-Locked Loops, Third Edition*
Clayton   *McGraw-Hill Illustrated Telecom Dictionary*
Faynberg   *Intelligent Network Standards*
Feit   *TCP/IP, Second Edition*
Gallagher   *Mobile Telecommunications Networking with IS-41*
Goralski   *Introduction to ATM Networking*
Harte   *Cellular and PCS: The Big Picture*
Harte   *GSM Superphones*
Heldman   *Information Telecommunications*
Heldman   *Competitive Telecommunications*
Kessler   *ISDN, Third Edition*
Kuruppilai   *Wireless PCS*
Lachs   *Fiber Optic Communications*
Lee   *Mobile Cellular Telecommunications, Second Edition*
Lee   *Mobile Communications Engineering, Second Edition*
Logson   *Mobile Communication Satellites*
Macario   *Cellular Radio, Second Edition*
Muller   *Desktop Encyclopedia of Telecommunications*
Muller   *Mobile Telecommunications Factbook*
Pecar   *Telecommunications Factbook*
Richharia   *Satellite Communications Systems, Second Edition*
Roddy   *Satellite Communications, Second Edition*
Rohde et al.   *Communications Receivers, Second Edition*
Russell   *Signaling System #7, Second Edition*
Russell   *Telecommunications Protocols*
Simon et al.   *Spread Spectrum Communications Handbook*
Smith   *Cellular Design and Optimization*
Smith   *Practical Cellular and PCS Design*
Tsakalakis   *PCS Network Deployment*
Turin   *Digital Transmission Systems*
Winch   *Telecommunication Transmission Systems, Second Edition*

TMN

Telecommunications
Management Network

Divakara K. Udupa

McGraw-Hill
New York • San Francisco • Washington, D.C. • Auckland • Bogotá
Caracas • Lisbon • London • Madrid • Mexico City • Milan
Montreal • New Delhi • San Juan • Singapore
Sydney • Tokyo • Toronto

McGraw-Hill

A Division of The McGraw·Hill Companies

1 2 3 4 5 6 7 8 9 0   DOC/DOC   9 0 3 2 1 0 9 8

ISBN 0-07-065815-3

The sponsoring editor for this book was Steve Chapman and the production supervisor was Pamela Pelton. It was set in Vendome by North Market Street Graphics.

Printed and bound by R. R. Donnelley & Sons Company.

McGraw-Hill books are available at special quantity discounts to use as premiums and sales promotions, or for use in corporate training programs. For more information, please write to Director of Special Sales, McGraw-Hill, 11 West 19th Street, New York, NY 10011. Or contact your local bookstore.

Product or brand names used in this book may be trade names or trademarks. Where we believe that there may be proprietary claims to such trade names or trademarks, the name has been used with an initial capital or it has been capitalized in the style used by the name claimant. Regardless of the capitalization used, all such names have been used in an editorial manner without any intent to convey endorsement of or other affiliation with the name claimant. Neither the author nor the publisher intends to express any judgment as to the validity or legal status of any such proprietary claims.

 This book is printed on recycled, acid-free paper containing a minimum of 50% recycled, de-inked fiber.

DEDICATION

To Father, Ramakrishna
   Mother, Varija
   Wife, Rajalakshmi
   Brother, Dr. Sudhakara

CONTENTS

Preface   xvii

Acknowledgments   xxiii

Part 1   TMN CONCEPTS   1

Chapter 1   TMN Overview   3

1.1 Introduction   4
1.2 Evolution of TMN   4
1.3 What Is TMN?   6
1.4 TMN Standards Bodies   7
1.5 Network Management, Systems Management, and TMN   11
1.6 Systems Management Functional Areas   11
1.7 Managed Object, Managed Object Class, and
      Management Information Model   12
   1.7.1 Managed Object   13
   1.7.2 Managed Object Class   14
   1.7.3 Information Model   15
1.8 Manager, Agent, and Management Information   15
1.9 TMN Management Layers   19
1.10 Conventions Used in This Book   21
1.11 Summary   22
1.12 References   22

Chapter 2   TMN Architecture, Interfaces, OAM&P, and CNM   23

2.1 Introduction   24
2.2 TMN and Telecommunications Networks   24
2.3 TMN Architecture   25
   2.3.1 Functional Architecture   26
   2.3.2 Physical Architecture   31
   2.3.3 Interfaces   33
   2.3.4 Information Architecture   35
2.4 OAM&P   37

2.5 CNM	38
2.5.1 CNM Functional Architecture	39
2.5.2 CNM Physical Architecture and Interfaces	40
2.5.3 CNM Management Services	41
2.5.4 ANSI-based CNM	42
2.6 Conformance	44
2.7 Summary	45
2.8 References	45

Chapter 3   TMN Management Services and TMN Functions   47

3.1 Introduction	48
3.2 TMN Management Services	48
3.2.1 Mapping of SMFAs and TMN Management Function Set Groups	53
3.3 TMN Management Function Sets and Management Functions	54
3.4 Performance Management	54
3.4.1 Performance Quality Assurance	55
3.4.2 Performance Monitoring	55
3.4.3 Performance Management Control	56
3.4.4 Performance Analysis	56
3.5 Fault Management	57
3.5.1 RAS Quality Assurance	57
3.5.2 Alarm Surveillance	57
3.5.3 Fault Localization	58
3.5.4 Fault Correction	59
3.5.5 Testing	59
3.5.6 Trouble Administration	60
3.6 Configuration Management	60
3.6.1 Network Planning and Engineering	60
3.6.2 Installation	61
3.6.3 Service Planning and Negotiation	62
3.6.4 Provisioning	62
3.6.5 Status and Control	63
3.7 Accounting Management	64
3.7.1 Usage Measurement	64
3.7.2 Tariffing/Pricing	64
3.7.3 Collections and Finance	65
3.7.4 Enterprise Control	66
3.8 Security Management	66

3.8.1 Prevention   67
3.8.2 Detection   67
3.8.3 Containment and Recovery   67
3.8.4 Security Administration   68
3.9 Implementation Notes   69
3.10 Summary   75
3.11 References   75

Part 2   TMN INFORMATION MODEL AND PROTOCOLS   77

Chapter 4   TMN Terms and Concepts   79

4.1 Introduction   80
4.2 Service Access Point   81
4.3 Service Provider and Service User   81
4.4 Service Definition and Protocol Specification   82
4.5 Connection and Connectionless Modes   83
4.6 Service Primitives   84
4.7 Communication Between Managed Objects and Agents   85
4.8 Management Domain   86
4.9 Management Information Hierarchies   89
4.9.1 Registration Hierarchy   90
4.9.2 Inheritance Hierarchy   91
4.9.3 Containment Hierarchy   92
4.10 Object Naming   92
4.11 Scoping   94
4.12 Filtering   95
4.13 Synchronization   97
4.14 Polymorphism   98
4.15 Allomorphism   99
4.16 Management State   99
4.16.1 Generic State Attributes   100
4.16.2 Status Attributes   101
4.17 Attributes for Relationships   103
4.18 General Relationship Model   104
4.19 Management Information Tree (MIT)   105
4.20 Intelligent Agents   105
4.21 Summary   107
4.22 References   107
4.23 Further Reading   108

Chapter 5   Abstract Syntax and Transfer Syntax   109

          5.1 Introduction   110
          5.2 Abstract Syntax Notation One (ASN.1)   110
                5.2.1 Simple Types   112
                5.2.2 Structured Types   115
                5.2.3 Tagged Types   117
                5.2.4 Module Definitions   122
                5.2.5 Subtypes   123
          5.3 X.680   125
                5.3.1 X.208 Versus X.680   125
          5.4 Basic Encoding Rules (BER)   132
                5.4.1 Identifier Field   133
                5.4.2 Length Field   135
                5.4.3 Data Contents Field   136
          5.5 Notes on the Use of ASN.1 and BER   142
          5.6 Summary   143
          5.7 References   143
          5.8 Further Reading   144

Chapter 6   Structure of Management Information and
          TMN Information Model   145

          6.1 Introduction   146
          6.2 Overview of the Structure of Management Information
                (SMI) Documents   146
          6.3 Managed Object Class   147
          6.4 Guidelines for the Definition of Managed Objects
                (GDMO) Templates   148
                6.4.1 Attribute   150
                6.4.2 Attribute Template and Definition   151
                6.4.3 Attribute Group   153
                6.4.4 Action Template   154
                6.4.5 Behavior Template   155
                6.4.6 Notification Template   155
                6.4.7 Parameter Template   156
                6.4.8 Package Template   157
                6.4.9 Name Binding Template   158
                6.4.10 Managed Object Class Template   159
          6.5 Notes on the ITU-T SMI Documents   161
          6.6 TMN Information Model   164
          6.7 Example of GDMO and ASN.1 Definitions   168

Contents

6.7.1 GDMO Definitions 169

6.7.2 ASN.1 Definitions 170

6.8 Summary 171

6.9 References 172

Chapter 7   ACSE, ROSE, CMISE, and CMIP 175

7.1 Introduction 176

7.2 Application Layer Component Concepts 176

7.3 Systems Management Service Elements 178

7.4 ACSE Services 180

7.4.1 ACSE Application Protocol Data Units (APDUs) 182

7.4.2 A-ASSOCIATE 182

7.4.3 A-RELEASE 186

7.4.4 A-ABORT 187

7.4.5 A-P-ABORT 188

7.4.6 Connectionless ACSE 188

7.5 Remote Operations Service Element (ROSE) 189

7.5.1 RO-INVOKE 191

7.5.2 RO-RESULT 192

7.5.3 RO-ERROR 192

7.5.4 RO-REJECT 192

7.6 Common Management Information Service Element
(CMISE) 193

7.6.1 M-EVENT-REPORT 196

7.6.2 M-GET 196

7.6.3 M-CANCEL-GET 198

7.6.4 M-SET 199

7.6.5 M-ACTION 199

7.6.6 M-CREATE 199

7.6.7 M-DELETE 200

7.7 Functional Units 200

7.7.1 Kernel Functional Unit 200

7.7.2 Multiple Object Selection Functional Unit 200

7.7.3 Multiple Reply Functional Unit 201

7.7.4 Filter Functional Unit 201

7.7.5 Extended Service Functional Unit 201

7.7.6 Cancel GET Functional Unit 201

7.8 Common Management Information Protocol (CMIP) 202

7.9 Systems Management Operations on Objects and
Attributes 203

7.10 Pass-through Services   204
7.11 Summary   206
7.12 References   206
7.13 Further Reading   207

Chapter 8   Internet Network Management: SNMPv1, SNMPv2,
                 and SNMPv3   209

8.1 Introduction   210
8.2 Internet Network Management Framework (SNMPv1)   213
8.3 Internet Objects   215
8.4 Management Information Base (MIB-II)   218
      8.4.1 Internet Registration Hierarchy   219
      8.4.2 Object Instance Identification   220
      8.4.3 Table Manipulation   222
      8.4.4 MIB-II Details (RFC1213)   223
8.5 SNMPv1 Protocol and Protocol Details   223
      8.5.1 Functioning of SNMPv1 PDUs   225
8.6 Proxy   229
8.7 SNMP over Different Protocols   230
8.8 SNMPv2   231
      8.8.1 SNMPv2 Structure of Management Information (SMI)   232
      8.8.2 SNMPv2 Textual Convention   236
      8.8.3 SNMPv2 Protocol Messages   237
      8.8.4 Transport Mapping for SNMPv2   239
      8.8.5 SNMPv2 MIB   240
      8.8.6 Coexistence Between SNMPv1 and SNMPv2   242
      8.8.7 Device-Dependent Objects   243
8.9 SNMPv3   243
      8.9.1 SNMPv3 Architecture   244
      8.9.2 SNMP Engine   246
      8.9.3 SNMPv3 Applications   249
      8.9.4 Abstract Service Interfaces and Primitives   250
      8.9.5 SNMPv3 Textual Conventions   252
      8.9.6 User-Based Security Model   254
      8.9.7 View-based Access Control Model   255
      8.9.8 SNMPv3 MIB Modules   255
8.10 Advantages of SNMP   260
8.11 Notes on SNMP   260
8.12 Coexistence Between SNMP and CMIP   263
8.13 Interoperability with ITU-T/OSI   263

Contents

8.14 Implementation Notes   264
8.15 Internet Standardization Process   265
8.16 Summary   265
8.17 References   266
8.18 Further Reading   267

Part 3 TMN APPLICATIONS   269

Chapter 9   Network Management for Mobile Communications 271

9.1 Introduction   272
9.2 Overview of Network Management for Mobile
    Communications   273
9.3 ANSI Network Management for PCS   274
9.4 ETSI Network Management for DCS   276
    9.4.1 GSM Architecture   276
    9.4.2 Overview of Network Management of PLMN   278
    9.4.3 Operation, Administration, and Maintenance (OAM)   279
    9.4.4 PLMN Information Model   280
    9.4.5 Common Management Functions   282
    9.4.6 Different Protocol Layers and Standards   283
9.5 Summary   286
9.6 References   286
9.7 Further Reading   287

Chapter 10   Broadband Network Management   289

10.1 Introduction   290
10.2 B-ISDN Protocol Reference Model   290
10.3 SDH Network Management   292
    10.3.1 Fault Management   295
    10.3.2 Performance Management   296
    10.3.3 SDH Managed Object Classes   297
    10.3.4 SDH Management Protocol Stack   298
10.4 SONET Network Management   298
    10.4.1 Overview of SONET Architecture   298
10.5 Operation and Maintenance (OAM)   303
10.6 ATM Network Management   306
    10.6.1 ATM Forum Network Management   307
10.7 Important Issues in Broadband Network Management   319

10.8 Summary 319
10.9 References 320

Chapter 11   Recent Trends: Distributed Network Management,
CORBA, Java, Web, and TMN 323

11.1 Introduction 324
11.2 Distributed Processing 324
11.3 Open Distributed Processing 325
11.4 Distributed Network Management 328
11.5 Open Distributed Management Architecture (ODMA) 329
11.6 CORBA 331
   11.6.1 Overview of CORBA Architecture 331
   11.6.2 CORBA Services 332
   11.6.3 How CORBA Applications Work 334
   11.6.4 CORBA-based TMN 335
   11.6.5 TMN and CORBA Integration 338
   11.6.6 Joint Interdomain Management (JIDM) 340
   11.6.7 CORBA Implementation Notes 343
11.7 Web-based TMN 344
11.8 Web-based Enterprise Management 347
   11.8.1 WBEM and TMN 351
11.9 Java and TMN 353
11.10 Java Management API 354
11.11 Summary 355
11.12 References 356
11.13 Further Reading 357

Chapter 12   Software Management Frameworks, TMN Challenges,
and Trends 359

12.1 Introduction 360
12.2 Management Frameworks 361
   12.2.1 Communication Infrastructure 361
   12.2.2 MIB Manipulation Tools 363
   12.2.3 GDMO and ASN.1 Compilers 364
   12.2.4 Manager and Agent Code Generators 364
   12.2.5 GUI and Presentation Service Generators 366
   12.2.6 Persistent Storage 366
   12.2.7 Process Management 367
   12.2.8 Management Applications 367
   12.2.9 Implementation Notes 368

12.3 Unresolved Issues and Challenges in TMN   369
    12.3.1 Integration of Legacy Systems and Standard
            TMN Solutions   369
    12.3.2 Impact of Changes in Regulatory Environments   370
    12.3.3 Integration of TMN Solutions for Different
            Technologies   370
    12.3.4 Automation   371
    12.3.5 Information Model Differences   371
    12.3.6 Protocol Differences   371
    12.3.7 Language Independence   372
    12.3.8 Platform Independence   372
    12.3.9 Presentation Services/GUI   373
    12.3.10 Standards Lag Solutions   373
    12.3.11 TMN Solutions Are Not Open   374
    12.3.12 Integrated Network Management for Computers,
            Telecommunications, and Televisions   374
12.4 Future Trends   375
    12.4.1 Focus on Standardization   375
    12.4.2 Distributed Network Management   375
    12.4.3 TMN Solutions on Windows-based Platforms   376
    12.4.4 Increased Use of Object-oriented Paradigms   376
    12.4.5 Integration of the Web and TMN   376
12.5 Summary   376
12.6 References   377

Appendix A   How to Keep Up to Date and Procure the Latest
TMN Standards   379

Appendix B   Important TMN and Network Management Standards   383

Appendix C   Suggested Exercises   393

List of Acronyms   401

List of Trademarks   411

Index   413

PREFACE

The telecommunications industry is intensively competitive because of liberalization and globalization of the telecommunications market. TMN is growing in importance as a means to provide a competitive edge for telecommunications service providers.

Although there is a large amount of material on TMN, unfortunately there is no good book that covers broadly most aspects of TMN. Lack of treatment of various topics of TMN in a single book motivated me to write this book.

This book focuses on how different standards relate to the TMN field. I have avoided the TMN work based on vendor-sponsored "standards" bodies and consortiums. Also, I have kept away from vendor-specific products that can quickly become obsolete. The alliances formed by leading vendors change frequently, and giving much importance to them is not appropriate while covering TMN in a general manner.

Objectives

To use this book, a certain amount of basic knowledge of computer networking and telecommunications is assumed, since there are many good books on these two topics. Here I would like to mention that a smooth and logical flow to many different TMN standards and protocols is maintained. I have also provided some insight into the issues of architecture, design, and implementation.

The rapid changes occurring in the computer and telecommunications industry are also having their impact on TMN. For this reason, I include discussions on some important topics such as CORBA, Java and the World Wide Web. For those interested in these developing areas, the discussions that center on these topics should lay the groundwork for further reading.

Comprehensive references are supplied at the end of each chapter. In addition, several chapters end with a list of further reading materials to enable the reader to further pursue a given topic. Also, Appendix A contains lists of important Web sites, and how to procure the pertinent standards. I have listed important and useful TMN standards in Appendix B.

This should be a useful reference material and pointer to those who wish to pursue further the subject matter covered in this book.

There are exercises for each chapter in Appendix C. Solving these should enable the reader to get a firm grip on the topics discussed here. Some exercises are complex and time consuming, suitable for independent study courses. My primary objective for including the exercises is to cultivate the spirit of innovation and to develop creative problem-solving skills.

Intended Audience

This is an introductory book with a wide range of TMN topics. It should serve to generate a keen interest and gain a good depth on the subject of TMN. This book is intended for the following audience:

- Telecommunications industry professionals interested in TMN.
- Architects, designers and implementors of TMN.
- Computer professionals interested in TMN.
- Undergraduate and graduate level TMN courses. TMN is sufficiently mature and should become a part of computer science, electrical and telecommunications courses.

How to Use the Book

This book has been logically organized. Those who know ASN.1, BER, GDMO, and M.3100 well may skip Chapters 5 and 6. Readers are encouraged to read Chapters 11 and 12 which cover many important and interesting topics. Basic material and different versions of SNMP are covered in Chapter 8. Those who are interested more in Internet Network Management should refer to the RFCs listed in the chapter references, or to other literature on Internet Network Management, found in the Further Reading section of Chapter 8.

How the Book Is Organized

TMN is a vast area. Therefore it is difficult to cover all the aspects of TMN in a single book. So I have focused on the important areas of TMN in order to provide a good insight into the subject. Those interested in specific details should consult the references listed at the end of each chapter and in Appendix B. With these points in mind, we will cover TMN concepts in Part 1, the TMN information model and TMN protocols in Part 2, and TMN applications in Part 3. See the following chart for an overview of the structure of the book.

Telecommunications Management Network

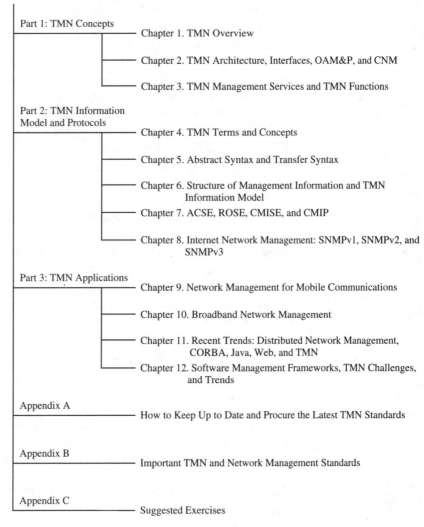

Part 1: TMN Concepts
— Chapter 1. TMN Overview
— Chapter 2. TMN Architecture, Interfaces, OAM&P, and CNM
— Chapter 3. TMN Management Services and TMN Functions

Part 2: TMN Information Model and Protocols
— Chapter 4. TMN Terms and Concepts
— Chapter 5. Abstract Syntax and Transfer Syntax
— Chapter 6. Structure of Management Information and TMN Information Model
— Chapter 7. ACSE, ROSE, CMISE, and CMIP
— Chapter 8. Internet Network Management: SNMPv1, SNMPv2, and SNMPv3

Part 3: TMN Applications
— Chapter 9. Network Management for Mobile Communications
— Chapter 10. Broadband Network Management
— Chapter 11. Recent Trends: Distributed Network Management, CORBA, Java, Web, and TMN
— Chapter 12. Software Management Frameworks, TMN Challenges, and Trends

Appendix A
— How to Keep Up to Date and Procure the Latest TMN Standards

Appendix B
— Important TMN and Network Management Standards

Appendix C
— Suggested Exercises

Part 1: TMN concepts. Part 1 is primarily devoted to introducing to the topic of TMN. It forms the basis for understanding the other parts.

Chapter 1 contains an overview of basic TMN concepts. It begins by defining TMN and exploring the evolution of TMN. We furnish a brief overview of standards bodies and consortiums that have an impact on TMN, and introduce the concept of managers and agents right in the beginning, as it is an important concept in network management. Then we look into different ITU-T TMN layers such as business management, service management, network management, element management, and network elements.

Chapter 2 basically covers functional architecture, physical architecture, and information architecture. In this chapter, we look into TMN physical components such as the OS, DCN, MD, WS, NE, and QA; reference points such as q, f, x, g, and m; and interfaces such as Qx, Q3, X, and F. The ANSI-defined operations, administration, maintenance, and provisioning (OAM&P) category is useful as an insight into network management in telecommunications area. This chapter ends with a brief introduction to customer network management (CNM).

The topic of TMN management services and TMN functions is interestingly quite different from data communication network management and SMFAs. Chapter 3 is devoted to TMN management services and functions.

Part 2: TMN information model and TMN protocols. Part 2 covers how the equipment involved in resources in telecommunications networks can be modeled as managed object classes. Equipment, along with the managed objects that can be manipulated by managers, are modeled as network elements. The manipulation of managed objects in NEs are performed by managers using different management protocols. With these points as the basis for our discussions, we cover the important standards used for modeling and the management protocols such as CMIP and SNMP.

Chapter 4 discusses important TMN-related ITU-T terms such as management information hierarchies, object naming, scoping, filtering, MIBs, and directories.

Chapter 5 concerns explanations of ASN.1 and BER.

Chapter 6 is devoted to the structure of management information (GDMO, X.722). In this chapter, we discuss how to define managed object classes, and also TMN-specific M.3100, the Generic Network Information Model.

In Chapter 7, we discuss at length the ITU-T management protocol CMIP and ACSE.

In addition to the ITU-T management protocols, Internet management protocols such as SNMPv1, SNMPv2, and SNMPv3 are also used in the telecommunications industry. Chapter 8 is devoted to these protocols. This chapter ends with a discussion of comparison of the CMIP and SNMP.

Part 3: TMN applications.   It is not enough to investigate information modeling and management protocols. It is also necessary to determine how these are being applied in real life. For this reason, we examine how different TMN standards are applied in mobile communications, SONET, SDH, and ATM. Part 3 also discusses the impact of CORBA, the World Wide Web (WWW), and Java on TMN. Also included are management frameworks used in building managers, agents, and TMN applications. No book on TMN would be complete without discussion of the challenges and trends in TMN.

Chapter 9 covers network management for mobile communications. ANSI and GSM standards for management are important aspects of the discussion.

Chapter 10 describes TMN for SDH, SONET, and ATM.

Recent advances in distributing network management are very appealing from the scalability aspect of network management solutions. So we devote a good amount of discussion to distributed network management, and to how we can incorporate CORBA in TMN solutions. Chapter 11 is devoted to some of these important topics. Also, TMN solutions are being influenced by advances in the Web and Java. These issues are covered in detail in this chapter.

The last chapter is devoted to TMN topics such as object-oriented toolkits and challenges in TMN. This chapter ends with a discussion of how TMN is going to evolve in future.

There are continuous changes and advances in the TMN area. It is essential to keep up to date. The amount of knowledge update required by professionals can be daunting. So there is a need for access to the latest material on TMN and other significant areas. This is the primary motivation for including this information in Appendix A.

Appendix B contains a list of important TMN documents for easy reference.

Appendix C provides suggested exercises for each chapter to aid in achieving a better understanding of the material presented in this book. There are also some challenging exercises that may be used for independent study courses on TMN.

ACKNOWLEDGMENTS

I would like to warmly thank Steve Chapman, the editor of the book. He was very patient, understanding, and very encouraging despite my missing many deadlines. I also like to thank other staff members including the editorial board of the McGraw-Hill for giving me the opportunity to write the second book for them. Thanks also to copyeditor Stephanie S. Landis, paginator Lisa Kochel, and art director Patti Kahler, all of North Market Street Graphics, for doing an excellent job.

Notice that I have used of many standards developed by various standards bodies. These standards are the collective effort of many leaders in the industry who devoted much time, energy and effort to develop them. I have presented their work in this book in the best possible manner. While taking the blame for any mistakes, I would like to sincerely thank the vast number of original contributors to the standards.

As this book relies heavily on standards, I have made use of ITU-T, OSI, ETSI, ANSI, ATM Forum standards, and Internet RFCs. Wherever required I have acquired the necessary permission. I would like to thank the following organizations for granting permission to reproduce or adapt material from their copyrighted publications:

- The International Telecommunication Union (ITU) has granted permission to modify material for which they hold the copyright. The selection of material is my sole responsibility and can in no way be attributed to the ITU.
  - Figure 2-1 is modified from Figure 1, "General relationship of a TMN to a telecommunication network," of ITU-T Recommendation M.3010 (5/96), "Principles for a Telecommunications management network."
  - Figure 2-4 is modified from Figure 5, "Example of typical Functional Blocks containing Functional Components," of ITU-T Recommendation M.3010 (5/96), "Principles for a Telecommunications Management Network."
  - Figure 2-5 is modified from Figure 4, "Relative roles of MCF and DCF," of ITU-T Recommendation M.3010 (5/96), "Principles for a Telecommunications Management Network."
  - Figure 2-6 is taken from Figure 14, "An example of a simplified physical architecture for a TMN," of ITU-T Recommendation

M.3010 (5/96), "Principles for a Telecommunications management network."

- Figure 2-8 is modified from Figure 12, "Sharing management knowledge between systems," of ITU-T Recommendation M.3010 (5/96), "Principles for a Telecommunications management network."
- Figure 2-10 is taken from Figure 1, "Functional Architecture of Customer Network Management," of ITU-T Recommendation X.160 (10/96), "Architecture for customer network management service for public data networks."
- Figure 2-11 is taken from Figure 4, "Example 3 of Physical Architecture," of ITU-T Recommendation X.160 (10/96), "Architecture for customer network management service for public data networks."
- Figure 10-3 is modified from Figure 3-4, "TMN, SMN, SMS model," of ITU-T Recommendation G.784 (1/94), "Synchronous Digital Hierarchy (SDH) Management."
- Table 7-6 is modified from Table 4, "Correspondence between CMISE primitives and CMIP Operation," of ITU-T Recommendation X.711 (3/91), "Common management information service definition for CCITT applications."

■ The Institute of Electrical and Electronic Engineers, Inc (IEEE) has granted permissions as related to the following figures.
- Figure 2-2 is modified from Figure 3.2 (page 76), "TMN Function Blocks and Reference Points," of *Telecommunications Network Management into the 21st Century* (1994), edited by Salah Aidarous and Thomas Pleyvak.
- Figure 2-9 is from Figure 10.1 (page 303), "OAM&P/OSI Functions," of *Telecommunications Network Management into the 21st Century* (1994), edited by Salah Aidarous and Thomas Pleyvak.
- Figure 9-2 is taken from Figure 1 (page 122), "GSM Architecture," of *IEEE Communications Magazine* (vol. 35, no. 10, October 1997) "General Packet Radio Service in GSM," by Jian Cai and David J. Goodman.
- Figure 12-1 is modified from Figure 3.4 (page 120), "Platform Components," of *Telecommunications Network Management Technologies and Implementations* (1998), edited by Salah Aidarous and Thomas Pleyvak.

I thank McGraw-Hill for permitting me to use the materials in Chapters 3, 4, 5, 6, 8, and 10 from my book *Network Management Systems Essentials*. I have updated and revised a good amount of materials in these chapters.

I thank the reviewers of different chapters of the book. A good review is very essential to flush out technical mistakes and turn the book into a good one. I would like to thank Dr. Raymond Raud, Dr. Ingo Busse of GMD FOKUS, Ferenc Kocsic of Ericsson-Hewlett Packard Telecommunications, Tetsuya Yamamura of NTT Network Service Systems Laboratories, Dr. Dev Roy of Siemens Information and Communication Networks, and Dr. Ravi Shankar of Motorola for carefully reading and providing very good comments on the chapters they reviewed. Whatever mistakes remain in this book, I am responsible for them.

I would like to thank my managers Pedro Bello, and Joe McGhee of Siemens Information and Communication Networks, for extending me help in writing this book.

My thanks to readers of my first book, *Network Management Systems Essentials,* who quickly made it a success.

—DIVAKARA K. UDUPA

TMN
Concepts

CHAPTER 1

TMN Overview

1.1 Introduction

The telecommunications management network (TMN) concept has become vital to the survival of telecommunications service providers because of competitive pressures. In many nations, deregulation and globalization have dramatically changed how telecommunications service providers operate. Many service providers, who were protected with complex regulations, realize all of a sudden that they have to face competition for consistent and better service at a reduced cost.

In addition to the pressures of deregulation and globalization, demand for transfer of a variety of digital data including voice and video has increased bandwidth requirements. Also, the telecommunications networks have to integrate computer networks of different configurations. Internet services are also having their impact in the telecommunications arena. The days of video and Internet phones are almost here.

To meet these new requirements of being able to carry different kinds of data at a faster rate, new technologies and improvements to the existing technologies and protocols are being introduced. Examples of some of the new technologies are the different kinds of digital subscriber line (DSL) technologies. Though standards for synchronous optical network (SONET), synchronous digital hierarchy (SDH), and asynchronous transfer mode (ATM) are well established, implementations are at varying stages. So, in many cases, the migration from plain old telephone service (POTS) has to be realized quickly by telecommunications service providers.

Different services and technologies over diverse telecommunications and computer networks make the management problem a huge ordeal. As a result, TMN becomes very critical for the success of the operation of these telecommunications and computer services.

1.2 Evolution of TMN

TMN has an expanding role when telecommunications, computers, and television are merging. In addition, in the telecommunications arena itself, more and more services are being added to the traditional telephone services offered by telephone service providers. As a result, equipment involved in providing telecommunications services is expanding and is also becoming more complex. The ability to deliver voice, video, and data at higher speeds is also becoming a critical requirement.

In addition, fiber optics and wireless communications have added their own complexity and speeds quite different from that of POTS. These days, and in the future, telecommunication switches have to handle a variety of equipment and data instead of only voice.

This complex and diverse equipment makes controlling networks and resources quite a daunting task. So TMN has been gaining ground as a panacea to solve problems involved in carrying different kinds of data at different data rates with different levels of equipment sophistication.

In the early days, network management in the telecommunications industry was mostly proprietary. These proprietary solutions were good enough for the limited services and limited geographical coverage of telecommunications service providers. Because of the regulatory and protected environments, telecommunications service providers could afford to take their time in implementing new technologies. They could control the introduction and implementation of technological solutions. However, in many nations, led by the United States, deregulation has changed the scenario. This has introduced fierce competition among telecommunications service providers.

In addition, deregulation has also provided the impetus to major telecommunications service providers to expand their area of operations. This has led them to look beyond their own national borders. This tendency toward globalization has also increased competition. Competition is becoming fierce in the area of services provided. As an example, many telecommunications service providers are offering additional services such as Internet access in addition to telephone services. We are also witnessing a mushrooming of different services such as wireless and paging services.

These illustrations show that there has been a major paradigm shift in the telecommunications industry. Proprietary network management solutions are limited in their ability to meet the challenges of this paradigm shift. Proprietary network management cannot provide interoperability between diverse technologies and network management solutions. This has made the need for standard network management solutions vital and urgent. Some proprietary network management systems can also be grouped under the classification of *legacy systems.*

However, the legacy network management systems add another problem in providing network management solutions. A high degree of investment has been made in these legacy solutions. It is difficult to discard solutions that have been working and in which heavy investments were made. This necessitates that legacy systems coexist with the new standard network management solutions.

1.3 What Is TMN?

In the telecommunications industry, TMN is a loosely used term that covers all kinds of network management solutions. However, in the strict sense, TMN refers only to network management solutions that satisfy and conform to the network management standards of the International Telecommunications Union-Telephony (ITU-T).

TMN specifies a layered architecture for management of telecommunications networks. TMN is concerned with the monitoring, control, and coordination of resources in telecommunications networks. *Resources* are components of a system that provides services. These resources can be equipment, software, hardware, or customers. The telecommunications networks include the advanced intelligent networks (AIN) as well. Some of the TMN functions are:

■ Remote management of system components and the different hardware and software involved in the transmission of voice, video, graphic images, Internet data, and others.

■ Providing easy interface and easy interaction with customers to configure and request the required services. The interface with customers has to take into account the different skill levels of end users or customers.

■ Providing increasing automation to rectify problems concerning the resources involved and end users. Automation also includes self-healing and self-correction in networks.

■ Achieving seamless integration and management of legacy equipment and protocols in different networks with the new equipment and protocols. This is very vital in regards to the new vistas being continuously unfolded by the telecommunications industry.

Telecommunications network components encompass the whole range of equipment involved in our telephone lines. Some of the components are as follows:

■ Remote digital terminals

■ Public and private networks, including mobile networks

■ Transmission terminals

■ Transmission systems

■ Operations systems and their peripherals

■ Digital and analog exchanges

- Area networks
- Intelligent networks
- Circuit and packet-switched networks
- Signaling terminals and systems
- Bearer services and teleservices
- Switching equipment
- Routers and gateways

In addition to the hardware, software is used to enhance the functionality of telecommunications equipment. This software has also to be managed. In this category, we can also add software applications. TMN applications themselves also need to be managed to function properly. Services provided to users include resource and service provisioning.

The role of TMN is not static and is evolving to meet new customer requirements for services and the equipment used to provide these services. As an example, in the early days telephone services covered only the transmission of voice data and provision of telephone service. However, these days there is a need for the same telephone lines or wireless services to carry voice, digital data, video, and Internet and intranet data.

To cater to the requirements of faster data, there are established protocols such as ATM, SDH, and SONET, and different DSL technologies are emerging. So TMN has to cover these new protocols and technologies as well.

1.4 TMN Standards Bodies

Having stated that TMN solutions follow ITU-T standards, let us look into the standards bodies that have an impact on TMN.

The International Organization for Standardization (ISO) defines a standard this way: "Standards are documented agreements containing technical specifications or other precise criteria to be used consistently as rules, guidelines, or definitions of characteristics, to ensure that materials, products, processes and services are fit for their purpose."

There are different types of standards. When discussing industry standards, there are primarily two types. One is a *de facto industry standard* and the other is a *formal standard*. When a large segment of the user population accepts or a majority of vendors use the same technical specifications, then these technical specifications are termed *de facto industry standards.* These de facto industry standards are the result of prominent players in an industry forming cooperative bodies and introducing products that conform to the guidelines developed by the standards bodies.

Formal standards are the result of the work of international, regional, or national standards bodies. In many cases, there is a close cooperation between these standards bodies. Also, international and regional bodies are members of national standards bodies. This is done deliberately to foster cooperation between these bodies. The International Telecommunications Union (ITU) and the ISO are examples of international standards organizations. The American National Standards Institute (ANSI) is an example of a national standards organization.

The International Electrotechnical Commission (IEC) was founded in 1906. The IEC did some pioneering work in electrotechnical standardization and currently oversees electrical and electronic engineering standardization. The ISO came into existence in 1947 and comprises many international organizations and governmental and nongovernmental agencies. The ISO works closely with the IEC. A joint ISO/IEC technical committee, JTC1, addresses standardization related to the information technology field. In the systems management arena, the ISO and IEC have published many standards that are accepted in the computer and telecommunications industry.

The ITU has its headquarters in Geneva, Switzerland and has been a specialized branch of United Nations (UN) since 1947. Its telecommunications standardization sector, known as ITU-T, was previously called the International Telephone and Telegraph Consultative Committee (CCITT). The ITU-T publishes standards on global telecommunications networks and services. ITU-T recommendations are areas of primary interest in TMN.

TMN standards are broadly divided into generic and technology/service specific areas. *Generic standards* are applicable to more than one technology or service. These are covered by the ISO and IEC. These generic ISO/IEC standards are also accepted by the ITU-T. As an example, ISO/IEC 10165-4, Guidelines for the Definition of Managed Objects (GDMO), is also known as ITU-T X.722. However, there are many TMN-related specific standards and these are the result of ITU-T work on telecommunications standards.

The European Telecommunications Standards Institute (ETSI) is a European standards organization operating under a system of technical subcommittees. One of the subcommittees, NA4, is responsible for the network architecture, operations, and maintenance principles and performance. Another subcommittee, ETSI TM2, is active in traffic management. ETSI NA4 focuses on TMN standards activity and provides input to the ITU-T. ETSI's Global System for Mobile Communications (GSM) standards are widely accepted TMN standards for wireless communication and are followed in many European countries.

In the United States, the Telecommunications Industry Association (TIA) and the Electronic Industry Association (EIA) together develop telecommunications standards. Their standards are adapted by ANSI, the standards body in the United States. T1 is the ANSI-accredited committee for developing standards for the telecommunications industry. T1M1 is the subcommittee within T1 devoted to TMN standardization. T1M1 basically adopts the ITU-T standards wherever they are available. In areas where ITU-T standards are not available, T1M1 provides input to the ITU-T.

In Japan, telecommunications standardization activities are carried out by the Telecommunications Technology Council and the Telecommunications Technical Committee. The Telecommunications Technology Council has a TMN working group and provides input to the ITU-T. The Telecommunications Technical Committee is responsible for publishing Japanese telecommunications standards and has a working group that covers relevant TMN standards that are applicable to Japan.

In the Internet arena, the Internet Activities Board (IAB) broadly guides Internet standards activities. The Internet Engineering Task Force (IETF) is a subgroup of the IAB and is responsible for the development of protocols and standardization activities related to the Internet. From a network management perspective, the development of Simple Network Management Protocol Version 1 (SNMPv1), SNMPv2 and SNMPv3 management protocols is one of the important contributions of the IETF.

In addition to the national and international standards bodies just mentioned, there are many vendor-based consortiums. These consortiums also have significant impact on TMN. The TeleManagement Forum is one such body. The TeleManagement Forum is a global consortium of over 210 leading service providers and suppliers, with a prominent role in the implementation of OSI and TMN standards. The TeleManagement Forum has different OMNIPoint releases. Each OMNIPoint release is devoted to guiding the specific needs of network management implementations. Each release explains standards and includes software development tools and implementation and procurement guides.

The Object Management Group (OMG), a nonprofit organization founded in 1989, is another industrial consortium with over 800 members. The OMG's charter is to develop technically feasible, commercially viable, and vendor-independent specifications for the software industry. Its primary focus is on object-oriented software. One of its significant contributions has been the development of technical specifications for Common Object Request Broker Architecture (CORBA). The OMG is also very active in the object-oriented database field.

The ATM Forum is an international consortium with over 700 members. It is devoted to accelerating the implementation of ATM products and services by bringing out common ATM-related standards. Its specifications are quite popular in the ATM industry.

There are many other important consortiums such as the Desktop Management Task Force (DMTF). The DMTF is devoted to the development, support, and maintenance of management standards for desktop computers and products. It was started in 1992 by some of the PC industry leaders. Now the DMTF includes most of the computer industry leaders.

The Telecommunications Information Technology Networking Architecture Consortium (TINA-C) started its activities in 1992. TINA-C is composed of telecommunications network operators, telecommunications service providers, telecommunications hardware and software vendors, and telecommunications research organizations. NTT, Bellcore, and British Telecom are the founder members of TINA-C. The primary objective of TINA-C is to reduce the cost of introducing new telecommunications network information infrastructures and services in a multiplayer and multivendor environment.

In addition, there are organizations such as Bellcore that are actively involved in telecommunications standardization. Because of the history of Bellcore, many Bell companies in the United States follow Bellcore documents.

At this juncture, a note of caution and some explanation are appropriate. In addition to the standards bodies, consortiums, and industry groups just mentioned, there are many organizations, consortiums, and bodies that tout their work as standards-based. We will not cover the work done by these bodies. In many cases the work of some of the consortiums does not have much impact in the TMN arena in the long run. Besides, some industry-formed bodies and consortiums do not command much respect in the telecommunications industry due to the short span of their existence and shifting allegiances. In some cases, proprietary standards are also touted as "industry standards." Taking these factors into consideration, we prefer to exclude many such consortiums and bodies altogether. Where it is absolutely essential, we have made only passing references to them.

1.5 Network Management, Systems Management, and TMN

Even the terms used in network management are not uniform. Different vendors and standard bodies use different terms to refer to similar activities. In the Internet arena, the term *network management* is popularly used. The Institute of Electrical and Electronics Engineers (IEEE) uses *network management* liberally to apply to the standards it publishes on layer management. The OSI and IBM use the term *systems management* in these cases.

Many network management functions are covered in TMN. In one sense, network management and TMN both mean the management of networks and services. However, in the case of TMN the focus is on the telecommunications network, equipment, and services provided to customers. In addition, in the TMN world the standards bodies have more impact and the telephone carriers have to satisfy strict national and international regulations. So most of the TMN tools, by and large, follow one form of standards or other. We say "by and large" because in the vastly expanding mobile communications arena, many vendors in the United States have their own proprietary protocols. Some in the United States follow the Bellcore documents, whereas many European nations follow the GSM standards.

In the telecommunications industry, end user configurations and services are also included as a part of TMN. So we have terms such as *service and resource provisioning* that are not found in data communication network management. We will look into the details of provisioning in Chapter 3.

1.6 Systems Management Functional Areas

In the OSI systems management arena, *systems management functional areas* (SMFAs) is a very frequently used term. The overall systems management function is broken down into easily distinguishable smaller network management functions. This breakup of systems management functions into SMFAs is done by OSI. The SMFAs are configuration management, fault management, performance management, accounting management, and security management.

Let us look into what each of these SMFAs mean. *Configuration management* is used to locate resources, including failed ones, and also to keep track of the resources and their details. Primarily, configuration management provides the support services to keep the systems and resources operational. It is necessary to clarify what is meant by configuration management. Sometimes, this term is synonymous with configuring equipment. In the systems management and TMN sense, configuration management is not the same as configuring equipment. Configuration management covers areas such as view management, topology management, software management, inventory management, and provisioning.

Fault management primarily covers the detection, isolation by analysis, and correction of unusual operational behaviors of telecommunications network and its environment. These unusual operational behaviors include conditions such as deterioration of service or error situations. Effective fault management may require that errors be logged in a database. Broadly, fault management covers areas such as problem reporting and detection, problem diagnosis, problem correction, and problem tracking. Trouble ticket application is one of the popular applications for problem tracking.

Performance management covers performance data collection, analysis of performance data, reporting of problems, and display and formatting of performance data. Performance management is also concerned with the behavior and evaluation of the effectiveness of resources.

Accounting management covers the usage of resources, controlled collection of data, and charging for the usage of these resources. The process of charging for the usage of resources is also known as *billing*.

Security management functions cover areas such as detecting security violations; tracking and reporting security violations; and creating, deleting, and maintaining security-related services such as encryption, key management, and access control. Distributing passwords and secret keys to bring up systems is also a function of security management.

For more details on these SMFAs, refer to Reference 1.1.

1.7 Managed Object, Managed Object Class, and Management Information Model

Managed object (MO), *managed object class* (MOC), and *management information model* are commonly used terms in network management. So it is best to introduce these terms at the beginning to get a better understanding of topics we are going to discuss. We will revisit these terms in detail in Chapter 6.

1.7.1 Managed Object

The data communication or TMN resources provide services. A printer, digital cross-connect, PBX, or line card within a PBX is a *resource*. A resource may be physical or logical. A printer is an example of a *physical resource*; application programs, log files, and network services are examples of *logical resources*.

The conceptual view of a resource that can be managed is known as a *managed object*. In other words, in order for a resource to be managed, it must be represented as a managed object. Sometimes, a managed object is also referred to as a *managed object instance*. A resource may be physical, such as a card in a circuit pack, or logical, such as a cross-connection map. circuitPackCard1 is an example of a managed object.

There need not be one-to-one mapping between a resource and a managed object. A resource may be modeled by more than one managed object. In this case, each managed object represents a different abstract view of a managed object. A managed object may also represent a relationship between different resources, as in the case of a network.

A managed object is defined by the following characteristics (Figure 1-1):

- *Attribute:* This refers to the properties of a managed object. A managed object can have one or more attributes. In the definition of a *network* managed object class (M.3100), networkId is an attribute. The type of printer—for example, dot matrix, laser jet, or laser printer— can be one of the properties; therefore, printerType is another example of an attribute. An attribute has one or more values.

- *Operation:* This is a set of activities performed on a managed object or one or more attributes to achieve a network management action. Create an object and Get an attribute value are operations. Get the value of networkId attribute of network managed object class is an example of an operation.

- *Notification:* This is an unsolicited message that contains details including why a notification has occurred, where it occurred, and for whom the notification is intended.

- *Behavior:* When the characteristics of a managed object such as attributes, operations, and notifications are defined, there must be a way to express their semantics and how they are related. This is done by behavior. Behavior is a text description.

Between a managed object and a resource, we perceive a conceptual boundary known as a *managed object boundary* (Figure 1.1). At this boundary, the characteristics of a managed object, such as attributes, operations,

Figure 1-1
Concepts of managed
object and managed
object class.

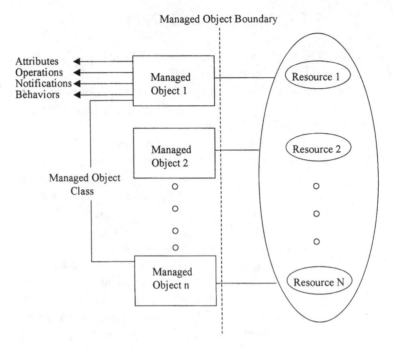

and notifications, are visible for management purposes. Items inside the managed object boundary pertaining to a resource are not needed for management purposes.

1.7.2 Managed Object Class

The common management characteristics of a group of managed objects are collected together in a managed object class. In TMN, the managed object classes are defined using principles involved in Management Information Model (X.720/ISO 10165-1), the templates provided in guidelines for the definition of managed objects (GDMO) (X.722/ISO 10165-4), and abstract syntax notation 1 (ASN.1) (X.208/ISO 8824). Separate chapters are devoted to ASN.1 (Chapter 5) and the GDMO and management information model (Chapter 6).

Of course, we have similar information models for Internet network management. However, we use the structure of management information (SMI) for defining the managed object classes. Notice that the information models for SNMPv2 and SNMPv3 extend the management information model for SNMPv1.

The process of creating a managed object according to rules is known as *instantiation*. As an example, if circuitPackCard is a managed object class, circuitPackCard1 is a managed object instance or a managed object of the circuitPackCard managed object class. A managed object class is defined in terms of attributes, notifications, operations, and behaviors. Each managed object has a unique name to identify it.

We will look in detail on the topic of managed object class in Chapter 6.

1.7.3 Information Model

A set of managed objects and the manner in which these managed objects are related to one another is known as an *information model*. The relationship between managed objects is depicted by inheritance hierarchy and containment hierarchy. We will look into what inheritance hierarchy and containment hierarchy mean in Chapter 4. Information models can be of two types:

- *Generic Information Model:* The standard objects are gathered in this model. Of course, this model does not include all standard objects, only those required for a specific implementation.

- *Specific Information Model:* An interface definition includes a protocol stack (for example, an OSI seven-layer stack) and an information model supported by the interface. There are different types of interfaces depending upon the application. Q3 (Chapter 2, Section 2.3.3) is an example of an interface. The specific information model is a subset of the generic information model.

1.8 Manager, Agent, and Management Information

Managers and agents are very important basic concepts in network management and TMN. Because manager and agent concepts are important topics and are needed for discussion later on, we have introduced these terms in this introductory chapter. The interaction of managers and agents is shown in Figure 1-2.

A manager plays a key role in the monitoring and controlling of different agents in its span of control. Agents, in turn, interpret the commands sent from managers. Managers and agents communicate by exchanging management information as shown in Figure 1.2. The

Figure 1-2
Manager, agent, and management information.

exchange of management information between manager and agents can be done either by passing messages between them or by an object-oriented approach.

In the telecommunications industry, message-based exchange of management information uses Transaction Language 1 (TL1) developed by Bellcore in North America, or ITU-T Recommendation Z.300, Man Machine Language (MML). TL1 consists of ASCII string-based message sets for applications such as alarm reporting, performance monitoring, testing, and provisioning. TL1 has commands, responses to commands, and autonomous notifications for exchange of management information between manager and agents. As the TL1-based systems are slowly being replaced by the object-oriented approach, we will not deal with TL1 any further. The TL1-based systems are being relegated to the legacy systems. For more information on TL1, refer to Reference 1.2.

TMN and data communication networks use the object-oriented approach for representing resources and exchanging management information between managers and agents (Figure 1-3).

A manager may have different SMFAs. As an example, one manager may have a configuration management application and another may have a fault management application running. However, for these network management applications to run, data must be collected. To collect the data for, say, configuration management, a manager sends commands or operations to agent(s) to collect it. In return, the manager receives replies to its commands. In between, if something goes wrong in the agent, the manager may get notifications. Thus the managers interpret the management protocols and convert them into useful network management functions in SMFAs.

The commands sent from a manager are interpreted by agents and are sent to managed objects. These managed objects have the inherent intelligence to act on the basis of commands received. They send replies to agents, and the agents dispatch the replies to one or more appropriate managers.

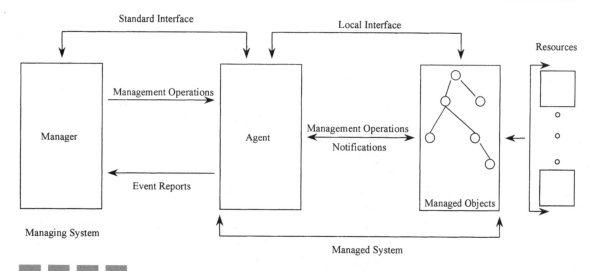

Figure 1-3
Manager and agent relationship.

Sometimes agents may receive notifications from managed objects. As an example, when a threshold has been crossed, one of the managed objects may send a notification to an agent. Then the agent sends notifications in the form of event reports to one or more managers. From this we see that a managed object emits notification and that this notification, when conveyed to external systems, becomes an event report.

A manager may be involved in exchanging management information with one or more agents. Similarly, an agent may also be involved in exchanging management information with one or more managers. An agent may deny operations from a manager for reasons such as security violations. So a manager must be able to handle negative responses from an agent.

Managers and agents communicate using *management protocols*. The network management protocols and applications are considered part of the application layer in the OSI seven-layer communication architecture. These management protocols can be common management information protocols (CMIP), SNMPv1, SNMPv2, SNMPv3, or proprietary protocols.

Between managers and agents are *standard interfaces*. The local interface between agents and managed objects is not covered by standardization. In OSI parlance, sometimes a manager is also known as a managing system (Reference 1.3). Similarly, an agent is known as a *managed system*. Note that the roles of managers and agents are not rigidly defined in OSI. As an example, a manager in one interaction may take up the role of an agent in another interaction.

Let us now examine the case of a cascaded environment (Reference 1.4), as this is one of the practices used to extend management capability in TMN. In a cascaded environment, a manager and an agent may be present in the same system (system B), as shown in Figure 1-4.

A manager in system A can manage the agent in system B. The manager in system A sees and processes the information model of system B. Similarly, the manager in system B manages the agent in system C. Here, manager in system B uses the information model presented by the system C. In system B, the agent may forward some of the notifications received from system C to the manager in system A. Similarly, some operations from the manager in system A may be forwarded by the agent in system B to the agent in system C via the manager in system B. The management protocols between the agent and manager in system B are not standardized and are dependent upon the implementation.

The management protocols use a communication stack to communicate with the agents, using communication stacks such as the seven-layer OSI stack, Transmission Control Protocol (TCP)/Internet Protocol (IP) (TCP/IP), and Internet Packet Exchange (IPX)/Sequenced Packet Exchange (SPX) (IPX/SPX). Sometimes proprietary protocols are also used in the communication stacks.

The managers can be in workstations along with operating systems such as Sun's Solaris, HP-UX, Windows NT, Windows 95/98, or any other operating systems that provide processing functions required by managers. The recent trends are to have managers on Windows NT and agents

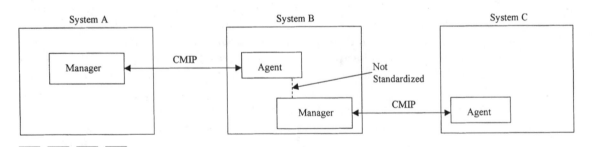

Figure 1-4
Managers and agents in a cascaded environment.

on Windows 95/98. The communication stacks are also available separately or as a part of the operating systems.

In large telecommunications or data communication networks it is a major problem to manage agents because a huge number of agents are involved. A large number of agents reporting to a manager can create performance bottlenecks. To overcome this problem, the concepts of management domains and distributed network management have evolved. A management domain may have one or more managers and zero or more agents. However, these managers are under one administrative control. Network management becomes difficult when we have to consider the coordination of these managers in different management domains.

Manager and agents can be organized in different ways, such as the centralized model. In this model, one manager oversees many agents. SNMPv1 is one example. When the management of agents becomes unwieldy for one manager, a flat model can be used (Reference 1.5). As per this model, more than one manager manages the agents. Here, there is a need for manager-to-manager communication to coordinate different managers. In TMN, we use a hierarchical model where management activities are partitioned into different layers.

1.9 TMN Management Layers

When anything becomes complex, it is the normal practice to break down the functions. In computers and telecommunications, this is done by breaking into layers. The same principle is followed in TMN. Each layer has its own functions and roles as well as rules for interfacing with layers above and below. The scope of the layer above is broader than the one below. By this, it is apparent that the lower layers perform specific functions and the upper layers are progressively responsible for a broader set of functions. The different TMN layers are termed *management functional layers* and are explained in Reference 1.4. The TMN functional layers (Figure 1-5) are:

■ Business management layer (BML)

■ Service management layer (SML)

■ Network management layer (NML)

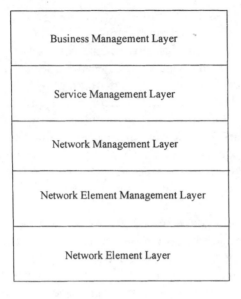

Figure 1-5
Different TMN
management layers.

- Network element management layer (NEML)
- Network element layer (NEL)

The breakdown of TMN functions just described facilitates easy step-by-step implementation. Let us examine the role and function of each layer in a top-down fashion.

The *business management layer* is concerned with the network planning, agreement between operators, and executive-level activities such as strategic planning. The BML is the topmost layer and, as a result, is responsible for management at the enterprise level. BML functions have more to do with setting and tracking the overall goals than with implementation of details. The BML has to interact with other TMN management layers to achieve BML layer functions.

The *service management layer* provides the customer interface. The SML performs functions such as service provisioning; opening new accounts; closing accounts; resolving customer complaints, including those related to billing; fault reporting; and maintaining data on quality of service (QOS). SML layer functions do not include the managment of physical entities.

The *network management layer* is concerned with the management of the whole network. It provides an end-to-end view of the network. The NML receives data from the lower NEML and synthesizes the data into meaningful total-network-level views. The NML communicates with other layers using standardized interfaces. This layer corresponds to the operations system (OS) functions. We will look into how OS functions in

Chapter 3. If we consider the NEML as corresponding to a manager, the NML layer can be viewed as a manager of a manager.

The *network element management layer* is used for managing a subnetwork—for example, a telecommunications network attached to a wire center. In this layer, data from network elements within the layer's span of control are analyzed and interpreted in a meaningful manner to monitor and control the subnetwork. As a subnetwork is a subset of the whole network, relevant data are passed on to the NML applications for integration of the views of the whole network. Sometimes the NEML is also referred to as the *element manager.*

The NEML is an intermediary layer between the NML and NEs. If a large number of network management functions are concentrated in the NEML, then the functionality required in the NML will be comparatively reduced. Therefore a judicious partition of network management functions is required between the NEML and the NML.

The *network element layer* (NEL) is the key to the TMN. It functions as an agent. This software or hardware component is present in physical entities that need to be managed. Some of the NEL functions are performance data collection, self-diagnostics, alarm monitoring and alarm data collection, traffic data collection, address translation, protocol conversion, data conversion, and data analysis.

Though the TMN functions are broken into the five layers just mentioned, implementations may not follow these textbook-style divisions. Also, with more and more emerging new demands on the telecommunications networks, new functions have to be aligned carefully and from a realistic implementation point of view.

1.10 Conventions Used in This Book

In view of the confusion in the network management terminology, it is a good idea to come to grips with what each term means. We refer to the network management based on ITU-T standards as *TMN.* In the context of the Internet, we use the term *network management.* In the case of OSI network management, we refer to *systems management.* Note that for IEEE-related management of resources and layer management, the IEEE uses *network management* (IEEE-related network management is not covered in this book).

Telecommunications companies can be broadly divided into different categories. Some companies only provide telephone and other telephone-related services—AT&T, BT, and MCI are a few examples. These companies are referred to as *telecommunications service providers*. Some other telecommunications companies manufacture telecommunications equipment and provide services to telecommunications service providers. Lucent, Nortel, and Siemens are examples of these telecommunications companies. These companies are referred to as *telecommunications vendors*.

1.11 Summary

This introductory chapter provides a baseline for the remainder of the book. Therefore we start with what TMN is and why TMN is an important part of the telecommunications industry. Since TMN is a loosely defined and used term in the telecommunications industry, we examine what TMN actually means and the scope of TMN. Then we look into the standards bodies involved in TMN. As some of the terms are frequently used in subsequent chapters, the topics of managed object, managed object class, management information model, manager, agents, and different TMN layers are introduced at the start.

1.12 References

1.1. Udupa, D. K., *Network Management Systems Essentials*, New York: McGraw-Hill, 1996.

1.2. TR-TSY-00831, *Operations Technology Generic Requirements (OTGR): Operations Application Messages—Language for Operations Applications Messages*, Issue 2, Bellcore, 1988.

1.3. ITU-T Recommendation X.701, Information Technology, Open Systems Interconnection, Systems Management Overview, 1992.

1.4. ITU-T Recommendation M.3010, Principles for a Telecommunications Management Network, 1996.

1.5. Pavlou, G., OSI Systems Management, Internet SNMP, and ODP/OMG CORBA as Technologies for Telecommunications Network Management. In *The Telecommunications Network Management, Technologies and Implementations*, Aidarous, S. and Plevyak, T. (eds.), New York: The Institute of Electrical and Electronics Engineers, Inc., pp. 63—110, 1998.

CHAPTER 2

TMN Architecture, Interfaces, OAM&P, and CNM

2.1 Introduction

We introduced the concept of TMN in Chapter 1. In this chapter we expand TMN concepts further. TMN is explained in different M-Series recommendations from ITU-T. ITU-T document M.3010 (Reference 2.1) lays the foundation for TMN architecture, discussed in this chapter. In TMN, terms such as *TMN function blocks, TMN functional components,* and *interfaces,* which are used to communicate management information between TMN components and also between TMN and non-TMN components, are quite common. At this stage it is necessary to introduce these terms and explain what they mean.

ANSI-based OAM&P is popular, at least in North America, so there is a need to look into this concept. OSI systems management functions are broadly used as yardsticks to explain other TMN functions. So, for understanding these concepts, it is prudent to explain how OAM&P is related to OSI systems management function. OAM&P explanations in this chapter are based on ANSI standard T1.210 (Reference 2.12).

In the telecommunications industry, ETSI standards are quite popular in European countries and some other nations around the world. ETSI uses operation, administration, and maintenance (OAM), which is slightly different from OAM&P. In ETSI standards, the provisioning function is part of the service and business areas. We will look into OAM in Chapter 9.

Customer network management (CNM) is a subset of the TMN functions exposed to customers. It is essential to standardize CNM so that customers experience a uniform look and feel. With this point in mind, we need to understand what CNM is all about.

Conformance is an important and vast topic. Conformance is very essential for interoperability. There are many ISO standards and ITU-T recommendations devoted to conformance. Also, conformance requirements are included in most of the protocol specification documents. In this chapter, we have only introduced the topic. For more details on conformance, refer to the standards documents. Also, there are some books that have detailed discussions of conformance (Reference 2.13).

2.2 TMN and Telecommunications Networks

Figure 2-1 shows the relationship between TMN and a telecommunications network, which TMN manages. TMN provides the management

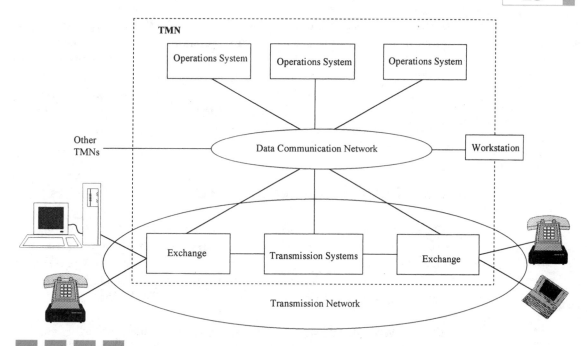

Figure 2-1
Relationship between TMN and telecommunications network.

support to plan, provision, install, maintain, operate, and administer telecommunications networks and services. The scope of TMN is broader than providing OSI SMFAs. TMN architecture can vary from simple to complex. As an example, there can be a single operations system (OS) managing a few pieces of equipment, or a number of OSs and a large, complex telecommunications network as in Figure 2-1. An OS is analogous to a manager; we will look into it in more detail.

A telecommunications network can include a variety of components such as equipment for analog, digital, or wireless transmission and support functions. This equipment can be switching systems, multiplexers, signaling terminals, front-end processors, cluster controllers, file servers, base stations, mainframes, and so on.

2.3 TMN Architecture

TMN architecture explains overall management of different telecommunications network components in a cooperative manner. For facilitating the ease of design and development of TMN, the management of a telecommunications network is subdivided into easily understandable and manageable components. These different TMN components are then combined into the total TMN functionality with proper coordination between the manageable TMN components. With this point in view, TMN architecture primarily consists of three different components: functional architecture, physical architecture, and information architecture. We will look into each in detail.

2.3.1 Functional Architecture

TMN functional architecture divides a TMN domain into different function blocks. Each function block in TMN functional architecture performs a specific TMN management function. Function blocks are similar to building blocks. By combining function blocks in different ways, we can derive TMN functionality of any complexity.

2.3.1.1 TMN Function Blocks.   Some of the function blocks can be within and some outside the TMN boundary, as can be seen in Figure 2-2. The different types of function blocks are as follows:

- *Operations systems function (OSF):*   Provides the management and planning functions for the telecommunications network and the TMN component itself. There are four OSF function blocks—namely element OSF, network OSF, service OSF, and business OSF—to support the element management layer, network management layer, service management layer, and business management layer functions, respectively (Figure 2-3). Here we may note that an OSF is separated by higher- and lower-level OSFs with a q_3 reference point. A peer OSF or OSFs in other domains are separated by x reference points. We will look into reference points in Section 2.3.1.3.

- *Network element function (NEF):*   Monitored and controlled by TMN. Telecommunications network components are represented by one or more NEF function blocks for the purposes of management.

- *WorkStation function (WSF):*   Enables management information to be viewed by human users. This involves translation of management data from F interface format to G interface format. F and G interfaces are explained in Section 2.3.3.

- *Mediation function (MF):*   A sort of a gateway for exchanging management information when the function blocks have different reference

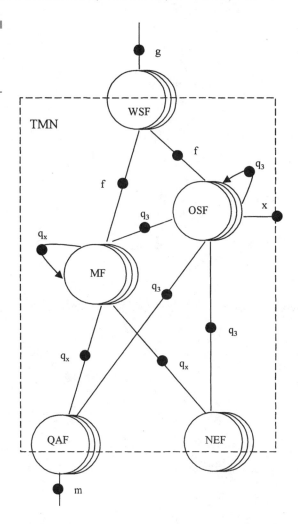

Figure 2-2
Functional
architecture of TMN
(© 1994 IEEE).

points. MF function blocks may store, convert, route, perform address mapping, filter, threshold, and condense management information.

- *Q adaptor function (QAF):* Used to translate management information between TMN reference and non-TMN reference points. Thus in Figure 2-2 a portion of QAF is outside the TMN boundary.

2.3.1.2 TMN Functional Components. Each function block contains functional components. The functional components are elementary building blocks. As an example, a NEF function block is obtained by grouping NEF-MAF, DSF, DAF, and SF (see the following list for explana-

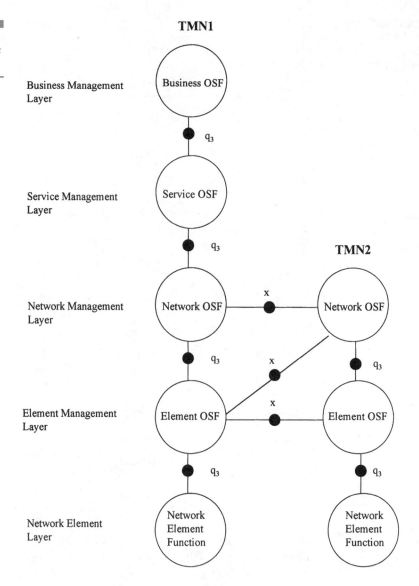

tion of each term). Another example of an OSF function block with functional components is shown in Figure 2-4. The different functional components are as follows:

- *Management application function (MAF):* Provides functionality for one or more management services. Management services are explained in Chapter 3. MAF also includes the management information. When a MAF is included in other TMN function blocks to

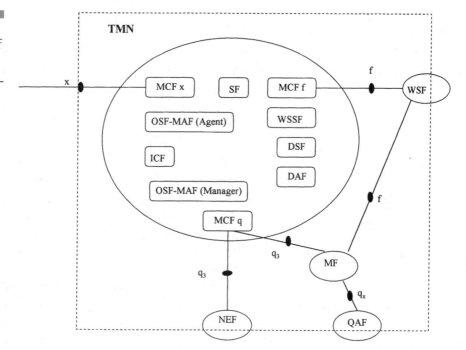

Figure 2-4
Exploded view of OSF
with functional
components.

provide support for TMN function blocks such as MF, OSF, NEF, and QAF, these are referred to as MF-MAF, OSF-MAF, NEF-MAF, and QAF-MAF, respectively.

- *Mediation function—management application function (MF-MAF):* Present in an MF to support manager and agent roles of the MF.

- *Operations systems function—management application function (OSF-MAF):* Present to support simple to complex management functions. Some of the management functions in OSF-MAFs are alarm correlation, trouble tracking, statistics, performance analysis, and the like.

- *Network element function—management application function (NEF-MAF):* Present in an NEF to support the agent role.

- *Q adaptor function—management application function (QAF-MAF):* Present in a QAF to support manager and agent roles.

- *Information conversion function (ICF):* Provides a mechanism to convert information models from one form to another. ICF is required in MF and QAF as there is a need to transform information models.

- *WorkStation support function (WSSF):* Required for the realization of WSF management function.

- *User interface support function (UISF):* Translates user information to the TMN information model and vice versa, and makes the information in an information model available in a displayable format at the human-machine interface. The human-machine interface can be a workstation screen, a printer, or another device.

- *Message communication function (MCF):* Provides a means for exchanging management information between peers using a protocol stack (Figure 2-5). This protocol stack need not necessarily be an OSI seven-layer stack. MCF is necessary for all function blocks which need a physical interface. An MCF may be connected to a data communication function (DCF) as shown in Figure 2-5 and basically provides an information transport mechanism.

- *DCF:* may provide routing, relaying, and interworking functions. DCF provides OSI layers 1 to 3 or their equivalent. DCF capability can be point-to-point links, local area networks (LANs), wide area networks (WANs), and embedded operations channels (EOCs).

- *Directory system function (DSF):* Required for realizing directory support to the TMN. The directory used in TMN is based on the ITU-T X.500 directory document (Reference 2.10). Note that there are many ITU-T recommendations on different aspects of directory services. A directory contains information about systems with which associations can be made along with association details, application context details, security details, list of managed objects, managed object classes supported, and so on. Directories also include functions to manipulate directories, such as adding entries, deleting entries, searching entries, and modifying entries.

- *Directory access function (DAF):* Required for accessing directories. It is required for OSF and may also be required for WSF, MD, QAF, and NEF depending upon whether they use directories.

- *Security function (SF):* Required for providing security to function blocks. The security services are authentication, access control, data

Figure 2-5
DCF functions.

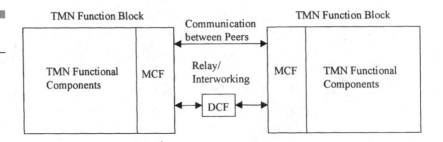

confidentiality, data integrity, and nonrepudiation. The details of these security services are provided in ITU-T X.800 (Reference 2.11).

2.3.1.3 Reference Points.   The function blocks are separated by conceptual boundaries known as reference points (Figure 2-2). As can be seen in Figure 2-2, there are q, f, x, g, and m reference points. There are two type q reference points, namely q_3 and q_x. g and m reference points delineate TMN and non-TMN boundaries.

2.3.2 Physical Architecture

Physical architecture explains the implementation of function blocks on physical systems and the interfaces between them. Implementations of function blocks on physical systems can be treated as building blocks from which complex TMN systems can be developed. For exchange of management information between building blocks, these building blocks must be connected by a communication path and each building block must have a similar interface with the communication path.

The components of physical architecture (Figure 2-6) are as follows:

■ *Operations system (OS):*   Supports information processing related to operations, administration, maintenance, and provisioning of telecommunications networks. Operation systems are analogous to managers. In Figure 2-6 there is only one OS. It is not necessary that there be only one OS within a TMN boundary: there can be more than one OS interconnected. As a matter of fact, when the TMN workload is heavy for a large telecommunications network, distributed architecture is required. This will lead to more than one OS, as in Figure 2-1.

■ *Data communication network (DCN):*   Has routing and transport capabilities used to exchange management information between OS and OS, OS and NE, WS and OS, and WS and NE. The DCN supports the DCF functional component and provides support for only one to three OSI layers. ANSI T.210 (Reference 2.12) defines a gateway network element (GNE) as a DCN. A GNE also has routing and relaying capabilities. Here, relaying means forwarding of data from one network to another. There is no data format conversion involved. Relays can be bridges, routers, or network relays based on the layer of support of the OSI protocol stack. As an example, repeaters provide connectivity and relays at the OSI physical layer.

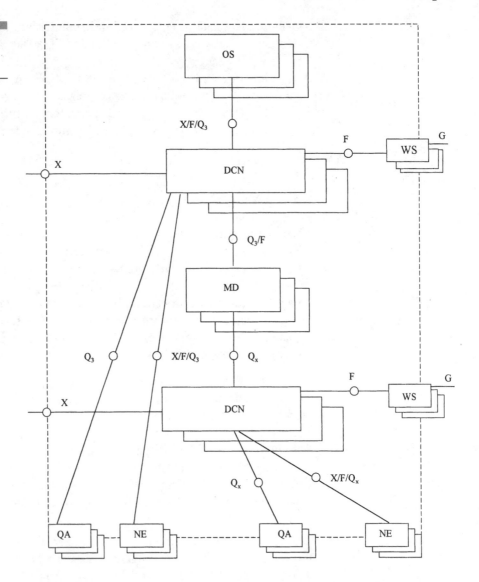

Figure 2-6

Physical architecture for TMN.

- *Mediation device (MD):* Has a relay or gateway function. An MD includes many functions such as protocol conversion, message conversion, signal conversion, address translation, and routing. An MD also may be required to perform information processing functions such as execution of functions, information processing, storing data, and filtering data.

- *Workstation (WS):* The entry or exit point that permits human users such as operators of a system to access management data. These systems are normally data processing systems such as mainframes, Unix-based workstations, or Intel PCs using Windows NT. Human users need to interpret management data received from MDs and OSs and are presented data on the computer screens and by means of reports.

■ *Network element (NE):* Has intelligence. An item, a group of items, or a piece of telecommunications equipment that is part of a telecommunications network and performs NEF functions is known as an NE. An NE is similar to an agent and has a NEF function block and support for a Q interface. We will look into Q interfaces in the next section. An NE also may have optional support for F and X interfaces. NE functionality is realized by microprocessors and software. Legacy NEs, which may not support TMN standards, are connected to the TMN environment using Q adaptors.

■ *Q Adaptor (QA):* Converts the non-TMN data to the TMN data format and vice versa. As an example, the non-TMN data may be TL1 messages from nonstandard devices. These TL1 messages are converted to CMIP data and transmitted to the DCN. A similar but reverse conversion of CMIP data from OS to TL1 messages suited for the non-TMN environment is also performed.

2.3.3 Interfaces

We have looked into reference points in functional architecture. When these reference points are implemented in physical systems, they become interfaces. For management information to be exchanged between two or more building blocks, there has to be a communication path between the building blocks and similar interfaces. An interface consists of a protocol suite and messages carried over the protocol. These messages are a mechanism to convey information to manage objects defined in an information model.

2.3.3.1 Q Interface. A Q interface is used at a q reference point. However, a Q interface can be either a Q3 interface or a Qx interface.

Q3 INTERFACE. The Q3 interface is a very popular interface in the TMN world. It uses a full OSI seven-layer stack. It refers to the interfaces provided by ITU-T recommendations Q811 (Reference 2.2) and Q812 (Reference 2.3). Q811 provides the details of the physical interfaces, the data communication layer, and the networking layer, while Q812 defines standards to the upper layers of the OSI stack.

Qx INTERFACE. In many cases it is not necessary to have the full OSI seven-layer stack. There is a lot of overhead involved in supporting a full OSI seven-layer stack. To overcome this lacuna, the Qx interface is quite useful. So, when NEs need to use less than the full seven OSI layers, the Qx interface is sufficient. As we have seen, the Q3 interface uses the full seven OSI layers.

2.3.3.2 X Interface. The X interface is used to interconnect OSs in different TMNs or to connect a TMN to other network management systems with TMN-like interfaces. OSs can be connected using different configurations. The X interface can be used to connect OSs in a peer-to-peer relationship, as in the case of the cooperative management model shown in Figure 2-7. There can also be a manager-to-agent relationship between OSs, as shown in the joint management model shown in Figure 2-7. The X interface needs security requirements in addition to the proto-

Figure 2-7
X interface examples.

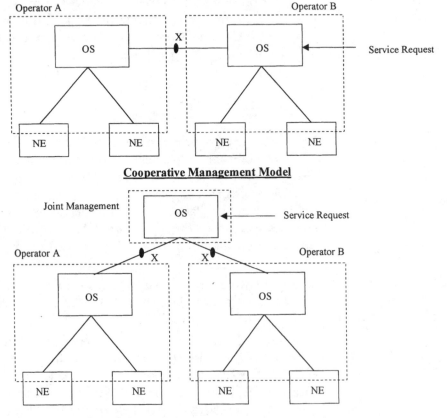

Cooperative Management Model

Joint Management Model

col stacks as management information is exchanged with other TMNs. For more details on the X interface, refer to Reference 2.4.

2.3.3.3 F Interface. The F interface supports functions to interconnect workstation OSF and MF using data communication networks. Users access TMN data via the F interface (Reference 2.5).

2.3.3.4 M Interface. The M interface corresponds to the m reference point. It is located outside the TMN boundary. The M interface provides connection between QAF and non-TMN managed entities or managed entities that do not conform to TMN standards.

2.3.3.5 G Interface. The G interface corresponds to the g reference point. The G interface is not considered part of TMN. The G interface provides access to the human user interface in a workstation. A human user can access TMN information via the G interface.

2.3.4 Information Architecture

Information architecture explains how OSI systems management and X.500 principles can be applied to TMN. Information architecture describes the resources that have to be managed by TMN using the guidelines for the definition of managed objects (GDMO) and abstract syntax notation one (ASN.1). Separate chapters are devoted to ASN.1 (Chapter 5) and GDMO (Chapter 6). Information architecture uses object-oriented approach in providing TMN solutions.

We looked into manager and agent concepts in Chapter 1. Managers and agents exchange management information about the resources controlled by agents using management protocols. These protocols in TMN are based on CMIP. However, in some cases, the exchange of management information can be done using file transfer, access, and management (FTAM) protocols.

There are two aspects of management information. One is what constitutes management information. The resources to be managed and the management operations that can be performed on the resources are contained in a management information model. These are application-level activities. Another important aspect of management information is how this management information is transferred. The transfer of management information is done using communication stacks involving DCFs and MCFs.

2.3.4.1 Shared Management Knowledge. *Management knowledge* refers to the management information required by an open system to associate and perform management operations on another open system. For a manager and agent to communicate, manager and agent must share a common body of management knowledge. This common management knowledge is known as *shared management knowledge* (SMK). This is analogous to the ability of two people to communicate with each other: For this to occur, there have to be some commonalties such as languages or interests. The shared management knowledge includes the following:

- Protocol knowledge such as application context
- Function knowledge such as TMN function blocks
- Managed object knowledge such as managed object classes and available managed object instances
- Constraints on functions supported and the relationships between those functions and managed objects
- Similar name bindings

SMK must be established before transfer of management information between two systems. Sometimes, this may require negotiation between the two communicating systems. SMK between interdependent systems can be different (Figure 2-8). As an example, while there can be one type of SMK between the manager in system A and the agent in system B, SMK between the manager in system B and the agent in system C can be of an entirely different type. However, communication protocols between the agent and manager in system B are an internal matter.

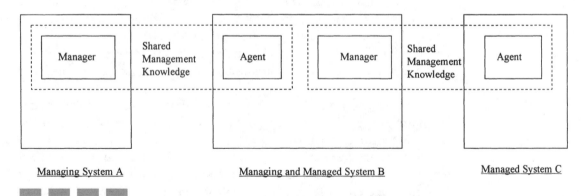

Figure 2-8
Shared management knowledge between different systems (© 1994 IEEE).

2.4 OAM&P

OAM&P is explained in Reference 2.12. OAM&P categories are shown in Figure 2-9. For a better understanding of OAM&P, OAM&P is mapped to OSI systems management functions (Figure 2-9). We will now look into each of the OAM&P categories.

Operations are related to the activities for providing telecommunications services to end users or subscribers. Operations include traffic management and billing. Note that accounting management includes functions beyond billing. Similarly, performance management includes more functions beyond traffic management.

Administration refers to the functions involved in providing efficient services to customers or subscribers and meeting the quality of service requirements. Administration includes traffic management and network management. As can be seen in Figure 2-8, traffic management and network management are part of OSI performance management.

Maintenance activities include detection of faults, location of faults, and restoration of a unit to a specific state by repairing the faults. Maintenance is further subdivided into *corrective maintenance* and *preventive*

Figure 2-9
OAM&P functions and mapping between OAM&P and OSI systems management functions.

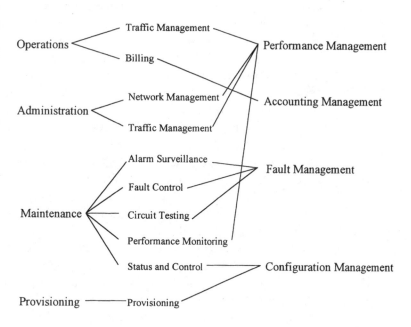

OAM&P

OSI Systems Management Functions

maintenance. Corrective maintenance covers procedures to restore normal operations after a failure has occurred. Instead, the preventive maintenance procedures are used to track and correct possible failures before the occurrence of failures. The objective of preventive maintenance is to minimize the failures. Despite preventive maintenance, failures are unavoidable and this is where the corrective maintenance comes into the picture. Maintenance includes the functions shown in Figure 2-9.

Provisioning refers to the management activity that makes different telecommunications resources available to telecommunications services. Provisioning includes *resource provisioning* and *service provisioning.* Resource provisioning refers to the deployment of resources to satisfy service demands of end users. Service provisioning is related to the activities involved in providing timely services and features to end users.

2.5 CNM

External users of a telecommunications network may need to be provided with limited control and view of the network. This facility is provided by customer network management (CNM). With the globalization of telecommunications services, customer interfaces with service providers have to be uniform from the point of view of cost and ease of use by customers. It is also important that these common customer interfaces be required within nations and across national boundaries. Hence, it is necessary to focus on the standards available in CNM. Internationally, there is no substitute for ITU-T standards.

With this important point in focus, we look into ITU-T standards as related to CNM. However, note that the ITU-T standards on CNM X.160 (Reference 2.6), X.161 (Reference 2.7), X.162 (Reference 2.8), and X.163 (Reference 2.9) are specifically defined for public data networks (PDNs). Still, these standards are generic enough to be applicable to other network technologies with slight modifications. The CNM domain is in the non-TMN environment and it is a vast topic. So we restrict the discussion of CNM to an overview. To complement the ITU-T description of CNM, we also look to ANSI standards on CNM at a high level.

CNM is used for the exchange of management information relating to the services provided between customers and network service providers. These customers can be subscribers of network services or private network administrators who manage a portion of the public networks. The management information used in CNM is more restricted than the normal management information used by service providers to manage their networks. The CNM information provided to customers is more related to service provisioning.

2.5.1 CNM Functional Architecture

CNM functional architecture is shown in Figure 2-10. The boundary between CNM function and the customer's management function is the CNM reference point. The CNM reference point can be mapped to the X reference point. We have discussed the X reference point earlier in this chapter. CNM function is analogous to the function of an OS. CNM function contains the following function blocks:

■ *CNM information:* Contains service management-related information and provides a customer's view of network services.

■ *Access control:* Used to restrict access to the services provided by the network to authorized customers.

■ *CNM application:* Acts in the agent role and implements the CNM services.

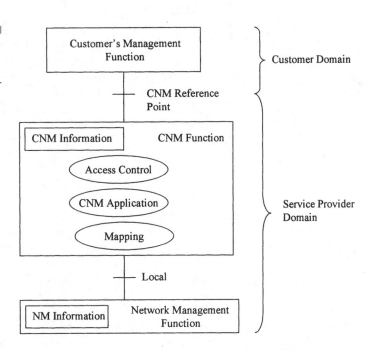

Figure 2-10
CNM functional
architecture.

■ *Mapping:* Provides customer-related management information. As already mentioned, customer-related management information is a subset of the management information used by a service provider.

2.5.2 CNM Physical Architecture and Interfaces

Figure 2-11 explains the CNM physical architecture. As shown in the figure, between the customer's management system and the service provider's CNM system, either a customer network management using CMIP (CNMc) interface or a customer network management using EDI (CNMe) interface can be employed.

The CNMc interface uses CMIP protocols and is useful for supporting interactive and real-time monitoring applications. The CNMc interface provides real-time/asynchronous notification, object-oriented support, and the ability to pick and choose OSI systems management software. For

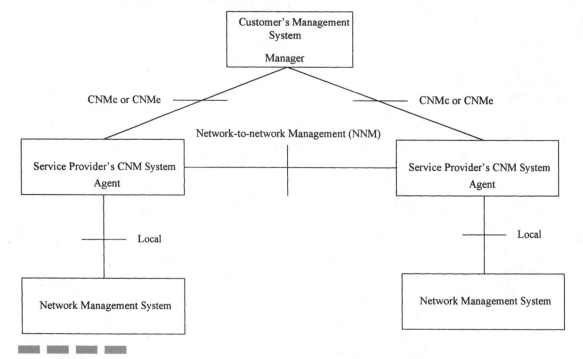

Figure 2-11
CNM physical architecture and interfaces.

more information, including management information on the CNMc interface, refer to Reference 2.8.

The CNMe interface uses electronic data interchange (EDI) messages with message handling services (MHS) as the supporting protocol. The CNMe interface is useful for supporting cases where there is a need for auditing data exchanged between a customer and service provider, such as in contractual obligations.

EDI messages are explained in ISO 9735, Electronic Data Interchange for Administration, Commerce, and Transport (EDIFACT)—Application Level Syntax Rules. MHS is defined in ITU-T Recommendation F.400/X.400, Message Handling Services: Message Handling System and Service Overview. The CNMe interface uses storing and forwarding of information for communication between the customer's management system and the service provider's CNM system. The CNMe interface permits buffering of messages, use of mailboxes, and protection against communication failures. The advantage of using mailboxes is that there is no need to form an association between the CNM customer and the service provider. For more details on the CNMe interface, refer to X.163 (Reference 2.9). Management information flowing across the CNMe interface is also defined in X.163.

Between service providers, the interface for exchange of management information is network-to-network management (NNM). The NNM interface is not standardized. Service providers can choose their own protocols for the exchange of management information across the NNM interface.

In Figure 2-11, two CNM service providers service the customer's management system. Typically, one customer's management system uses the services of a CNM service provider. The motivation for including two service providers is to explain the NNM interface.

In Figure 2-11, the customer's management system provides manager role activities and is located on the customer premises. The service provider's CNM system supports the agent role. Note that there can be one or more associations between a manager and an agent. The topic of association between manager and agent is discussed in detail in Chapter 7.

2.5.3 CNM Management Services

CNM management services are provided to customers by service providers across CNM interfaces. CNM management services are a subset of TMN management services (Chapter 3). As we have seen, CNM interfaces can be CNMc or CNMe. CNM management services are divided into the following groups:

- *Fault management:*   Includes alarm notification service, fault history service, trouble report service, loop setup service, test host service, and protocol monitoring service.

- *Accounting management:*   Includes billing service, detailed accounting service, quota control service, and real-time charging information service.

- *Configuration management:*   Subdivided into configuration inquiry service, reconfiguration service, ordering service, cancellation service, systematic call redirection service, and inventory inquiry service.

- *Performance management:*   Includes traffic information service, quality of service information service, and network statistics service.

- *Security management:*   Concerned with password change service and access rights definition service.

- *CNM supporting services:*   Provides service request function. The service request function enables a customer's management system to request service provisioning or usage from a service provider.

We have briefly looked into different CNM management services; for more details on this subject, refer to X.161 (Reference 2.7).

2.5.4 ANSI-Based CNM

Customers of CNM are the network managers of a telecommunications service. Mapping of CNM to OSI systems management functions is shown in Figure 2-12, and CNM components are as given here:

- *Configuration management:*   Applies to the networks and equipment used in providing telecommunications services. Configuration management includes following categories of functions:
  - *Service establishment:*   Deals with service order—related activities such as receiving a service order, initiating a service order, checking service order status, modifying a service order, canceling a service order, and cross-referencing related service orders.
  - *Service reconfiguration:*   Relates to changing and rearranging assignments, for example adding or deleting a directory number hunt group (DHNG) member in Centrex.
  - *Service information:*   Has to do with listing of circuits and telephone numbers with the services offered. In addition, it also provides the capability to obtain information for planning purposes such as availability of network resources, capacity of resources, compatibility of resources, and so on.

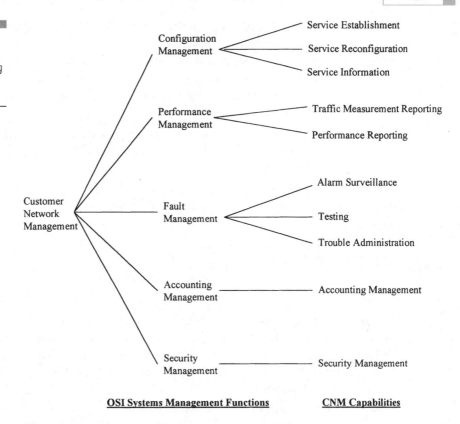

Figure 2-12
CNM management services and mapping to OSI systems management functions.

OSI Systems Management Functions   CNM Capabilities

■ *Performance management:* Consists of the following:
  • *Traffic measurement reporting capability:* Relates to the ability to create, delete, and modify schedules and reports.
  • *Performance monitoring capability:* Refers to the ability to obtain and evaluate the conditions of network resources. Performance monitoring capability may also include real-time performance monitoring and modifying the criteria for real-time performance monitoring, logging performance data, retrieving performance data and modifying performance data logging criteria.

■ *Fault management:* Includes the following:
  • *Alarm surveillance:* Concerned with alarm reporting, logging of alarms, retrieving of alarms logged, modifying alarm logging criteria, and other activities related to performance degradation.
  • *Testing:* Includes a whole range of activities related to the testing of resources and isolating faults. Some of the activities are scheduling

of tests, modifying the parameters related to testing of resources, cancellation of tests, and getting reports on tests.

- *Trouble administration:* Includes activities connected with trouble tickets. These activities include entering trouble, tracking trouble status, canceling trouble information, and getting different kinds of trouble reports.

■ *Accounting management:* Concerned with billing information, billing payment, usage data, and reconciling billing differences and other billing-related activities.

■ *Security management:* Relates to management of security audit trials and alarms, access security, and recovery from intrusion.

2.6 Conformance

Conformance is very important to interoperability. For interoperability, the protocols, formatting of data, and application environments must be similar so that applications developed on different platforms can work together. An application developed by one vendor must work with a similar application from another vendor. For example, two electronic mail systems must work together regardless of which vendors developed the systems.

By and large, standards do not go into the details of implementation; also, standards are either not available or incomplete in some areas. As a result, during implementation some assumptions are made. However, these assumptions may result in incompatible implementations. To overcome this problem, a set of guidelines should be clearly stated for checking whether an implementation has adhered to the standards.

Checking whether an implementation really matches the protocol specifications mentioned in standards such as ITU-T recommendations is done by conformance testing. One of the key aspects of conformance testing is to model the implementation as a set of states and transitions to these states; thus, protocol specifications and implementations are modeled as finite state machines (FSMs).

There are many ITU-T recommendations on how conformance testing is to be done. In addition, most protocol specifications also have portions solely devoted to conformance. So, when interoperability is a key issue, it is important to perform rigorous conformance testing. Conformance is a very vast topic. There are many standards documents and books that have separate chapters devoted to conformance. Refer to these for more details.

2.7 Summary

This chapter explains the basic concepts of TMN. We have examined different types of TMN architecture, namely functional architecture, physical architecture, and information architecture. Detailed explanations are also furnished on interfaces and the closely related topic of reference points.

We also describe different components of OAM&P. This explanation is primarily based on ANSI standards. It is very important to examine the user interfaces to TMN. From this point of view, there is a limited discussion on customer network management (CNM). Though CNM as treated in this chapter is related to public data networks, it can be extended to telecommunications networks based on protocols such as SDH, ISDN, and ATM. From an interoperability standpoint, conformance is an important topic. Therefore we have included a brief description of conformance.

2.8 References

2.1. ITU-T Recommendation M.3010, Principles for a Telecommunications Management Network, 1996.

2.2. ITU-T Recommendation Q811, Lower Layer Protocol Profiles for the Q3 and X Interfaces, 1997.

2.3. ITU-T Recommendation Q812, Upper Layer Protocol Profiles for the Q3 and X Interfaces, 1997.

2.4. ITU-T Recommendation M.3320, Management Requirements Framework for the TMN X-Interface, 1997.

2.5. ITU-T Recommendation M.3300, TMN Management Capabilities Presented at the F Interface, 1992.

2.6. ITU-T Recommendation X.160, Architecture for Customer Network Management Service for Public Data Networks, 1996.

2.7. ITU-T Recommendation X.161, Definition of Customer Network Management Services for Public Data Networks, 1997.

2.8. ITU-T Recommendation X.162, Definition of Customer Network Management Service for Public Data Networks to be used with CNMc Interface, 1997.

2.9. ITU-T Recommendation X.163, Definition of Customer Network Management Services for Public Data Networks to be used with CNMe Interface, 1995.

2.10. ITU-T Recommendation X.500, The Directory: Overview of Concepts, Models and Services, 1993.

2.11. ITU-T Recommendation X.800, Security Architecture for Open Systems Interconnection for CCITT Applications, 1991.

2.12. ANSI T1.210, *Telecommunications—Operations, Administration, Maintenance, and Provisioning (OAM&P)—Principles of Functions, Architectures, and Protocols for Telecommunications Management Network (TMN) Interfaces,* New York: American National Standards Institute, 1993.

2.13. Udupa, D. K., *Network Management Systems Essentials,* New York: McGraw-Hill, 1996.

2.14. Sen Subhabrata, B., Network Performance Management. In *Telecommunications Network Management into the 21st Century,* Aidarous, S. and Plevyak, T. (eds.), New York: The Institute of Electrical and Electronics Engineers, Inc., pp. 302—336, 1994.

2.15. Sahin, V., Telecommunications Management Network, Principles, Models, and Applications. In *Telecommunications Network Management into the 21st Century,* Aidarous, S. and Plevyak, T. (eds.), New York: The Institute of Electrical and Electronics Engineers, Inc., pp. 72—121, 1994.

CHAPTER 3

TMN Management Services and TMN Functions

3.1 Introduction

There are some basic differences in network management for data communications and telecommunications. The scope of network management in telecommunications is broader and slightly different. Some of the major areas of differences are related to user activities in provisioning, alarm surveillance, and traffic management. This is partly due to the more stringent regulatory environments in the telecommunications industry. As a result, in TMN more network management functionality has to be covered.

The basic TMN documents are M.3000-series documents. These documents define different TMN architectures, interfaces, management services, and functions. In Chapter 2 we discussed TMN architecture and interfaces; in this chapter we will discuss different TMN management services and TMN functions.

From a TMN standards point of view, telecommunications management network management services (TMN-MSs) are described in ITU-T Recommendation M.3200 (Reference 3.1). TMN management functions are described in ITU-T Recommendation M.3400 (Reference 3.2). The overall structure of how the TMN management services and TMN management functions are related is explained in ITU-T Recommendation M.3020 (Reference 3.3). In addition, M.3020 ties together the concepts of TMN users, management services, management functions, operations, attributes, notifications, and managed object classes.

3.2 TMN Management Services

TMN-MSs are modeled from a user perspective. They provide the operations, administration, maintenance, and provisioning (OAM&P) support for a telecommunications network. A TMN-MS can reside in different systems and is not part of standardization.

The hierarchy of TMN-MSs is shown in Figure 3-1. The TMN-MS is partitioned into TMN management function set groups, which are further subdivided into TMN management function sets. A TMN function set includes two or more TMN management functions. In the hierarchy of relationships between TMN-MSs and TMN functions, a TMN function is the smallest functional part of a TMN-MS and the TMN function is at the lowest level of the hierarchy.

By combining elementary building blocks such as TMN management functions, we can form simple to complex TMN applications in a modu-

Figure 3-1
Hierarchy of
management services
and management
functions.

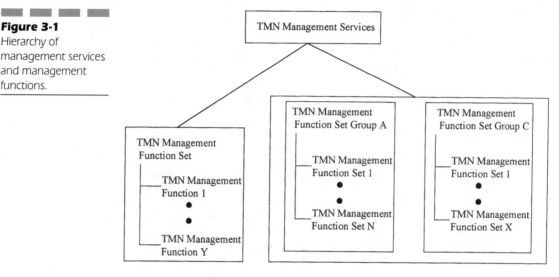

lar manner. This is analogous to building simple to complex and sophisti-
cated houses or building complexes with the elementary bricks or concrete slabs with gluing and supporting materials.

Let us look into another specific example of a TMN management function set group. Alarm surveillance consists of an alarm reporting function
set, an alarm summary function set, an alarm event criteria function set, an
alarm indication management function set, and a log control function set.
The alarm reporting function set, in turn, includes a report alarm function, an inhibit/allow alarm reporting function, a request alarm report
route function, a condition alarm reporting function, and a route alarm
report function.

A TMN-MS can be provided by one or more TMN management functions. TMN management functions are mapped to TMN systems management (SM) services and these TMN SM services exchange management
information with the managed objects as shown in Figure 3-2. The
exchange of management information between TMN SM services is done
by a series of operations and notifications on one or more managed
object instances using CMIS services.

TMN management functions such as performance monitoring usually reside in a manager or an OS. The data related to these management
functions are collected from the agents or NEs by an exchange of messages between the NEs and the OS. This exchange of messages is done by
using management protocols. Usually, in TMN, the management protocol

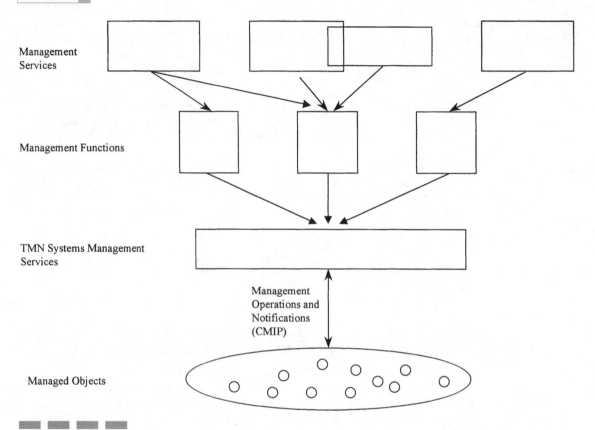

Figure 3.2
TMN systems management services.

is CMIP. CMISE services are M-GET, M-CANCEL-GET, M-SET, M-ACTON, M-CREATE, M-DELETE, and M-EVENT-REPORT. We will look in detail at CMISE services in Chapter 7. Note that the exchange of messages between managers and agents can also be done by FTAM as an alternative to the use of CMIP.

TMN SM services (Figure 3-3) are provided by one or more OSI systems management functions such as log control functions, event report management functions, security audit trail functions, and so on. The OSI specification documents of interest to us are the 10164 series.

In this section, only a summary of management services is provided. For more details refer to Reference 3.1. Also, M.3400 Appendix has detailed flows on each of the management services.

The details of the management services are as follows:

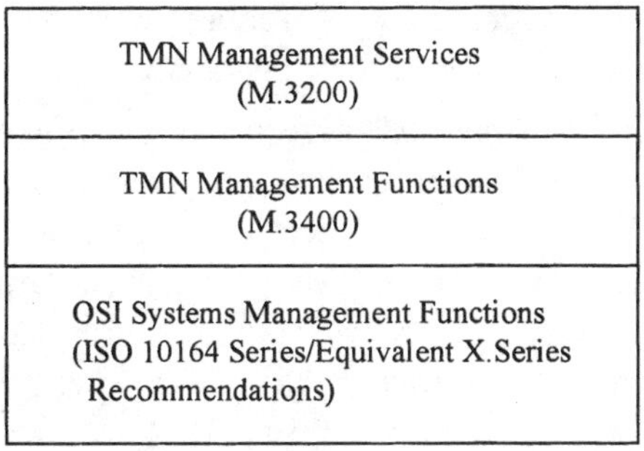

▬▬ ▬▬ ▬▬ ▬▬

Figure 3-3
Basis for TMN systems
management services.

TMN Management Services (M.3200)
TMN Management Functions (M.3400)
OSI Systems Management Functions (ISO 10164 Series/Equivalent X.Series Recommendations)

- *Customer administration:* Concerned with fulfilling customer require-ments and interfacing with customers on the telephone services offered. Customer administration needs to transmit these telephone service—related data, such as the services and features, to the network administration to satisfy customer requirements. This MS includes service provisioning management, configuration administration, fault administration, charging administration, complaints administration, quality of service administration, and traffic measurement adminis-tration. Some of the customer administration functions are service activation, customer request to make changes to the services, customer request for information about the status of services and network resources, and reporting of customer trouble to the trouble ticket mechanism.

- *Network provisioning management:* Encompasses the functions of management of processes for providing new and traditional services to customers in a very efficient and proactive manner. To provide new resources or features, an expansion of the existing resource capacity may be required.

- *Workforce management:* Responsible for the deployment of appropri-ate field staff to perform maintenance, repair, and installation. This MS may also involve deployment of field staff in customer premises.

- *Tariff, charging, and accounting administration:* Involves the whole gamut of billing and accounting management of customers. Some of the functions include billing the customers at regular intervals; taking action on unpaid bills; and resolving customer complaints on billing, including errors, changes in tariffs based on customer choices, detec-tion of fraud using traffic analysis, and so on. For new customers, billing and pricing processes have to be set up. Tariff, charging, and account administration also require usage measurement and testing.

Billing starts with service activation and necessary paperwork that has to be generated with the service activation.

■ *Quality of service and network performance administration:*   Customers need consistent telecommunications services with good transmission quality and assured performance. The QOS and network performance administration includes root cause elimination by investigation, interviewing, analysis, and testing. Some functions of this MS are traffic quality assurance; performance quality assurance; and reliability, availability, and survivability (RAS) quality assurance. Information from NEs on fault localization, network fault localization, and service outage reports provide input for RAS quality assurance.

■ *Traffic measurement and analysis administration:*   Sometimes, traffic load on a network may be larger or smaller than planned. Also, adding new services can change the traffic pattern. In such scenarios, a traffic administration process is required to resolve the congestion or underutilization problems. Traffic administration also includes a traffic measurement process.

■ *Traffic management:*   Kicked off to solve current traffic problems as a result of failures and outages of telecommunications resources, abnormal increases in traffic load, and so on. For traffic management, performance monitoring and performance management functions are required.

■ *Routing and digit analysis administration:*   Required for verifying routing information in an exchange, changing routing information in tables, and switching routing tables on a time schedule.

■ *Maintenance management:*   When a failure or a problem is detected in any resource in a network, a trouble ticket is opened. The failure/problem rectification is tracked with the trouble ticket opened as a reference. Here, mean time between failures is also helpful. Maintenance management includes proactive maintenance, network detected trouble, fault localization, and fault correction.

■ *Security administration:*   Concerned with the security of switches, customers, and billing and accounting information. It also deals with establishing and changing customer privileges, detection of security violations, and taking steps to prevent security violations.

■ *Logistics management:*   Required for offering telecommunications services to customers and for achieving improvements in the availability of equipment in a telecommunications network. Materials management is responsible for procuring items and making them available to the transmission equipment and other equipment in the telecommunications network in a timely manner. Logistics management enables timely deployment of resources to meet customer and internal demands, keeping the cost factor in focus.

3.2.1 Mapping of SMFAs and TMN Management Function Set Groups

As we have seen in Chapter 1, SMFA is an OSI systems management term. The same term is also popular in TMN. Figure 3-4 shows the mapping of SMFAs to different TMN Management Function Set Groups. We discuss each of the TMN management function set groups in detail in the following sections.

Figure 3-4
Mapping of SMFAs and TMN management function set groups.

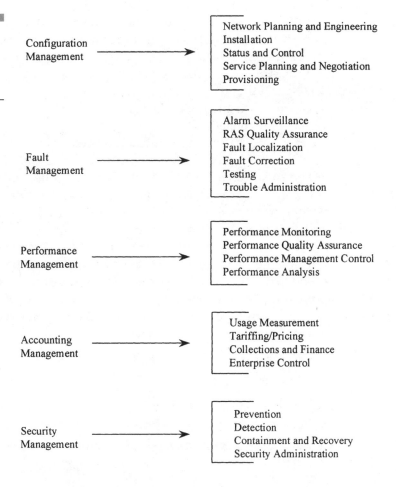

Configuration Management →
- Network Planning and Engineering
- Installation
- Status and Control
- Service Planning and Negotiation
- Provisioning

Fault Management →
- Alarm Surveillance
- RAS Quality Assurance
- Fault Localization
- Fault Correction
- Testing
- Trouble Administration

Performance Management →
- Performance Monitoring
- Performance Quality Assurance
- Performance Management Control
- Performance Analysis

Accounting Management →
- Usage Measurement
- Tariffing/Pricing
- Collections and Finance
- Enterprise Control

Security Management →
- Prevention
- Detection
- Containment and Recovery
- Security Administration

3.3 TMN Management Function Sets and Management Functions

In this section we examine how TMN management functions are relevant to network management. TMN management functions are defined in ITU-T Recommendation M.3400, TMN Management Functions. The material included here is patterned on the lines of M.3400. For details on each of the individual function sets, refer to M.3400, which has detailed descriptions.

3.4 Performance Management

One of the primary performance management functions is to collect performance-related data on the telecommunications networks and equipment. Once these data are collected from the resources in a manager or OS from network elements, the data have to be analyzed. The performance data—including the reports on the data, especially the bottlenecks—have to be identified and the problems have to be corrected. Performance management also includes traffic management. ITU-T Recommendation Q823 (Reference 3.6) defines many managed object classes. These should be utilized in the design of the traffic management application.

Performance management also involves collecting QOS-related data and improving the QOS. In addition, performance management includes the performance-related issues of NEs. Note that in the explanations given here, *NEs* refers to one or more NEs.

QOS is measured by characteristics such as the rate of information transfer; the probability of system failure, storage failure, and communication disruption; and the latency. QOS is measurable at the service access point and is quantified in terms of user-perceivable effects.

QOS is an important factor in the TMN. QOS is applicable to the following parameters:

- Customer connection establishment
- Customer connection retention
- Customer connection quality
- Billing integrity
- Keeping and examining logs of system state histories

- Cooperation with fault management to establish source of failure of a resource
- Cooperation with configuration management to change routing and load control parameters
- Performing tests to monitor QOS parameters

However, many issues are involved in the collection of performance data. As an example, if the performance data is collected in short intervals, then the network traffic will increase, impacting network performance. On the other hand, if too few data are collected, then usability of those data will be severely affected. Therefore care must be taken to use the right kind of schedule to collect the performance-related data.

There are four function set groups in performance management. These are discussed in the following text.

3.4.1 Performance Quality Assurance

The function of performance quality assurance is to establish processes to meet the customer's needs with respect to the performance management. Performance quality assurance has the following function sets:

- QOS performance goal setting
- QOS performance assessment
- Network performance goal setting
- Network performance assessment
- Subscriber service quality criteria
- NE performance assessment
- Data integrity check

3.4.2 Performance Monitoring

The function of performance monitoring (PM) is to continuously collect performance-related data on system, network, or service activities. PM is slightly different from alarm surveillance. Alarm surveillance is related to acute fault conditions, whereas performance monitoring is related to the very low-rate or intermittent error conditions not detected by alarm surveillance. PM includes the following function sets:

- Performance monitoring policy
- Network performance monitoring event correlation and filtering
- Data aggregation and trending
- Circuit-specific data collection
- Traffic status
- Traffic performance monitoring
- NE threshold crossing alert processing
- NE trend analysis
- Performance monitoring data accumulation
- Detection, counting, storage, and reporting

3.4.3 Performance Management Control

Performance management control is responsible for controlling the performance of a telecommunications network. Network traffic management includes traffic control, which affects routing of traffic and processing of calls. Transport performance includes functions such as setting thresholds and collecting performance data. Performance management control includes the following function sets:

- Network traffic management policy
- Traffic control
- Traffic administration
- Performance administration
- Execution of traffic control
- Audit reporting

3.4.4 Performance Analysis

Performance analysis is involved in the analysis of performance data of an entity. It supports the following function sets:

- Recommendations for performance improvements
- Exception threshold policy
- Traffic forecasting
- Customer service performance summary

- Customer traffic performance summary
- Traffic exception analysis
- Traffic capacity analysis
- Network performance characterization
- NE performance characterization
- NE traffic exception analysis
- NE traffic capacity analysis

3.5 Fault Management

Fault management is responsible for detecting and isolating abnormal conditions that affect the operation of a telecommunications network and its environment. Fault management also includes quality assurance measurement for RAS. Effective fault management may require errors to be logged in a database. The fault management functional area covers the fault management function set groups presented in the next sections.

3.5.1 RAS Quality Assurance

RAS quality assurance establishes guidelines for reliability of other fault management—related functions and the design of redundant equipment. RAS quality assurance includes the following function sets:

- Network RAS goal setting
- Service availability goal setting
- RAS assessment
- Service outage reporting
- Network outage reporting
- NE outage reporting

3.5.2 Alarm Surveillance

Alarm surveillance provides the capability for real-time monitoring and interrogation of NE failures. When there is a failure in an NE, it reports the failure, sometimes along with the nature and severity of the fault. If there is intelligence in an NE, it will send notifications to the manager or OS with the details of failure. In simple cases, the NE may just indicate that a failure has occurred. These details of the failure may be reported at the time of its occurrence or logged for future use. An alarm, because of a failure, may lead to some other management actions within an NE.

At this juncture it is appropriate to look into the distinctions between an alarm and an event. An *alarm* is a notification for a specific event indicating a problem condition. An alarm may or may not represent an error. An *event* is an instantaneous occurrence that changes at least one of the attributes representing the global status of an object. This status change may be persistent or temporary, and it may be monitored by alarm surveillance or performance measurement functionality. Events may or may not generate reports, and may be spontaneous or planned.

For alarm surveillance, an NE must permit monitoring of the alarm in real time or in a scheduled manner, and the NE must be enabled to query on the alarm conditions and allow logging and retrieval of the historical alarm information. There is a separate ITU-T recommendation for alarm surveillance (Reference 3.5) that should also be used while designing alarm surveillance. Alarm surveillance includes the following function sets:

- Alarm policy
- Network fault event analysis, including correlation and filtering
- Alarm status modification
- Alarm reporting
- Alarm summary
- Alarm event criteria
- Alarm indication management
- Log control
- Alarm correlation and filtering
- Failure event detection and reporting

3.5.3 Fault Localization

When a fault occurs, it is necessary to identify its location. This may require tests to pinpoint the problem and its cause. This functionality is the domain of the fault localization function. Fault localization has the following function sets:

- Fault localization policy
- Verification of parameters and connectivity
- Network fault localization
- NEs fault localization
- Running of diagnostics

3.5.4 Fault Correction

Fault correction is responsible for repairing or replacing the faulty equipment or using redundant equipment to replace the faulty equipment after a fault has been detected. This area has plenty of scope for automation, thereby improving productivity for telecommunications service providers and bettering the customer satisfaction. Fault correction has the following function sets:

- Management of repair processes
- Arrangements for repairs with customer
- Scheduling and dispatching administration of repair forces
- NE fault correction
- Automatic restoration

3.5.5 Testing

Testing of equipment to check its characteristics or analysis of circuits is done routinely. The management application is responsible for receiving requests from an NE to conduct tests and reporting the results of the tests. The tests and the processing of test results are done in the NE. These test results may be sent to management applications immediately or on a delayed basis. In another method of testing, the management application requests access for testing an NE. The main testing and processing is done by the management application. Testing includes the following function sets:

- Test point policy
- Service test
- Circuit selection, test correlation, and fault location
- Selection of test suite
- Test access network control and recovery

- Test access configuration
- Test circuit configuration
- NE test control function
- Results and status reporting
- Test access path management
- Test access

3.5.6 Trouble Administration

Trouble administration is related to the administrative aspects of trouble reports generated by trouble tickets. Trouble reports are generated due to problems reported by customers or due to proactive equipment failure detection checks. Trouble administration has the following function sets:

- Trouble report policy
- Trouble reporting
- Trouble report status change notification
- Trouble information query
- Trouble ticket creation notification
- Trouble ticket administration

3.6 Configuration Management

The scope of configuration management covers areas such as collecting data from NEs, providing data to NEs, and exercising control over data collection from NEs.

3.6.1 Network Planning and Engineering

The network planning and engineering function is devoted to determining the needs for growth in capacity and the introduction of new technologies. It also involves evaluating alternate plans, and the output of this function becomes input to provisioning to implement the plan for introducing new technology and services. Network planning and engineering includes the following function sets:

- Product line budget
- Supplier and technology policy
- Area boundary definition
- Infrastructure planning
- Management of planning and engineering process
- Demand forecasting
- Network infrastructure design
- Access infrastructure design
- Facility infrastructure design
- Routing design
- NE design

3.6.2 Installation

The installation function set group is responsible for installing the telecommunications network, equipment, and NEs. Installation may also involve extending or shrinking the telecommunications network; installing hardware and software and initial data loading; and testing that a piece of equipment works in a desired fashion and meets the requirements. Installation includes the following function sets:

- Procurement
- Management of installation
- Contracting
- Real estate management
- Arrangement of installation with customer
- Network installation administration
- Materials management
- Scheduling and dispatch administration of installation
- Installation completion report
- Software administration
- NE installation administration
- Loading software into NEs

3.6.3 Service Planning and Negotiation

Service planning and negotiation is concerned with new services, upgrading of services and features, and disconnecting services. Service planning and negotiation has the following function sets:

- Service planning
- Service feature definition
- Marketing
- Management of sales process
- External relations
- Customer identification
- Customer need identification
- Customer service planning
- Customer service features
- Solution proposal

3.6.4 Provisioning

Provisioning involves the procedures required to bring equipment into service. It does not include installation. Provisioning may also control the state of a unit—such as in service, out of service, on standby, reserved—and other important parameters. We also briefly covered the topic of provisioning in Chapter 2, Section 2.4. Provisioning includes the following function sets:

- Provisioning policy
- Materials management policy
- Access route determination
- Directory address determination
- Leased circuit route determination
- Request for service
- Service status administration
- Network resource selection and assignment
- Interexchange circuit design
- Access circuit design

- Leased circuit design
- Facility design
- Management of pending network changes
- Network connection management
- Circuit inventory notification
- Circuit inventory query
- NE configuration
- NE administration
- NE database management
- Assignable inventory management
- NE resource selection and assignment
- NE path design
- Loading program for service features
- NE inventory notification
- NE inventory query
- Management of pending changes in NEs
- Storage of parameters and cross-connects
- Storage and execution of service
- Self-inventory

3.6.5 Status and Control

Status and control has the responsibility of monitoring and controlling the activities of NEs, checking and changing the service status of an NE, and initiating diagnostic tests within the NE. Status and control can also be part of routine maintenance. Status and control has the following function sets:

- Priority service policy
- Priority service restoration
- Message handling systems network status
- Leased circuit network status
- Transport network status
- NE status and control
- Access to state information
- Notification of state changes by NEs

3.7 Accounting Management

Accounting management is devoted to the measurement of costs to the network service provider and charges to customers for the usage of network services and features. The description of the function set groups in accounting management is furnished in the following sections.

3.7.1 Usage Measurement

The data for charging customers is collected from NEs and stored in an OS. Data collection for charging and processing of data has to be reliable and, sometimes, has to be done in real time. There is also a need to keep records of billing to resolve discrepancies that may arise later. Usage measurement includes the following function sets:

- Planning of the usage measurement process
- Management of the usage measurement process
- Usage aggregation
- Service usage correlation
- Service usage validation
- Usage distribution
- Usage surveillance
- Usage error correction
- Usage testing
- Measurement rule identification
- Network usage correlation
- Short-term usage storage
- Long-term usage storage
- Usage accumulation
- Usage validation
- Administration of usage data collection
- Usage generation

3.7.2 Tariffing/Pricing

A *tariff* is a set of data used to determine the charges for services used. A tariff may depend on the service, origination and destination, tariff period, and day of call. A tariff has the following function sets:

- Pricing strategy
- Tariff and price administration
- Costing
- Settlements policy
- Feature pricing
- Provision of access to tariff/price information
- Rating usage
- Totaling usage charges

3.7.3 Collections and Finance

The collections and finance TMN functional set group includes administration of customer accounts, informing customers on payment dates, payment amount, and collection of payments. This function set group includes the following function sets:

- Planning of the billing process
- Management of the billing process
- General accounting operations
- General ledger
- Accounts receivable
- Accounts payable
- Payroll
- Benefits administration
- Pension administration
- Taxation
- Human resources
- Invoice assembly
- Sending invoices
- Customer tax administration
- In-call service request
- Storage of invoice
- Receipt of payment
- Inquiry response
- Collections

- Customer account administration
- Customer profile administration

3.7.4 Enterprise Control

Enterprise control is responsible for the proper financial management of an enterprise. It also includes identifying and ensuring financial account-ability of officers and the flow of funds between the enterprise and its owners and creditors. Enterprise control includes checks and balances needed for a smooth financial operation of an enterprise. Enterprise control has the following function sets:

- Budgeting
- Auditing
- Cash management
- Raising equity
- Cost reduction
- Profitability analysis
- Financial reporting
- Insurance analysis
- Investments
- Asset management
- Tracking of liabilities

3.8 Security Management

Security management is concerned with security in communication between systems, between customers and systems, and between internal users and systems. Security services include authentication, access control, data confidentiality, data integrity, and nonrepudiation. These security services are defined in ITU-T Recommendation X.800 (Reference 3.8). Security services are also required for event detection, security audit trail management, and security recovery. Security violations such as access by unauthorized users and tampering with important data are reported to appropriate security violation tracking layers.

3.8.1 Prevention

The prevention function set group is related to activities such as prevention of intrusion by unauthorized users. Prevention also includes access control and has the following function sets:

- Legal review
- Physical access security
- Guarding
- Personnel risk analysis
- Security screening

3.8.2 Detection

Detection is both a proactive and an after-the-fact function. It is responsible for guarding against possible intrusion by keeping track of unusual activities, and has to take into account both detecting and tracking intrusions. Detection has the following function sets:

- Investigation of changes in revenue patterns
- Support element protection
- Customer security alarm
- Customer profiling
- Customer usage pattern analysis
- Investigation of theft of service
- Internal traffic and activity pattern analysis
- Network security alarm
- Software intrusion audit
- Support element security alarm reporting

3.8.3 Containment and Recovery

Containment and recovery has to do with prevention of intrusion, repair of damage, and recovery after intrusion and security violations have occurred. Containment and recovery has the following function sets:

- Protected storage of business data
- Exception report action
- Theft service action
- Legal action
- Apprehending
- Service intrusion recovery
- Administration of customer revocation
- Protected storage of customer data
- Severing external connections
- Network intrusion recovery
- Administration of network revocation list
- Protected storage of network configuration data
- Severing internal connections
- NE intrusion recovery
- Administration of NE revocation list
- Protected storage of NE configuration data

3.8.4 Security Administration

Security administration has to do with managing, planning, and administrating security-related policies and security related data. Security administration has the following function sets:

- Security policy
- Disaster recovery planning
- Management guards
- Audit trail analysis
- Security alarm analysis
- Assessment of corporate data integrity
- Administration of external authentication
- Administration of external access control
- Administration of external certification
- Administration of external encryption and keys
- Administration of external security protocols

- Customer audit trail
- Customer security alarm management
- Testing of audit trail mechanism
- Administration of internal authentication
- Administration of internal access control
- Administration of internal certification
- Administration of internal encryption
- Network audit trail management
- Network security alarm management
- NE audit trail management
- NE security alarm management
- Administration of key for NEs
- Administration of key by an NE

3.9 Implementation Notes

Development of network management solutions can be broadly divided into the following categories:

- Providing network management basic infrastructure such as implementing manager and agents.
- Providing network management application solutions. Note that in M.3020 (Reference 3.3), management application is also known as *management services*. As an example, we want to add new network management functionality such as trouble ticket application and integrate with help desk features. In this case, there are two scenarios. In one scenario, we will buy the software packages available for trouble ticket and help desk features. After buying these packages, we integrate the software packages and tailor them to meet the specific requirements of an organization. In the other case, we develop all the software packages in house and do the integration as well.
- Providing enhancements to the existing network management application functions. In this case, we are already using a network management application, but we are extending the functionality of the application by adding new features. As an example, we have the trouble ticket and help desk features. Now, we want to add some automa-

tion features to the trouble ticket and help desk features, such as automatic paging of the appropriate repair technician and sending an e-mail with all the details of a given problem so the technician can attend to and rectify the problem.

In all cases, the first activity involved in development is to gather the user needs. From the user needs, detailed requirements are prepared. The more detailed and stable the requirements are, the fewer problems will be encountered in the design and development stages. In most of the TMN implementations, TMN solutions are staged into different phases/releases for convenience and easy development. Therefore the requirements should be broken down into different stages.

From the list of requirements follow design, development, and testing. Testing includes system test, conformance tests, and acceptance tests. This is the basic flow of activities for developing network management solutions. Note that this development scenario is almost similar to normal development activities encountered in any software development. However, in telecommunications, due to regulatory environments, the quality requirements are stringent.

Now we examine the specific development cycle and activities involved in providing network management solutions. First, identify and prepare the list of telecommunications resources to be managed. Also, identify the management information needed and the operations to be performed on the telecommunications resources. From this, prepare a list of requirements on how these resources are to be managed.

From the list of requirements, prepare the list of TMN management services and management functions. We have already examined what the management services and management functions mean. After this step, develop a management information model—this process is also known as *object modeling.* The management information model is a means to specify interfaces between resources and managing systems. This is known as the *top-down approach.* This approach is time consuming, but it permits refinement of object classes in an iterative manner.

In another approach, known as the *bottom-up approach,* managed object classes are modeled from the resources. This approach saves time, but it has the limitation of creating complex managed object classes and not permitting easy refinement of managed object classes. GSM 12.00 (Reference 3.8) suggests a pragmatic approach, which is a combination of the top-down and bottom-up approaches. We have deliberately introduced the pragmatic approach here, as it is an interesting alternative to the top-down and bottom-up approaches. For more details on the pragmatic approach, refer to Reference 3.8.

One of the principal activities of information modeling is the development of managed object classes with associated attributes, actions, behaviors, and notifications. The information model also contains relationships between managed object classes. Entity relationship (E-R) diagrams represent the relationship between managed object classes. The managed object classes represent the management aspects of the telecommunications resources. The telecommunications resources to be managed usually reside in managed systems.

The information model defines the interface between resources and the managing system and also the messages exchanged between resources and managed systems. CMIP or SNMP protocols can be used to exchange management information. We have specifically used the term *exchange* to convey that the management information flow can be from a managed system to a resource and also from a resource to a managed system.

From the management information model, it is clear when and how a resource has to report or reply to the managing system. And from the managing system's point of view, it is clear how the managing system will receive notifications and how it will process management operations such as CMIS M-SET, M-GET, and others. How the managing system analyzes the received information and reacts to the management operations is not included in the standardization process.

While designing object classes, there are many options. One of the options is to use the standard managed object classes defined in ANSI standards, GSM standards, ITU-T recommendations such as M.3100, and X.721 standards. In addition, there are many standard documents related to specific activities. These standard documents also define managed object classes. As an example, X.740 defines the managed object class securityAuditTrialRecord. Thus this managed object class can be used without changes if there is a need to record security-related activities.

Sometimes, these managed object classes do not satisfy the specific requirements. In such cases, one has to define one's own object classes. If one goes for proprietary definition of managed object classes, one has to define the inheritance hierarchy and the containment hierarchy as well. The definition of managed object classes is done using ASN.1 and GDMO definitions. In the case of TMN solutions using Internet network management, SMI for Internet has to be used for defining managed object classes.

The management information schema is derived from information model. It represents the view of the information model presented by a managed system to a managing system. The management information schema contains all managed object classes that are visible to a managing system, the naming hierarchy between managed object classes in the managed system, and all possible cases of information exchanged between a managed system and managing system.

A strategy to instantiate object classes is required. Note that in the following discussions on object instances, the way managed object classes are defined largely influences how object instances can be created. Let us take some examples of how to instantiate object instances. For bit error rate (BER) testing to be performed on a resource, one instance of the BER test object class is required in each NE and the operations system (OS). That means an OS will have as many instances of the BER object classes as there are NEs. As an example, if three NEs are to be subjected to BER testing, the OS will have three instances of the BER test object class (Figure 3-5). With this arrangement, all NEs can be subjected simultaneously to BER testing.

The design of the BER test object class may be changed such that we have only one object instance of the BER test object class in the OS and each NE has one object instance of each BER test object class. In this case it is possible to perform BER testing on only one NE at a time.

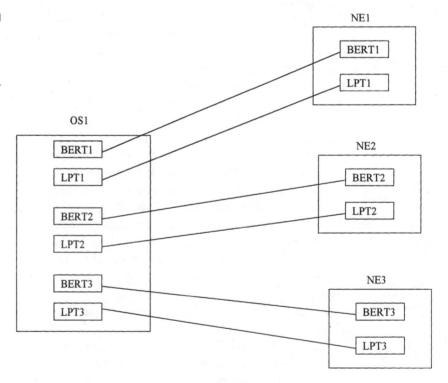

Figure 3-5

Instantiating object classes—separate BER and loopback tests.

However, if another test such as a loopback test is also to be performed on the resource, then we need another set of loopback test object instances in the NE and the OS (Figure 3-5).

We have to be careful while creating object instances. If too many are created, it may cause a performance bottleneck. To reduce the number of object instances, we can create a single managed object class for BER test and loopback test (Figure 3-6). In this case we need only one set of object instances each in an OS and an NE. However, this design imposes a restriction that a BER test and a loopback test cannot be performed at the same time. Besides, if a managed object class is complex and performs a large number of activities, design and implementation of the managed object class can present difficulties. In such cases, a trade-off is required.

Along with the design of the information schema, we have to determine the communication requirements, such as the type of transactions, file transfer, file access, and so on. Also, there can be requirements of throughput, reliability, restrictions on naming, and transit delay. The type of communication stack required should also be determined at this stage.

Figure 3-6

Instantiating object classes—combined BER and loopback tests.

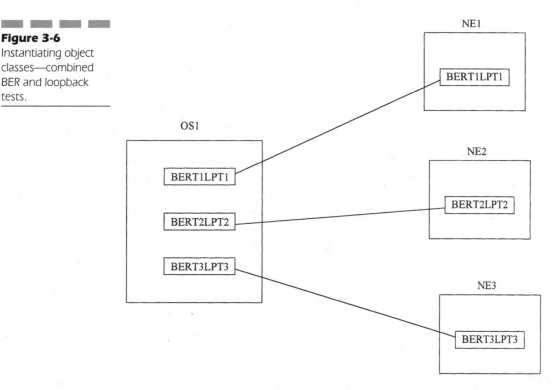

As an example, sometimes it may not be necessary to have a full OSI seven-layer stack. Instead of the OSI seven-layer stack, a partial OSI stack with fewer than seven layers may be enough to meet the needs of the management applications.

Let us take the case of developing a performance management application. As an example, for performance management, it is necessary to take into consideration ITU-T Recommendation M.3400, Workload Monitoring Function, X.739 (ISO 10164-11), Summarization Function, X.738 (ISO 10164-13), and Q.822, Description for the Q3 Interface—Performance Management (Reference 3.4). The managed object classes required for the performance management must be a collection of managed object classes defined in the standards.

The workload monitoring function defines object classes for monitoring performance, such as scanner, monitorMetric, gaugeMonitor, meanMonitor, movingAverageMeanMonitor, ewmaMeanVarianceMonitor, and ewmaMeanPercentileMonitor.

Similarly, the managed object classes defined in the summarization function aid in the preparation of summary reports on one or more attributes of observed managed objects. The managed object classes defined in the summarization function document are: simpleScanner, dynamicScanner, dynamicSimpleScanner, ensembleStatisticScanner, heterogeneousScanner, bufferedScanner, homogeneousScanner, meanScanner, meanVarianceScanner, minMaxScanner, and percentileScanner. The managed object classes for the workload monitoring function and the summarization function are explained in the respective standards or in Reference 3.9. Therefore they are not explained further.

ITU-T recommendation Q.822 also defines managed object classes for performance management, such as currentData, historyData, and thresholdData. currentData is a subclass of scanner. An instance of currentData contains the current performance data. An instance of currentData is contained in the managed object being monitored and has performance data of the containing managed object. The managed object class historyData is a subclass of *top*. The attributes of the historyData managed object are a copy of the attributes in the currentData object at the end of a recording interval. As a result, current data becomes history data at the end of a recording interval. Again, to collect the current data, a new instance of historyData is created. The thresholdData managed object class supports the attributes for threshold settings for performance monitoring. The thresholdData is a subclass of *top*.

While developing the performance management application, it is necessary to identify the resources on which performance data must be collected. Then it is necessary to decide how and in what frequency performance data have to be collected. Here it is necessary to check whether object classes that have been defined in the standards can be reused. If these standards do not satisfy the requirements, then one has to define one's own object classes. Reference 3.9 contains more details on how to develop different SMFAs.

NEs may require one or more OSs. If there are too many NEs to be managed by a single OS, then more than one OS will be required. In this case, we will become involved with distributed network management. We will look into distributed network management issues in Chapter 11.

In another case, the type of OS required is governed by the management functions to be provided. As we have seen in Chapter 2, an OS may be used to provide element management, network management, service management, or business management layer functions. As an example, for service management functions such as billing and customer support, a service management OS will be required.

Some of the tricky issues in the implementation are how to transfer data from NEs to an OS. In some cases, such as that of performance data, a large amount of data is to be handled. Scheduling of these performance data is also important. For scheduling, we can use one of the scheduling managed object classes defined in X.746, Scheduling Function. Or, for simple implementations, NEs may just collect the performance data and transfer the performance data to the OS using FTAM.

3.10 Summary

This chapter covers management services and management functions. There are detailed discussions on the management services and management functions. It is necessary to have an explanation and feeling for the management functions as they form the base for systems management applications such as configuration management. This chapter ends with implementation details on how to develop management applications, taking performance management as an example.

3.11 References

3.1. ITU-T Recommendation M.3200, TMN Management Services and Telecommunications Managed Areas: Overview, 1997.

3.2. ITU-T Recommendation M.3400, TMN Management Functions, 1997.

3.3. ITU-T Recommendation M.3020, TMN Interface Specification Methodology, 1995.

3.4. ITU-T Recommendation Q822, Stage 1, Stage 2 and Stage 3 Description for the Q3 Interface—Performance Management, 1994.

3.5. ITU-T Recommendation Q821, Stage 2 and Stage 3 Description for the Q3 Interface—Alarm Surveillance, 1993.

3.6. ITU-T Recommendation Q823, Stage 2 and Stage 3 Functional Specifications for Traffic Management, 1996.

3.7. ITU-T Recommendation X.800, Security Architecture for Open Systems Interconnection for CCITT Applications, 1991.

3.8. ETSI GSM 12.00 (ETS 300 612-1), European Digital Cellular Telecommunication System (Phase 2), Network Management (NM): Part 1: Objectives and Structure of Network Management, 1996.

3.9. Udupa, D. K., *Network Management Systems Essentials,* New York: McGraw-Hill, 1996.

TMN Information Model and Protocols

CHAPTER 4

TMN Terms
and Concepts

4.1 Introduction

Let us examine some of the important frequently used basic TMN concepts. As we alluded to in Chapter 1, many OSI systems management concepts, terms, and standards are also used in ITU-T TMN. As a result, we have the OSI prefix in many places. Some of the terms explained in this chapter, such as *polling* and *heartbeat*, are frequently used in TMN, systems management, and Internet network management.

This chapter will examine some important systems management concepts, such as management domains, management information hierarchies—the registration, inheritance, and containment hierarchies—object naming, scoping and filtering, synchronization, polymorphism, and allomorphism. Scoping and filtering will be useful in fault management. Also, we will discuss the topics of management state and the attributes used for relationships, which pertain to connecting managed objects. Management state and relationships between objects are very important concepts for configuration management. Though we have already identified fault management and configuration management, these terms will be used in other systems management functional areas as well. In addition, some of the terms will be used in discussing topics such as CMIP and managed object definitions.

We must be very careful in implementing ITU-T-related TMN standards. The standards documents provide broad guidelines but do not go into specific implementation details. Also, in some cases the definitions are in place but the details are still being worked out. Modifications may be made during implementation, and definitions and guidelines may be expanded to suit individual cases.

Also, in many cases the standard documents are in different stages of standardization. Standards should not be implemented while still in draft stage. Implementation has to be done when standards are fairly mature. Also, sometimes, to account for corrections and additions, amendments are made after standards are published. Therefore it is advisable to check whether any amendments to published standards are available during implementation.

The starting point in TMN and OSI systems management is the OSI seven-layer architecture. As per OSI seven-layer architecture, the different layers are the physical, data link, network, transport, session, presentation, and application layers. The topmost of these seven layers—the application layer—is important from the TMN and systems management point of view. TMN and systems management applications reside in the application layer.

Figure 4-1
OSI layer concepts.

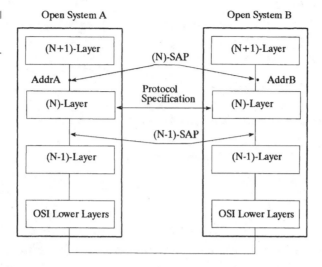

4.2 Service Access Point

In data communications and TMN, we often hear the term *entity.* Basically, an entity is an abstract concept (conceptual idea). An entity is that which provides services. Examples of services are error recovery, segmentation, and assembly. The entities in the (N) layer provide the services to the entities in the (N + 1) layer through a point known as the service access point (SAP). AddrA and AddrB are examples of SAP addresses.

The SAP is an addressing concept. A SAP is identified by a SAP address. It is a conceptual intersection between two layers. An (N + 1) entity may concurrently be attached to one or more SAPs attached to the same or different N entities and vice versa. So an entity in (N + 1) layer in open system A accesses the entity in the (N) layer using the intersection point address (AddrA) as shown in Figure 4-1. In a similar manner, an entity in the (N + 1) layer in open system B accesses the entity in the (N) layer using the SAP address AddrB.

4.3 Service Provider and Service User

An OSI service provider represents a collection of entities that provide an OSI service to an OSI service user. *OSI service user* refers to a single entity that makes use of an OSI service through an OSI service primitive as

Figure 4-2
OSI service provider
and OSI service user.

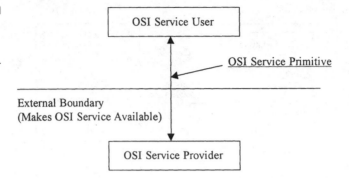

shown in Figure 4-2. OSI service can be defined as a capability provided by the OSI service provider and available for use by the OSI service user at the boundary demarcating OSI service provider and OSI service user.

OSI service primitive is an abstract concept; it represents an atomic implementation-dependent interaction between an OSI service provider and an OSI service user. Either the service provider or service user issues these service primitives. The service primitive contains information such as the semantics of the information carried in the service primitive, the constraints or conditions that must be met by the service provider or service user, and the actions to be performed on receiving the service primitive.

4.4 Service Definition and Protocol Specification

In ITU-T and ISO systems management documents, terms such as *service definition* and *protocol specification* are frequently used, so it is important to know what they mean. Some of the commonly used terms are:

- *Reference model:* The popular OSI seven-layer data communication architecture, used as the basis for the OSI standardization effort is an example of a reference model. Reference models provide the basic architecture for further standardization in an area. The B-ISD or Protocol Reference Model (Chapter 10) is another example of a reference model.

- *Service definition:* An abstract concept that includes the behavior of a service provider as seen by a service user. Alternatively, the service definition includes a set of capabilities provided to a service user by a service provider. A service definition does not include the internal behavior of a service provider.

- *Protocol specification:* Furnishes a set of complete rules that govern the interaction between a service provider and a service user and provides implementation guidelines. As conformance requirements and testing relate to the implementation of protocols, they apply to protocol specification only. Most of the seven OSI layers are covered by service definition and protocol specification documents.

Concepts such as service provider, service user, service primitive, and service definition are explained in X.210, Conventions for the Definition of OSI Services (Reference 4.2).

4.5 Connection and Connectionless Modes

Some important discussions in TMN and OSI systems management are centered around connection (or *connection-oriented*) and connectionless modes of data communication. The basic difference between these two modes also contributes to differences in the protocols and how data communication is done.

To develop the concepts of connection and connectionless modes of data communication, let us first examine what a connection is. A cooperative relationship between two entities is known as an *association*. An identifiable association with an agreed-upon set of rules for data communication between two or more peer entities is known as a *connection*. Note that entities in the same layer are known as *peer entities*.

The *connection mode* of data transfer involves three distinct phases: connection establishment, the actual data transfer, and connection release. This is analogous to a telephone call. As a starting point for talking to someone, we need to form a telephone connection with the person we want to talk to. Then we talk, and after the conversation we release the connection by placing the receiver back on the hook. Of course, one or more telephone companies do the connection establishment, maintenance, and release. The connection mode of data transfer is useful when data transmission has to be done over a period of time, as in the case of file transfers, remote connection of a computer terminal to a computer, and so on.

In the *connectionless mode* of data transfer, no connection is established before data transfer between a source service access point and one or more destination service access points. Connectionless data transfer does not have a distinguishable lifespan. All the required information, such as destination address, quality of service selection criteria, option, and so on, along with the unit of data to be transferred, are delivered to one or more service access points in a single service access. Notice that in the connectionless mode of data transfer, we do not employ the connection establishment and connection release phases used in connection mode of data transfer.

The connection mode, connectionless mode, and OSI seven-layer architecture are explained in X.200, Basic Reference Model: The Basic Model (Reference 4.1).

4.6 Service Primitives

Service primitives furnish further details on a state. There are four primitives associated with a connection mode: request, indication, response, and confirmation. When a request is sent, the sender may wait for a reply. In this case, the request is known as a *confirmed request*. In some cases the sender may not desire a reply to come from the responder. In such a case, the request is known as an *unconfirmed request*. A manager and an agent also use similar requests and responses, namely, request, indication, response, and confirmation. The behavior of these is shown in Figure 4-3. The commonly used generic terms *requester* and *responder* are used in this figure.

When a requester sends a message asking for a certain service to be performed by the responder, the requester sends it in the form of a *request*. On the responder side, correspondingly, the responder receives a message asking the responder to perform a service. This becomes an *indication* on

Figure 4-3
Requestor and
responder messages.

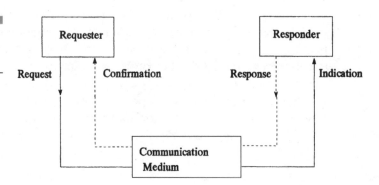

the side of the responder. When a responder has to send some message, it sends it in the form of a *response*. On the receiving side, the requester sees the message as a *confirmation*. In the connectionless mode, only request and indication primitives are used. A requester sends a request primitive and a responder gets the indication primitive.

In the preceding explanations, the broad term *message* is used to avoid confusion that might arise if we referred to this communication with names such as *event report, notification, command,* or *response*. When specific terminology is required or clear distinctions are necessary, such terms will be well defined and explained.

Each service will have an identifier for the layer, for example, A, which refers to an application layer; a verb such as ASSOCIATE; and a primitive such as request. An example of a service is thus A-ASSOCIATE.request. Each service has parameters that convey information including data and controls.

4.7 Communication Between Managed Objects and Agents

Exchanges of messages between managers and agents are done by *protocol data units* (PDUs). PDUs contain data from the layer above and control information of a layer. A PDU can take the form of a request or response. A manager can send a request to an agent, and the agent in turn sends a response. These requests and responses contain management information, which is contained in parameters. However, it is not cast in concrete that only a manager sends requests and only an agent sends responses. In some cases, an agent may send unsolicited messages or notifications to the manager. The manager, in turn, may send responses to the notifications sent by the agent.

An agent must access managed objects frequently to know what is happening to them or how they are performing. One way to do this is through *polling*, in which the managed object is queried at constant time intervals. Polling is somewhat like asking the managed objects "How are you doing?" Sometimes polling is not that simple, however. For performance-oriented queries, managed objects may be required to send back large amounts of information. In polling, the time interval is an important factor. If polling is done too often, there is increased network traffic. On the other hand, if it is done at infrequent intervals, up-to-date information on the state of the managed object may not be received. So the time interval used for polling is really a design decision that reflects the goals to be achieved.

In TMN, however, in case of unusual conditions, notifications are sent by the objects to an agent. These notifications, in turn, are converted to *event reports* in agents and sent to managers. This is a better way of learning the state of a managed object than polling. It avoids the unnecessary network traffic that results from polling. By and large, polling is unproductive and should be avoided.

Another way to access a managed object is to use another intermediary agent. This agent must be self-contained and is required to have intelligence to issue requests or responses, depending on the conditions observed in a managed object. Also, specific implementation-dependent methods can be used to access managed objects.

Sometimes a manager needs to know whether an agent is functional or "dead" due to some internal problem or a broken communication connection between a manager and an agent. In such a case, the manager uses *heartbeats*, whereby an agent sends a message to the manager at regular intervals saying "I am alive." Like polling, the heartbeat may also carry information on the state of an agent.

4.8 Management Domain

Management domain is an important concept that helps in distributing management functions. By carefully designing management domains, we are able to conveniently partition systems management into manageable portions. There may be some gateways, different computer systems belonging to different vendors, and different kinds of systems, from workstations to mainframes. How do we show these on the screen of a workstation? When we show topology, it must be of some use and make sense. One intuitive way is to break up the topology into easily manageable management domains. Imagine the case of a network that spans a large geographical area, connecting some continents. In this example, each nation could form one management domain.

A collection of managed objects for systems management and TMN purposes is known as a management domain. The division of management domains may be based on geography, functions, or technology, and it helps in the application of management policies to a group of managed objects. We show one example of the concept of management domain in Figure 4-4.

Figure 4-4

Management and administrative domains.

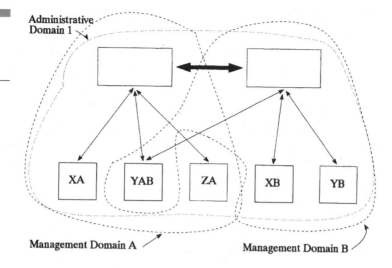

Management domains, to be useful, must have unique names, must include the objects that will be managed by that domain, and must know how the managed objects and agents will communicate with one another. One managed object in one management domain may also belong to another management domain, as shown in Figure 4-4. From Figure 4-4, notice that management domain A has managed objects XA, YAB, and ZA as members. Similarly, management domain B has managed objects YAB, XB, and YB as members. Thus, it is apparent that managed object YAB is a member of both management domains A and B.

After the whole network has been divided into management domains, what do we do? If there is no centralized control, there may be chaos. For this reason, we define another set of domains over this conceptual model. This is known as the management *administrative domain,* as shown in Figure 4-4. The functions of management administrative domains are as follows:

■ Exercise control over managed objects and agents in the domain.

■ Aid in changing the boundaries of management domains if, for example, after some time, certain managed objects need to be under the control of another management domain.

■ Facilitate coordination when a managed object belongs to more than one management domain.

X.749 (ISO 10164-19), Management Domain and Management Policy Management Functions (Reference 4.7), provides information on managed object classes for management domains and management policies, models for the behavior of management domains and management policy, the services that can be performed, mapping of the services to CMISE services, and a model for retrieving information on the managed objects associated with management domains. Managed object classes defined for management domains are shown in Figure 4-5. The explanations of these managed object classes are as follows:

- *domainCoordinator* provides an interface to a management domain for management operations. domainCoordinator represents the functional aspects of a management domain, such as the members of the domain, the relationship with a managementPolicy managed object, and the management policy as applied to members of a domain. domainCoordinator can coordinate domains, superdomains, and subdomains. A domain within another management domain is known as a *subdomain*. The parent management domain is known as the *superdomain*.

- *managementPolicy* is responsible for the management policies that can be applied to the members of a management domain. This managed object class contains a list of the authorities allowed to access and modify the management policies.

- *conflictDetector* detects conflicts in management policies of managed objects in a management domain or domains.

Some of the management operations that can be performed on a management domain are subdomainCreate, domainDelete, enrollMember, de-enrollMember, changeLocalName, listParents, listMembers, and list-Subdomains. These management operations are used as action-type parameters in CMIS M-ACTION (M-ACTION will be discussed in Chapter 5.) Similarly, the action types associated with management policies are policyCreate, policyDelete, policyScope, enrollRule, and de-enrollRule.

A management domain is created by a manager or an administration by creating an instance of a management relationship among management policy, a member of a domain, and a domain coordinator. In management domains, there are still some unresolved issues, including:

Figure 4-5

Managed object classes for management domains.

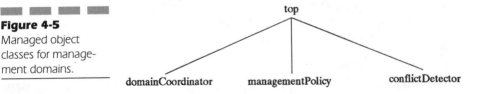

- Security issues involved in accessing other domains and managed objects in other domains.

- The strategy for backup when one domain fails. Do we allow one domain to be the backup for another domain? The ISO 10164-19 document does not address this issue.

- X.701, Systems Management Overview (Reference 4.3) mentions the administrative domains. For implementation purposes, administrative domains must be formally defined.

4.9 Management Information Hierarchies

Managed objects have relationships with one another. These relationships can be organized in a systematic manner by indicating how one managed object is related to another object. These relationships can serve different purposes. If managed objects are to be globally known to all, then they must have relationships indicating where they stand in a global naming structure. For this purpose, a *registration hierarchy* is used.

Because OSI management standards use object-oriented principles, it may be possible to use some characteristics already defined for other objects. This is done through *inheritance*. This relationship between managed object classes is provided by an *inheritance hierarchy*.

We may wish to have a relationship for naming a managed object. This relationship is shown by a *containment hierarchy*, also sometimes known as a *naming hierarchy*. These three hierarchies that are used for management purposes are shown in Figure 4-6. It should be noted that these hierarchies are independent of each other and are used for different purposes.

Figure 4-6
OSI management
information
hierarchies.

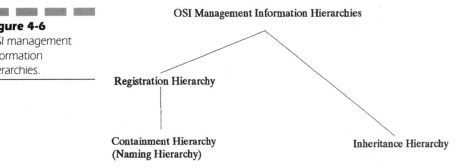

4.9.1 **Registration Hierarchy**

A managed object class is identified by an ASN.1 object identifier. These object identifiers are formed by taking a sequence of integers in the registration tree. These numbers are registered; the registration hierarchy tree is shown in Figure 4-7. The registration number for the Internet is {1.3.6.1}. All systems management object identifiers, which are used in standard documents, are derived from {joint-iso-itu-t ms(9)}.

These numbers, from the root to the leaf of the registration hierarchy tree, are concatenated to form an *object identifier.* An object identifier is a series of integers used to uniquely identify a managed object class. We should note here that an attribute also has an object identifier to uniquely identify it.

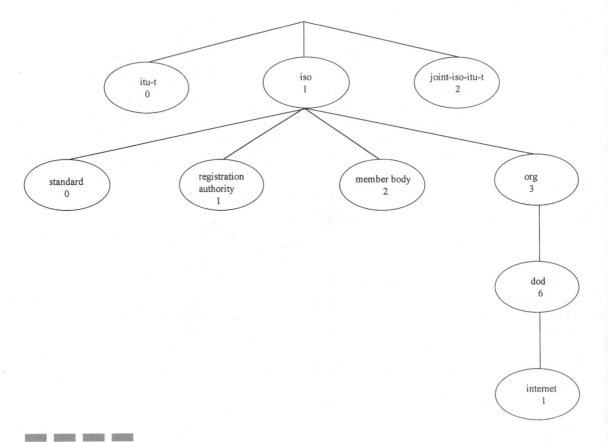

Figure 4-7
Registration hierarchy.

4.9.2 Inheritance Hierarchy

It is important to know where a managed object class is positioned in the inheritance hierarchy tree. The property of inheritance is very useful, because we can derive characteristics from parents. In other words, it is not necessary to define the characteristics that parents already have. Parents, in turn, inherit properties from their parents; thus, a new managed object class definition reduces to properly positioning a managed object class in the inheritance hierarchy tree and adding some more characteristics.

Inheritance hierarchy is derived from the managed object class *top*. From *top*, various organizations and countries are derived. An example of an inheritance hierarchy tree is shown in Figure 4-8. Again, a managed object class may be derived from one or more managed object classes, which facilitates inheriting characteristics from those managed object classes. We call this *multiple inheritance*. Figure 4-8 also illustrates multiple inheritance.

The managed object class *lanNetworks*, which is the parent of another managed object class *lanNet*, is known as a superclass with respect to the managed object class *lanNet*. Similarly, a managed object class *lanNet*, which is the child of managed object class *lanNetworks*, is known as a subclass.

Figure 4-8
Inheritance hierarchy.

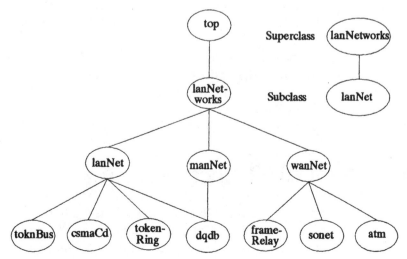

Figure 4-9
Containment
hierarchy example.

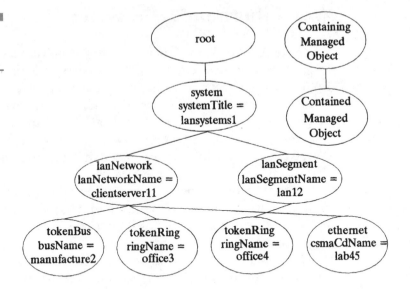

4.9.3 Containment Hierarchy

One managed object can represent a part of another managed object. This relationship is commonly known as *containment* and the structure is used for constructing global names. This containment relationship is shown in Figure 4-9. Here, system *lansystems1* is known as a contained managed object in relation to *root*. And *root*, in turn, is known as a *containing object*.

The object instance of *lanNetwork* named *clientserver11* is a contained managed object with respect to the object instance of the system named *lansystems1*. The managed object *lansystems1* is the containing managed object.

The containment relationship is relevant to object instances. We must remember that it does not apply to managed object classes. Containment is a directed graph where arcs connect contained and containing objects. Containment relationships can refer to static and dynamic behaviors that must be specified when defining containment relationships.

4.10 Object Naming

We use names to recognize people. Similarly, we use a name to identify a managed object. Containment and naming are closely related to one another. A containment tree is used for naming a managed object. Every managed object must have a unique name. The containment hierarchy fans out from *root*. In the containment hierarchy, *root* is the starting point and represents a null object. Containment relationships can be described in the definitions of a managed object class, but are often described after classes are defined.

Referring again to Figure 4-9, some more terms used in defining a managed object class need to be explained. Here, the object instance of *lanNetwork* is a subordinate object in relation to the object instance of the managed object class *system*. The object instance of *system* is the superior object in relation to the object *lanNetwork*.

If we extend this relationship, *root* is the superior object class of *system*. This hierarchy of relationships forms a tree known as the *naming tree*. It is important to mention how we name a managed object of a class that we are defining. The relationship of a subordinate object class to the superior object class is known as *name binding*. In our discussions, *naming tree* and *containment tree* are used interchangeably.

Naming is important for uniquely identifying an object instance. In the containment tree, the distinguishing attribute, along with the name of an object instance, is known as the *relative distinguished name* (RDN). Referring to Figure 4-9, the RDN for *tokenRing* is {ringName=office3}. The RDN need not be unique at the same level; however, in relation to a superior managed object, the RDN must be unique.

The distinguishing attribute used for uniquely identifying a managed object is part of the mandatory package and, obviously, should have a fixed value throughout the life of the managed object. However, there need not be just one distinguishing attribute; there can be multiple attributes used for different name bindings.

In Figure 4-9, how do we distinguish between object instances of *token-Ring* with the RDNs *ringName=office3* and *ringName=office4* under the managed object classes *lanNetwork* and *lanSegment?* To uniquely identify the *tokenRing* object instances, we must move up the containment tree. For this we need the help of the RDN of the parents. Starting from the beginning of the containment tree, if we concatenate the RDNs, we can derive the globally unique names. A globally unique name is known as a *distinguished name* (DN), and it is unique across the entire containment tree. The DN for *tokenRing* is {systemTitle=lansystems1, lanNetwork-Name=clientserver11, ringName=office3}. It is important to note that the containment tree and the physical containment of one resource by another need not be similar.

For naming a systems managed object, we use systemID or systemTitle. The ASN.1 for systemID can be a GraphicString, Integer, or Null. A Null value is used when a system has not been configured or a systemID attribute is not used in naming. A system title is a layer-independent name. In systemTitle, the ASN.1 type can be a distinguished name, Object Identifier, or Null.

There are two forms of naming for systems management purposes: local or global. For global naming, we start from the root in the containment tree and proceed down the naming tree, concatenating the RDN until we arrive at the managed object desired. In contrast, for the local name of a managed object, we can start from any managed object in the naming tree. However, for OSI systems management, we take the systems managed object as a starting point for local names. The local name of a systems managed object is an empty sequence shown by {}. A local name may not be globally unique.

Let us examine this with the example shown in Figure 4-9. The global name for *tokenRing* is {systemTitle=lansystems1, lanNetworkName= clientserver11, ringName=office3}. In global naming, we use *root* as the reference point. Global names cannot be used for a system when the systemID and systemTitle are both Null, because this would show that the system is unaware of its global name. In this case, the local name is {lanNetworkName=clientserver11, ringName=office3}. Because a systems managed object is represented by {}, {} is not included in the local name.

4.11 Scoping

When management operations are done on managed objects, *scoping* enters into the picture. These management operations are provided by CMISE services. Scoping selects one or more managed objects for management operations such as Action, Delete, Get, and Set requests. The scoping is applied to a naming tree. The base object can be anywhere in a naming tree, but, to be successful, the request should be sent to the agent with the base object. The base object specified in the request is the reference point for scoping operations. Base object level is referred to as level zero, and sometimes the subtree below a base object is used in scoping.

There are different levels of scoping, as follows:

1. A base object alone is selected. This is the default action for scoping. In Figure 4-10, if the argument of a scoping operation is the base object only and the base object specified in a request is A, then the result is a selection of A. Note that the base object is A.

2. The *n*th-level subordinates can be selected. For example, if *n* is the first level in Figure 4-10, the objects selected are B, C, D, and E.

Figure 4-10

Scoping example.

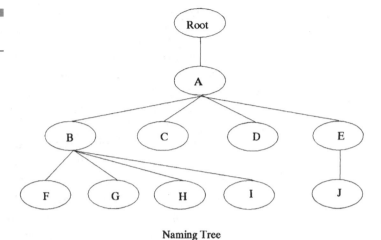

Naming Tree

3. Scoping can be applied to objects that include the base object and the subordinates up to the nth level. In Figure 4-10, take n as one; then managed object A will be selected in addition to B, C, D, and E.

4. Scoping can be extended to cover all objects in the subtree below the base object. If we take A as the base object, the selected objects from this scoped operation, are A, the objects in the first level (B, C, D, and E), and the objects in the second level (F, G, H, I, and J).

4.12 Filtering

Filtering is one more level of selection imposed on scoping. It can be used to choose a subset of managed objects that have been selected by the scoping operation. Those managed objects that have been chosen by scoping are further subjected to conditions furnished by filtering for the selection. If the managed objects pass the conditions, they are selected; otherwise, they are left out. These conditions are formed by grouping logical operations such as *or, and,* and *not.*

When all conditions are true, the *and* condition is satisfied and becomes true. In the case of the *or* condition, if one or more conditions are true, then the whole condition set is true. In the case of *not,* the condition is true only if the nested filter (a combination of filters) is false.

For evaluating whether an attribute value matches a certain rule, there are matching rules. The first condition is that the attribute must be present. If the attribute is not present, then the comparing value is regarded as false. There are eight explicit matching rules:

1. *Equality:*   We can test an attribute value to equality with an assigned value. As an example, in Figure 4-11, we can test whether *tokenRing-CardPrice* has a value of 300. In this case, we get the object instance D. An attribute may have more than one value, in which case we get a set of values. We can also use a set for comparison. This set also may have one or more members. For a matching rule to become true, members of the comparison set must be equal in value to all members of the attribute set. Otherwise, the matching rule evaluates as false.

2. *Greater than or equal to:*   Here, the value supplied for comparison must be equal to or greater than the attribute value. For example, in Figure 4-11, if we take a comparison value of 300, we are looking for object instance values for the attribute *tokenRingCardPrice* of 300 and less. The object instance is D. For sets, the comparison set has only one member. For the matching rule to become true, the value of the member of the comparison set must be greater than or equal to one or more members of the attribute set, or else the matching rule evaluates as false.

3. *Less than or equal to:*   In this test, the value used for comparison must be less than or equal to the attribute value. For comparison, let the value be 325. From Figure 4-11, for *tokenRingCardPrice*, the object instances with values greater than or equal to 325 are C and E.

Figure 4-11

Filtering example.

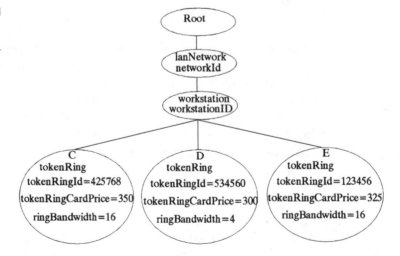

4. *Present:* This tests whether an attribute is present, and if so, then the comparison is evaluated as true. The attribute selected may be *collisionRate*. A cursory look at the *tokenRing* managed object class in Figure 4-11 reveals that there is no such attribute. In this case, there are no object instances that can be selected.

5. *Substring:* For this test, the attribute value substring must match the substring furnished for comparison. Let us check in Figure 4-11 for an object instance that has a *tokenRingId* of 123456. On comparing each element of the substring, the object instance of E is obtained.

6. *Subset of:* Here the set for comparison must be a subset of the attribute values. As an example, let the set of *tokenRingId* for comparison be {123456, 325}. On examination of the naming tree in Figure 4-11, only E matches. *Subset of* is applicable only to set-valued attributes.

7. *Superset of:* This test is applicable only to set-valued attributes, and all members must be present in the set presented for comparison. Referring to Figure 4-11 again, for *tokenRingId*, let the set for comparison be {123456, 325, 987234}. On comparison, there is no object instance matching this requirement.

8. *Non-null set intersection:* Again in Figure 4-11, let the set for comparison be {123456, 456789, 987234}. For this to be evaluated as true, there must be at least one *tokenRingId* with one of the above values. In our example, the object instance is again E.

We can combine these simple matching rules and evaluate them as true or false. For example, let the combination of filters used be (*objectClass=tokenRing*) *and* (*tokenRingCardPrice=350*). The object instance is C only. For variation, let the combination of filters be *tokenRingCardPrice=300*) *or* (*ringBandwidth=16*). Now the object instances are C, D, and E.

4.13 Synchronization

A manager may request information from an agent about how the agent performs operations on behalf of the manager. This is known as *synchronization*. Sometimes operations are performed on more than one managed object. Synchronization is part of managed object behavior definition. We will examine what behavior means in relation to the definition of a managed object in Chapter 6, Section 6.4.5.

Synchronization does not apply to a Create operation on an object. Here, intermediate operations are not visible. When operations on objects such as Get, Set, and Action include scoping, the issue of synchronization arises. The operations that can be performed on managed objects are explained in Chapter 5. The synchronization operation can be of two types. The first, *atomic* synchronization, is an all-or-nothing proposition. An initial check is made as to whether it is possible to satisfy the request for all objects. If it is not possible to retrieve all the objects, say for a Get operation, then an error is returned. Otherwise, all the objects are returned. The second type of synchronization is known as *best-effort* synchronization. For example, for a Get operation, all retrievals are tried and whichever objects can be retrieved are returned. For those cases where retrieval fails, an error is returned.

4.14 Polymorphism

Polymorphism means *having many forms* and is primarily an object-oriented concept. Managed object classes that respond to a common operation in a similar manner are said to exhibit the property of polymorphism. Referring to Figure 4-12, let us assume that we have many managed object classes in an undergraduate level based on a student's major. Thus, there are managed object classes such as *computerScience-*

Figure 4-12
Polymorphism
example.

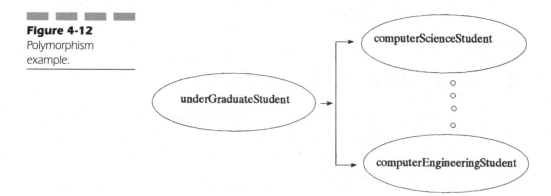

Student, computerEngineeringStudent, and so on. Suppose we have an operation such as Grading for the managed object class *underGraduateStudent.* As a result of the property of inheritance, this operation of Grading will be inherited by *computerScienceStudent* and *computerEngineeringStudent,* and may need only slight modifications for the subclasses of *computerScienceStudent* and *electricalEngineeringStudent.* Here the managed object classes *computerScienceStudent* and *computerEngineeringStudent* are termed *polymorphic.*

4.15 Allomorphism

Allomorphism refers to the ability of one object instance to function as if it were part of more than one object class. To understand this concept, let us slightly modify our earlier example. Assume that a student, Joe Smith, is majoring in computer science. Further assume that we have the managed object classes *xUniversityStudent, underGraduateStudent,* and *computerScienceStudent. Joe Smith* can be taken as an instance of the managed object class *computerScienceStudent.* However, the object instance *Joe Smith* can also be part of the managed object classes *underGraduateStudent* and *xUniversityStudent.* Here, *Joe Smith* has the characteristics of allomorphism. Allomorphism is used in OSI systems management and TMN to migrate to newer versions of the old or obsolete objects.

4.16 Management State

State describes operational and availability conditions of a managed object at a specific time. These conditions are included when appropriate in the definition of a managed object class as attributes. It is necessary to standardize the state for management purposes.

Management state attributes are broadly classified as *generic state* attributes and *status* attributes. The status attributes furnish further information on generic state attributes. The generic state attributes are operational, usage, and administrative, as shown in Figure 4-13. The status attributes used for management purposes are *alarm, procedural, availability, control, standby,* and *unknown.* Management state attributes and their values are listed in Table 4-1.

Figure 4-13
Management state
attributes.

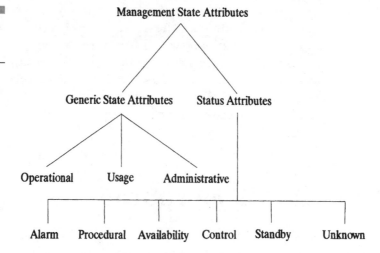

4.16.1 Generic State Attributes

The *operational* state attribute indicates whether a resource is working. Management operation can only read the operational state of a managed object; hence, this state has only a Read operation and is single-valued. There are two values for this attribute: *disabled* and *enabled*. When the operational state is not known, then the *unknown* status attribute with a value of *true* is used to reflect this condition.

TABLE 4-1

Different Manage-
ment State
Attributes.

State Attributes	Possible States
Generic State Attributes	
Operational	Disabled, enabled
Usage	Idle, active, busy
Administrative	Locked, unlocked, shutting down
Status Attributes	
Alarm	Under repair, critical, major, minor, alarm outstanding
Procedural	Initialization required, not initialized, initializing, reporting, terminating
Availability	In test, failed, power off, off line, off duty, dependency, degraded, not installed, log full
Control	Subject to test, part of services locked, reserved for test, suspended
Standby	Hot standby, cold standby, providing service
Unknown	Used when state of a resource is unknown

The *usage* state defines whether a resource is being actively used at a particular time. It mentions whether additional users can use this resource. There are three values: *idle, active,* and *busy.* The usage state attribute is also a read-only and single-valued attribute. When only one user is involved, the possible values are *idle* or *busy.* When a resource has an unlimited number of users, then the possible values are *idle* or *active.* As in the operational state, when resource state details cannot be furnished by the usage state, the unknown status attribute with a value of *true* is used.

The *administrative* state indicates how a resource is used under management operations. The possible values are *locked, unlocked,* or *shutting down.* Some managed object classes have only a subset of the three values. In some cases, there is no unlocked state. In some other cases, the *shutting down* value is absent, if there is no graceful shutdown characteristic. Administrative state values are stated while defining managed objects. Note also that the administrative state attribute is read-write and single-valued. That means that the value of an attribute can be read by using a Get operation and changed by doing a Set operation.

When defining a managed object class, it is possible to have one or more generic state attributes. However, when defining values, it must be ascertained that these values represent only a valid combination of possible values.

4.16.2 Status Attributes

Status attributes furnish further details on the generic state attributes, such as *operational, usage,* or *administrative.* Let us examine these status attributes individually.

The *alarm* status attribute indicates the status of alarms that have been generated. It can have a value of *under repair,* which states that the resource is being repaired, or *critical, major,* and *minor,* which indicate that one or more alarms have been detected and have not been cleared. In all of these cases, including the *under repair* value, the operational state can be enabled or disabled. The last possible value, *alarm outstanding,* states that one or more alarms are outstanding against the resource and the condition due to these alarms may or may not have been disabled. It is not necessary that the alarm status attribute have values. Instead, this attribute may be an empty set, which indicates that none of the aforementioned values are present. The alarm status attribute is read-write, indicating that Get and Set operations can be performed.

The *procedural* status attribute is used when a resource has many phases of operations. If this value attribute is an empty set, then the managed object representing the resource is *ready.* One of the attributes is *initialization required,* which indicates that this managed object has to be initialized before it can perform its normal role, and the operational state is disabled. On the contrary, a value of *not initialized* indicates that the managed object is capable of initializing itself and needs no initialization to perform its normal functioning; however, initialization has not been started. The operational state here can be enabled or disabled. The value of *initializing* indicates that the initialization process is in progress, and the operational state may be disabled or enabled, depending on the definition of the managed object class. *Reporting* states that the object is reporting the results of the operation that has been done, and the operational state is enabled. As the name suggests, the *terminating* value states that the resource is in a termination phase. Again, it is not necessary to have one of these values for an attribute; the value of an attribute can be an empty set.

The *availability* status attribute indicates whether a managed object is available. It has values of *in test, failed, power off, off line, off duty, dependency, degraded, not installed,* or *log full.* Here, *off line* indicates that the operational state is disabled and needs some sort of intervention to make it available for use. *Dependency* states that some dependent resource is unavailable and the operational state is disabled. Other values are obvious, so the meanings are not discussed. Availability status is a read-only attribute. It is worth noting that the alarm, procedural, and availability status attributes add further meaning to the operational state attribute. As mentioned earlier regarding other status attributes, this attribute can be an empty set.

The *control* status attribute is read and write, and the values are *subject to test, part of services locked, reserved for test,* or *suspended.* The value of *subject to test* indicates that the resource may be subjected to tests during normal operation, and it may sometimes lead to abnormal behavior. *Part of services locked* means that some services of a resource may not be available for users. *Reserved for test* states that a resource is not available for normal users and is undergoing a test. *Suspended* indicates that a resource is not available for users.

The *standby* status attribute states the condition of a backup resource. This is a read-only attribute. The value of *hot standby* means that the standby resource does not need initialization and contains all the information about the resource the standby resource is backing up; thus, whenever a resource needs the backup to take over, the backup will be immediately available. However, in the case of *cold standby,* the backup resource needs some sort of initialization before it can take over from a resource. The *providing service* value states that backup operation is already being done by the backup resource. *Unknown status* is used when the state of a resource is not known.

In addition to the state and status attributes used when defining a managed object class, there is also an attribute group of *state,* which represents a collection of all the state attributes. Using the state attribute group makes it easier to perform management operations on the collection, because this avoids the need for performing the same management operation on each individual state attribute. In Chapter 6, Section 6.4.3, we will examine in detail the meaning of attribute groups.

Whenever there are changes in the management state attributes of a managed object, an agent will send an M-EVENT-REPORT to the manager. This M-EVENT-REPORT can be a confirmed or nonconfirmed service. The parameters in the M-EVENT-REPORT for reporting management state changes are *event type, event information,* and *event reply.* Here, we must be clear that the management state includes generic states and status.

Let us briefly look into the parameters and the values that go in these parameters when using M-EVENT-REPORT to report management state changes. Event type is used to report a change in the value of a state attribute. Event information furnishes details of the event due to a change in state and has a source indicator with three values: *resource operation, management operation,* and *unknown.* Event information also has an *attribute identifier list* and a *state change definition.* The state change definition has an *attribute identifier, old attribute value,* and *new attribute value.* There is no event reply parameter specified for the state change notification. In addition, the parameters used with M-EVENT-REPORT, such as notification identifier, correlated notification, additional text, and additional information, can also be used to furnish further details on state change. We will revisit M-EVENT-REPORT, along with the parameters used, in Chapter 7. State and status attributes are explained in X.731, State Management Function (Reference 4.5).

4.17 Attributes for Relationships

A system may consist of many managed objects. If so, how these objects are related or grouped becomes important. It is also important to know how relationships change when certain operations are done. For this, the relationship attribute *role* is used. The role attribute may have a single value or a set of values. A managed object class such as *printerUsed* may have another backup managed object class such as *printerBackup*. How these managed object classes are related and how the backup managed object class *printerBackup* behaves when the original managed object class *printerUsed* fails is important. Different kinds of relationships are explained in X.732, Attributes for Representing Relationships (Reference 4.6). When a relationship changes, notification is produced. This notification can be sent as an M-EVENT-REPORT. An agent sends M-EVENT-REPORTs to a manager. Parameters of an M-EVENT-REPORT are tailored to identify managed objects participating in a relationship and changes in the relationship. Details of the parameters of M-EVENT-REPORT for reporting relationship changes can be found in X.732, Attributes for Representing Relationships (Reference 4.6).

4.18 General Relationship Model

X.725, General Relationship Model (Reference 4.4), primarily describes how to represent relationships between resources and the management operations that can be done on relationships. Managed objects can be tied to one another for management purposes by managed relationships, and the managed relationships that share the same definition can be grouped as a *managed relationship class*. A manager uses the managed relationships, and these managed relationships are useful for different systems management functions, especially for configuration management.

Management operations that can be performed on a managed relationship are BIND, Establish, Notify, Query, Terminate, Unbind, and User DEFINED. The meanings of some of the management operations are obvious, so we will discuss only certain ones. BIND refers to associating a managed object with a relationship. ESTABLISH stands for forming a managed relationship. NOTIFY is used to report on events associated with managed relationships. USER DEFINED, as the name suggests, can be employed to carry a user-defined management operation. These management operations are mapped to systems management operations such as attribute-based and managed object-based management operations.

For relationships, *relationshipObjectSuperClass* under *top* is defined. This managed object class contains the relationship attribute group and the following attributes:

- *Relationship name:*   Used for naming relationship objects
- *Relationship class:*   Identifies the relationship class
- *Role binding:*   Specifies how a managed relationship is represented

We have briefly discussed the general relationship model; for further details, readers should consult X.725, General Relationship Model (Reference 4.4).

4.19 Management Information Tree (MIT)

Managed object instances are arranged in a hierarchical fashion, forming a tree. This hierarchical tree forms the containment hierarchy for naming the managed objects instances and is known as a management information tree (MIT) (see Figure 4-9). An MIT is dynamic and changes with the deletions or additions of managed object instances. Management information is stored in the nodes of the MIT, including the internal and leaf nodes. Agents interface with the object instances in the MIT.

Normally, when an agent starts up, it creates managed object instances in an MIT. The number of object instances in the MIT can sometimes be very large in real-life situations. So the managed object instances can be arranged in the form of one of the variations of B trees for faster accesses and searches. To reduce access and search times, the object instances can also be arranged in the form of distributed trees.

The details of the managed objects, which are required for management purposes, are stored in a conceptual repository known as a management information base (MIB). A MIB is a conceptual model and it has no relation to how the data is physically or logically formatted and stored. MIB structure does not change dynamically like a MIT does.

4.20 Intelligent Agents

Not many functions are handled by agents. Agents control managed objects, send notifications to managers on unusual occurrences in agents and managed objects, and send responses to the commands from managers to management operations. Otherwise, most of the management functions reside in managers. In SNMP protocols, for extensibility reasons, the bare minimum functions and intelligence reside in agents.

This is good from one angle: It is easy to add new equipment and hence new MIBs into the management structure. At the same time, the centralized network management imposes a heavy workload on the managers. To overcome this, the distributed network management is also becoming increasingly popular. We will look into more on distributed network management in Chapter 11.

We briefly present the ongoing work and different approaches taken to incorporate more intelligence in agents. The motivation for this brief overview is to acquaint readers with some of the possible directions and solutions to divert the workload from the managers. This becomes a very critical issue as networks are becoming global and heterogeneous, and the mix of data carried on the networks is more complex than a few years earlier.

To reduce the workload on the managers, different approaches are taken. One of the solutions is to use distributed network management, but others are being suggested. One of the approaches involves adding more intelligence and processing in agents themselves by using decentralized management by delegation (Reference 4.8). This reduces the network bandwidth required for transferring network management data and reduces the processing needs of the managers. In management by delegation, a flexible elastic process in an agent is used. An elastic process can perform additional processing off-loaded by other processes. The management applications reside in agents and a good amount of processing is done in the elastic process. So, more intelligence is added to the devices or agents, reducing the management functionality required of managers.

Another approach taken by the authors of Reference 4.9 is related to service management. Here service management activities are separated from the network layer activities. The service management semantics, as well as data and logic to interpret data, are incorporated in service agents. These service agents are mobile in the sense that they are location independent.

One more idea is have an intermediate layer between a manager and agents. The intermediate layer has managing agents that act as managers to the agents below and perform like agents to the manager above. This concept shifts the workload from the manager to the managing agent. In the work cited in Reference 4.10, the managing agents have intelligence and perform functions as a rule-based expert system.

While different approaches are being tried, it is important to note that there are neither standards for the intelligent agents as such nor popular and well-accepted implementations.

4.21 Summary

In this chapter, we have discussed some of the important concepts in TMN such as service access points, service providers, service users, service definitions, and protocol specifications. We have also introduced the topics of connection and connectionless modes of data transfer. Connection and connectionless modes of data transfer are important concepts and are used in CMIP and SNMP management protocols.

We have also discussed the concepts of management domain and management information hierarchies. We have examined how managed objects and agents communicate. While discussing management information hierarchies, we have examined three different types of hierarchies: registration, inheritance, and containment.

The important concept of naming a managed object has been examined in detail. Scoping and filtering have also been discussed with examples, as well as synchronization, polymorphism, allomorphism, management state attributes, and the role attributes that govern the relationship between different managed objects. We have ended this chapter with a brief discussion on management information tree and intelligent agents.

4.22 References

4.1. ITU-T Recommendation X.200 (ISO 7498-1), Information Technology, Open Systems Interconnection, Basic Reference Model, The Basic Model, 1994.

4.2. ITU-T Recommendation X.210 (ISO 10731), Information Technology, Open Systems Interconnection, Basic Reference Model, Conventions for the Definition of OSI Services, 1993.

4.3. ITU-T Recommendation X.701 (ISO IS 10040), Information Technology, Open Systems Interconnection, Systems Management Overview, 1992.

4.4. ITU-T Recommendation X.725 (ISO 10165-7), Information Technology, Open Systems Interconnection, Structure of Management Information: General Relationship Model, 1995.

4.5. ITU-T Recommendation X.731 (ISO 10164-2), Information Technology, Open Systems Interconnection, Systems Management: State Management Function, 1992.

4.6. ITU-T Recommendation X.732 (ISO 10164-3), Information Technology, Open Systems Interconnection, Systems Management: Attributes for Representing Relationships, 1992.

4.7. ITU-T Recommendation X.749 (ISO DIS 10164-19), Information Technology, Open Systems Interconnection, Systems Management, Part 19: Management Domain and Management Policy Management Functions.

4.8. Meyer, K., M. Erlinger, J. Betser, C. Sunshine, G. Goldszmidt, and Y. Yemini, *Decentralizing Control and Intelligence in Network Management*. Integrated Network Management IV, Proceedings of the Fourth International Symposium on Integrated Network Management, 1995. Sethi, A. S., Raynaud, Y. and Faure-Vincent, F. (eds.), London: Chapman & Hall, 1995, pp. 4—15.

4.9. Hjalmtysson, G. and A. Jain, *An Agent-based Approach to Service Management—Towards Service Independent Network Architecture*. Integrated Network Management V, Integrated Management in a Virtual World, Proceedings of the Fifth IFIP/IEEE International Symposium on Integrated Network Management, San Diego, CA, May 12—16, 1997, Lazar, A., Saracco, R., and Stadler, R. (eds.), London: Chapman & Hall, 1997, pp. 715—729.

4.10. Trommer, M. and R. Konopka, *Distributed Network Management with Dynamic Rule-Based Managing Agents*. Integrated Network Management V, Integrated Management in a Virtual World, Proceedings of the Fifth IFIP/IEEE International Symposium on Integrated Network Management, San Diego, CA, May 12—16, 1997. Lazar, A., Saracco, R., and Stadler, R. (eds.), London: Chapman & Hall, 1997, pp. 730—741.

4.23 Further Reading

ITU-T Recommendation X.660 (ISO 9834-1), Information Technology, Open Systems Interconnection, Procedures for the Operation of OSI Registration Authorities: General Procedures, 1992.

ITU-T Recommendation X.660 (ISO 9834-1), Amendment 1, Information Technology, Open Systems Interconnection, Procedures for the Operation of OSI Registration Authorities: General Procedures, Amendment 1: Incorporation of Object Identifiers Components, 1996.

CHAPTER 5

Abstract Syntax and Transfer Syntax

5.1 Introduction

For two systems to communicate, each must understand the data sent from one to the other. This can be achieved by using a language that has the same syntax and semantics.

In the application layer, we use *abstract syntax,* which states only how data are arranged and what meaning they have. One of the possible abstract syntaxes is *Abstract Syntax Notation One* (ASN.1). Between the application layer and the presentation layer, a local set of rules can be used to transform data; however, the syntax of the data transferred between presentation entities must be understood by each end. This is known as *transfer syntax.* Abstract syntax and transfer syntax are negotiated at the beginning, during association time.

One transfer syntax is *basic encoding rules* (BER). BER state how data must be transformed before it is transferred to the other presentation entity. The local syntax can be purely dependent on the local protocols used. Figure 5-1 illustrates the concepts of abstract syntax and transfer syntax.

ITU-T Recommendations X.208 (Reference 5.1) and X.680 (Reference 5.2) describe standardized ways and steps to define data types and data values. Data types and data values are also referred to as *types* and *values,* respectively.

5.2 Abstract Syntax Notation One (ASN.1)

We will use a bottom-up approach to explain the concepts, starting with types and moving on to the definition of modules. In ASN.1, the starting

Figure 5-1
Abstract and transfer syntax concepts.

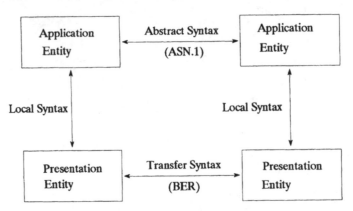

point is a *value*. An object instance can have a value. A collection of all these values is a *type*. These types are similar to the data types found in programming languages. Integer is an example of a data type. The whole idea in forming different data types is to define all possible simple data types first. Then these simple data types are combined in different manners to define complex data types.

X.208 is still widely used in TMN. Many commercially available ASN.1 compilers that perform syntax checking of ASN.1 definitions are yet to migrate to X.680. We will look into the topic of ASN.1 compilers in Chapter 12. ITU-T Recommendation X.680 is a refinement of X.208. It includes extensions and corrections to X.208. For this reason, we will discuss X.208 first. While examining X.208, we will not dwell much on the topics that have been dropped from X.680. Next we will state the differences between X.208 and X.680. This logical approach facilitates easier transition to the understanding of ASN.1 definitions to the X.680.

We broadly classify the ASN.1 built-in types as follows:

- Simple types
- Structured types
- Tagged types
- Subtypes

Like every formal programming language, ASN.1 has its own rules. Let us look into some of the important rules. They are explained as follows:

- *Keywords* appear in uppercase letters. An example of a keyword is:

  ```
  BOOLEAN
  ```

- A *type* and *module name* begin with an uppercase letter. A type consists of one or more letters, digits, and hyphens. Examples of types are:

  ```
  BOOLEAN (which is an ASN.1 built-in type)
  HouseNumber (described next)
  ```

- A new type can be formed using ASN.1 built-in types. This is done by *type assignment*. An example of a type assignment is:

  ```
  HouseNumber ::= INTEGER
  ```

  In the preceding definition, HouseNumber is a new type, ::= means *defined as*, and INTEGER is the ASN.1 built-in type. HouseNumber is also known as the *type reference*. We notice here that HouseNumber starts with the uppercase letter H.

- An *identifier*, like a type, consists of one or more letters, digits, and/or hyphens. However, there is one difference between a type and an identifier: The first character of an identifier starts with a lowercase letter. An example of an identifier is:

```
newModule
```

■ A type can have one or more values. We can assign a value to a type by *value assignment.* An example of a value assignment is:

```
houseNumber HouseNumber ::= 234
```

In the preceding example, houseNumber is a *value reference* (used for providing a value to a type), HouseNumber is the type for which the value is provided, ::= stands for the assignment of a value, and 234 is the actual value. Note that the value reference houseNumber starts with a lowercase letter. The syntax for a value reference otherwise is the same as for a type reference.

■ A comment starts with -- and ends with either another -- or a period. An example of a comment is:

```
-- this is a comment in ASN.1 --
```

ASN.1 built-in types are displayed in Table 5-1. Let us examine each one of them with examples.

5.2.1 Simple Types

We can choose the BOOLEAN type for cases that have two states. As an example, the simple type *Normal* can be defined as follows:

TABLE 5-1

ASN.1 Built-in Types (X.208).

AnyType*	NullType	SetType
BooleanType	OctetStringType	SetOfType
BitStringType	ObjectIdentifierType	TaggedType
CharacterStringType	RealType	UsefulType (GeneralizedTime)
ChoiceType	SelectionType	UsefulType (EXTERNAL)
EnumeratedType	SequenceType	UsefulType (ObjectDescriptor)
IntegerType	SequenceOfType	UsefulType (UTCTime)

*Removed in X.680.

```
Normal ::= BOOLEAN
-- the whole thing is a production --
```

In this example, Normal is a BOOLEAN type with two values, TRUE or FALSE. This case is an example of a *production*. A production has a name on the left, followed by ::= and then a collection of sequences, which simply means a list of names. If there is more than one name, the names are separated by a vertical bar (|), which stands for *or*, as in many programming languages. Here, note that Normal starts with an uppercase letter because it is a type reference.

If we are not satisfied with just two states for a type, we can use an enumerated type to model the type. For example, assume that a type, EthernetAdapterStatus, has possible values of normal, degraded, off line, and failed.

```
EthernetAdapterStatus ::= ENUMERATED {normal (0), degraded (1),
offline (2), failed (3)}
```

In this production, note that ENUMERATED is used for three or more states, and the first state (normal) has a value of 0. So the next state (degraded) has a value of 1.

We want to have a counter that keeps track of the number of collisions in Ethernet over a fixed period of time. Let us call this counter *Ethernet-NumberCollisions*. This can be defined in ASN.1 syntax as follows:

```
EthernetNumberCollisions ::= INTEGER
```

INTEGER can be used to model an integer variable. It can also be used to define cardinal variables. Here, *cardinal variable* refers to values as a set or sequence. Now let us assume that EthernetNumberCollisionsRange is a range of 0 (no collisions) to 1000 collisions. Then *range* can be defined as follows:

```
EthernetNumberCollisionsRange ::= INTEGER {minimum(0),
maximum(1000)}
```

Both BIT STRING and OCTET STRING can be used to define binary data. The main difference between them is that in BIT STRING, the number of bits used is not necessarily a multiple of 8 bits, whereas in OCTET STRING, the length of the bits is in multiples of 8.

Let us go back to our example of EthernetAdapterStatus, which we used in explaining the ENUMERATED data type. Using BIT STRING, this example can be defined as follows:

```
EthernetAdapterStatus ::= BIT STRING {normal (0), degraded (1),
offline (2), failed (3)}
```

In the preceding example, EthernetAdapterStatus will have a value of 1000 B or 8 H (hex string) for the normal.

Let us investigate the CharacterStringType. CharacterStringTypes are:

- NumericString

- PrintableString

- TeletexString

- VideotexString

- VisibleString

- IA5String

- GraphicString

- GeneralString

Of these different CharacterStringTypes, NumericString, Printable-String, and IA5String are important. NumericString consists of digits 0 through 9 and spaces. PrintableString consists of letters, which can be uppercase or lowercase, digits, punctuation marks (",", ".", ":", etc.), and spaces. IA5String stands for International Alphabet Number 5 and is the same as the ASCII character set. For details on TeletexString, refer to Reference 5.3, for more on VideotexString, refer to Reference 5.4. The following are some examples of character strings.

```
AdapterCardType ::= PrintableString
  -- Here card type can be Ethernet, token ring, token bus.
AdapterCardType ::= NumericString
  -- Card type can be mapped as Ethernet to 0, token ring to 1, and
  so on.
```

Note that OCTET STRING may be used when an appropriate CharacterStringType is not available. As an example, we can define Ethernet-AdapterNumber as follows:

```
EthernetAdapterNumber ::= OCTET STRING
```

The NULL type is, by and large, used as a placeholder and is used if there is no element in a sequence.

The REAL type is used to model real numbers.

```
AdapterCardPrice ::= REAL
```

Because the adapter card price can be a specific number, for example $254.90, it is realistic to model it as REAL.

5.2.2 Structured Types

Let us assume that, in some cases, an Ethernet adapter does not have a number to identify it. In that case, it can be modeled as follows:

```
EthernetAdapterNumber ::= CHOICE {NULL, OCTET STRING}
```

Here, the use of CHOICE states that the Ethernet card number need not be there or an OCTET STRING. We will come back to the use of CHOICE later.

The SEQUENCE type is used to model a variable that has zero or more elements, in which the order of elements is important. The SEQUENCE type can have different types of elements, while the SEQUENCE OF type has only one type of elements.

```
EthernetCollisionsCounter ::= SEQUENCE
                                    {highValue INTEGER,
                                    lowValue INTEGER}
```

In this case, values in a collisions counter are expressed between the high and low values. Also, highValue and lowValue are just identifiers used for understandability; hence, lowercase letters are used as the initial characters. EthernetCollisionsCounter can also be expressed with the SEQUENCE OF type, because both the high and low values are mentioned with the same INTEGER type.

```
EthernetCollisionsCounter ::= SEQUENCE OF
                                    {highValue INTEGER,
                                    lowValue INTEGER}
```

Let us define one more counter for tokens lost in a token ring network.

```
TokenRingTokensLost ::= SEQUENCE OF
                                {highValue INTEGER,
                                lowValue INTEGER}
```

These two counters, EthernetCollisionsCounter and TokenRing Tokens-Lost, can be combined into a LAN counter. Because the types are different, they are combined into a SEQUENCE type variable.

```
LanSimpleCounterLimits ::= SEQUENCE
        {ethernetCounter1 COMPONENTS OF EthernetCollisionsCounter,
    tokenRingCounter1 COMPONENTS OF TokenRingTokensLost}
```

In the preceding definitions, COMPONENTS OF used with Ethernet-CollisionsCounter and TokenRingTokensLost indicates that all elements of both sequences are included.

The use of SET and SET OF types is similar to that of SEQUENCE and SEQUENCE OF, except in one respect. In SEQUENCE and SEQUENCE OF, we noticed that the order of elements is important. If the order of elements is not important, then SET and SET OF can be used in place of SEQUENCE and SEQUENCE OF, respectively. While using SEQUENCE, SEQUENCE OF, SET, and SET OF, context-specific tagging helps to identify each variable. Context-specific tagging is explained under Section 5.2.3.

SET OF can also be used for variables in which the elements are of the same type and the order of data is not important.

```
LanWorkstationSerialNumbers ::= OCTET STRING (SIZE (32))
LanSegment ::= SET OF LanWorkstationSerialNumbers
```

In this example, LanSegment is modeled as a collection of workstations, and each workstation is identified by its serial number. The serial number has a length of 32 octets (8 bits each).

Next, let us examine the use of SET. A LAN network may have combinations of Ethernet and token ring networks. The types used to model Ethernet and token ring networks are deliberately kept different in the following example. We assume that the order of these is not important.

```
MacAddresses ::= OCTET STRING (SIZE (6))
EthernetNetworks ::= SET OF MacAddresses
TokenRingNetworks ::= SET OF LanSegment
LanNetwork ::= SET
                {etherNet [0] IMPLICIT EthernetNetworks,
                 tokenNet [1] IMPLICIT TokenRingNetworks}
```

In this example, MacAddresses has a length of six octets. The LanNetwork set has two elements: etherNet and tokenNet. In turn, etherNet is a collection of workstations identified by MacAddresses. However, in the case of tokenNet, there are sets of LAN segments, each of which in turn is a set of serial numbers as elements. IMPLICIT will be explained in the next section.

When only one of the alternative members of a collection has to be selected, then CHOICE is used. IMPLICIT tagging can be used if members belong to only a single data type.

```
ObjectName ::= CHOICE
                {localUniqueName GraphicString,
                 localUniqueIdentifier    NumericString OPTIONAL}
```

This states that ObjectName can be in one of the following forms: localUniqueName or localUniqueIdentifier. Here, the keyword OPTIONAL states that localUniqueIdentifier may or may not be sent during data transfer to the other end, depending on circumstances.

Selection type makes use of the alternative types defined in CHOICE.

```
ObjectNameUsed ::= SEQUENCE
                {easilyReadableName localUniqueName <
                ObjectName}
```

In this example, we have used one of the alternatives: localUnique-Name, modeled by the ObjectName type.

5.2.3 Tagged Types

A tagged type is used to model variables for removing ambiguities. In structured data types, which we have already seen, there are possibilities for confusion over such issues as how the receiving end interprets data, when it receives data on ObjectName, and whether the data refers to local-UniqueName or localUniqueIdentifier. Here, we need tagging to explicitly state that the data sent from the other end refers to localUniqueName or localUniqueIdentifier, removing the confusion.

A tag can be EXPLICIT or IMPLICIT. By using an IMPLICIT tag, there is no need to transfer the data type during data transfer to the other end, while in the case of an EXPLICIT tag, transfer of the data type is required. This is understandable. For example, a CharacterString that identifies a variable can mean a Numeric String or a Graphic String. In order for a CharacterString to be clearly understood on the receiving end of the application entity, it is necessary to know exactly what is meant by the CharacterString.

If no IMPLICIT tag is specified, then it is assumed that an EXPLICIT tag is used. There is no mention of EXPLICIT in such cases. However, in module definitions, things are slightly different. If an IMPLICIT tag is used along with the module definition, then all the tags in the module are IMPLICIT. If a tag is left out or states that it is EXPLICIT, then it is assumed that the tagging used is EXPLICIT. Details on module definitions are provided in Section 5.2.4.

A user-defined tag has a class and a number within the square brackets []. The four user-defined tag classes are listed in Table 5-2. Let us examine each of them.

TABLE 5-2

ASN.1 User-Defined
Tag Classes.

UNIVERSAL

APPLICATION

PRIVATE

CONTEXT-SPECIFIC

UNIVERSAL TAG. The UNIVERSAL tag is used for data types as provided in *X.208* (ISO 8824) (see Reference 5.1). The data types must be globally known and unique. Table 5-3 lists the different types of UNIVERSAL class tags. Let us look at an example of the UNIVERSAL class.

TABLE 5-3

Different UNIVER-
SAL Class Tags.

Tag	Type
UNIVERSAL 0	Reserved for use by encoding rules
UNIVERSAL 1	BooleanType
UNIVERSAL 2	IntegerType
UNIVERSAL 3	BitStringType
UNIVERSAL 4	OctetStringType
UNIVERSAL 5	NullType
UNIVERSAL 6	ObjectIdentifierType
UNIVERSAL 7	ObjectDescriptorType
UNIVERSAL 8	ExternalType and InstanceOfType*
UNIVERSAL 9	RealType
UNIVERSAL 10	EnumeratedType
UNIVERSAL 11	EmbeddedPDVType*
UNIVERSAL 12—15	Reserved for future editions of X.680
UNIVERSAL 16	SequenceType and SequenceOfType
UNIVERSAL 17	SetType and SetOfType
UNIVERSAL 18	NumericString
UNIVERSAL 19	PrintableString
UNIVERSAL 20	TeletexString (T61String)
UNIVERSAL 21	VideotexString
UNIVERSAL 22	IA5String
UNIVERSAL 23—24	Time
UNIVERSAL 25	GraphicString
UNIVERSAL 26	VisibleString (ISO646String)
UNIVERSAL 27	GeneralString
UNIVERSAL 28	UniversalString*
UNIVERSAL 30	BMPString*
UNIVERSAL 31	Reserved for addenda to X.680

* Added in X.680.

Assume that we are using an attribute, *Counter,* to keep track of beaconing in a token ring card. At a particular time, Counter may have a value of 21. This may be represented as an INTEGER. Here, INTEGER is the type.

```
Counter ::= [UNIVERSAL 2] IMPLICIT INTEGER
```

In this production, definition of the UNIVERSAL class tag is used. The INTEGER type is UNIVERSAL 2, as per Table 5-3.

APPLICATION TAG. The APPLICATION class is used to model the variables that are understood in the ASN.1 module being used. The presentation context understands the data type of the variable.

```
AnotherCounter ::= [APPLICATION 1] IMPLICIT INTEGER
```

In this example, [APPLICATION 1] is the tag. [APPLICATION 1] states that it is understood in the presentation context negotiated between the presentation entities, APPLICATION is the tag class and 1 is the number within the class. Here, IMPLICIT states that the explicit stating of Another-Counter as an INTEGER is not necessary during data transfer. In this example, AnotherCounter is understood to be INTEGER by receiving the presentation layer entity.

CONTEXT-SPECIFIC TAG. In structured types, there is the problem of distinguishing between different elements. There can be major confusion, especially when using CHOICE. Unless elements are specifically mentioned, it is hard for the receiver to understand which element was sent. To remove these ambiguities, we use context-specific tags. The number for these tags starts with 0. For example:

```
BeaconingCounter ::= SET
                    {counterName  [0] IMPLICIT VisibleString,
                     counterNumber    [1] IMPLICIT INTEGER }
```

In this production, BeaconingCounter is defined as a SET. Mentioning that it is a SET means that order is not important. Here counterName has a context-specific tag of [0] and it states that it is the first element. Similarly, counterNumber has a context-specific tag of [1], and it is the second element.

PRIVATE TAG. The PRIVATE tag may be used to identify data types used within an organization or a country.

```
BecCounter ::= [PRIVATE 3] IMPLICIT INTEGER
```

In this example, [PRIVATE 3] has been used to specify that this is a widely used type within an organization or country.

OBJECT IDENTIFIER AND ObjectDescriptor.   OBJECT IDENTIFIER is a set of names, numbers, or a mixture of the two associated with nodes from the root of the object identifier tree up to the object used, and it uniquely identifies an object. The object identifier tree is the same as the registration hierarchy tree (refer to Chapter 4, Figure 4.7). The root of the object identifier tree has three nodes: itu-t, iso, and joint-iso-itu-t. The basic principles of assigning identifiers are that an organization is responsible for the assignment of identifiers below it and the organization must ensure that the identifiers it issues are unique. As an example, iso, with a node value of 1, is responsible for assigning object identifiers below it. It has four children—standard, registration-authority, member-body, and identified-organization—with identifier values of 0, 1, 2, and 3, respectively. Identified-organization issues its own set of unique identifiers to the nodes below it. These parent and children nodes are connected by arcs.

Each value or name in OBJECT IDENTIFIER represents the values or names of nodes in the object identifier tree. Let us form an arbitrary OBJECT IDENTIFIER for lanNetwork:

```
lanNetwork OBJECT IDENTIFIER ::=
        {iso org dod internet private enterprises Xenterprises 85}
```

Here, org has a value of 3 for the node below the iso, dod has a value of 6 assigned to the node from org, internet has 1 for the node from dod, private has a label of 4 for the node from internet, and enterprises has 1 assigned to the node below private. Let us assume that Xenterprises has 140 given to its node and that in Xenterprises a value of 85 is assigned to lanNetwork. In this case, for the OBJECT IDENTIFIER of lanNetwork, instead of using the textual form as previously given, we can also use the numeric form as follows:

```
lanNetwork OBJECT IDENTIFIER ::= {1 3 6 1 4 1 140 85}
```

Please note that OBJECT IDENTIFIER can also have a mixture of names and values, instead of just names or just values as shown in these examples. The OBJECT IDENTIFIER of lanNetwork, as indicated here, is difficult to understand. So ObjectDescriptor, which represents easily readable texts, must be sent along with OBJECT IDENTIFIER. Sometimes

ObjectDescriptor may not end up being unique, but the combination of ObjectDescriptor and OBJECT IDENTIFIER will become unique globally.

```
etherlanNetwork ObjectDescriptor ::= [UNIVERSAL 7] IMPLICIT
GraphicString(SIZE(8))
```

Here, etherlanNetwork is the name of the ObjectDescriptor used and is a GraphicString of eight octets.

EXTERNAL. The EXTERNAL type is useful for modeling variables by abstract syntax other than ASN.1. This can refer to the types defined outside a particular module, and there are no restrictions on the use of the type. As can be seen from Table 5-3, the tag for EXTERNAL is UNIVERSAL 8.

```
DataTransferMode ::= EXTERNAL
```

Here, we are assuming that how we transfer the data is external to the module, which has DataTransferMode defined in it. We are assuming that for representation of data, we are using EBCDIC.

DATE AND TIME. Nations use different ways of reporting date and time. Thus, communication between different users around the globe is facilitated if the representation of date and time is standardized. The data type used for this purpose is *Time*, and the tags used are UNIVERSAL 23 for UTC (Coordinated Universal Time) and UNIVERSAL 24 for generalized time.

Three forms of generalized time are:

- *Calendar date:* 19940623235343.7.   In this example, the first four digits represent the year (1994), the next two digits represent the month (06), the next two digits represent the day (23), the next two digits represent the hour (23), the next two digits indicate minutes (53), and the last digits indicate seconds (43.7). So, the date and time are June 23, 1994, at time 11:53:43.7 P.M. This form represents local time.

- *Time of day:* 19940623235343.7Z.   All digits represent the same terms as they do in the local time, but the addition of the letter Z at the end indicates that the time refers to UTC time.

- *Time differential:* 19940623235343.7+1100.   Here, local time is furnished as in the local time example. We can derive the UTC time from the time differential form of date and time representation. The UTC required is obtained by adding 11 hours to the local time.

Now let us examine universal time represented by UTC time. In this form, the date is represented by YYMMDD. Here, YY stands for the last two digits of a year, MM stands for the month, and DD represents the day of the month. The time can be of the form hhmm with four digits, or hhmmss with six digits. In this case, hh stands for hours (00 to 23), mm stands for minutes (00 to 59), and ss indicates seconds (00 to 59). This can be followed by either Z or a time differential that indicates the hours that must be added or subtracted to get the UTC time.

For example, 940623235343Z is similar to the UTC time listed under generalized time. One difference is that 1994 becomes 94, and seconds are not carried to decimal places (43 seconds instead of 43.7 seconds). The other form, 940623235343Z+1100, means that to get the UTC time we must add 11 hours.

5.2.4 Module Definitions

Module definitions are primarily used for grouping ASN.1 definitions. They also help in using type definitions defined in other places by making use of IMPORT and EXPORT mechanisms. Modules are analogous to functions in C language or subroutines in Pascal. There are module definitions in the definitions of managed object classes in standards and other documents. The following example illustrates this.

```
LanNetworkModule {iso org dod internet private enterprises Xenter-
prises 95}
    -- Above, LanNetworkModule is the module name, and {iso org dod
    -- internet private enterprises Xenterprises 95} is the assigned
    -- identifier.
DEFINITIONS EXPLICIT TAGS ::= BEGIN
    -- We have module body below.
IMPORTS
    RelativeDistinguishedName  FROM      InformationFramework
    {joint-iso-ccitt ds(5) modules(1)
     informationFramework(1)}
-- End of IMPORTS.
EXPORTS
    LanNetworkName ::= SEQUENCE of RelativeDistinguishedName
-- End of EXPORTS.
MacAddresses ::= OCTET STRING (SIZE (6))
LanWorkstationSerialNumbers ::= OCTET STRING (SIZE (32))
LanSegment ::= SET OF LanWorkstationSerialNumbers
EthernetNetworks ::= SET OF MacAddresses
TokenRingNetworks ::= SET OF LanSegment
LanNetwork ::= SET
    {etherNet   [0] IMPLICIT EthernetNetworks,
     tokenNet   [1] IMPLICIT TokenRingNetworks}
END
```

In the preceding definitions, IMPORTS states that RelativeDistin-guishedName is defined in the InformationFramework and is used in this module. In the preceding module, LanNetworkName will be used in other module definitions. For this reason, it has to be mentioned in EXPORTS. Although it is not mandatory to have IMPORTS and EXPORTS, their use makes the definitions easier.

Notice that EXPLICIT TAGS immediately follows DEFINITIONS. We have deliberately introduced this to explain the idea behind using it. EXPLICIT TAGS is not necessary, because the default tag is "empty," which also means EXPLICIT TAGS. If we use IMPLICIT TAGS instead of EXPLICIT TAGS, then all of the tags we use in the module are IMPLICIT.

5.2.5 Subtypes

Subtypes, as the name suggests, make use of the existing types (see Figure 5-2). When subtypes are derived, they must have values. Subtypes are used in the following cases.

■ When two *or* more types have common characteristics, subtyping makes the definition easier, if we include the common characteristics in a parent type. Subtypes include parent type and individual characteristics.

■ If we want to limit the sizes or values of existing types, subtyping is helpful, making definitions of variables clear.

■ If we wish to explain a subset with values in more detail, then sub-typing is useful.

There are six subtypes. We will borrow some of the examples from previous sections to show how subtyping works.

Figure 5-2
Types, values, and subtypes. (Source: Reprinted with permission from OSI Upper Layer Standards and Practices by Baha Hebrawi, copyright 1993 by McGraw-Hill.)

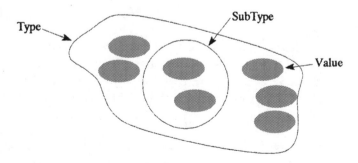

SINGLE VALUE. Single-value subtyping permits only one value out of many possible values of a subtype to be used.

```
TestResult ::= INTEGER (0 | 1 | 2)
```

In this case, we assign the values: pass is 0, fail is 1, and withdraw is 2. Thus, the results can be only one of these three states. The vertical bar (|) stands for *or.*

PERMITTED ALPHABET. Assume that house numbers can be only numbers that range in size from 1 to 5 digits. In such a case, we can come up with the following permitted alphabet subtyping:

```
HouseNumber     ::=     IA5String               (FROM
("0"|"1"|"2"|"3"|"4"|"5"|"6"|"7"|"8"|"9") SIZE(1..5))
```

CONTAINED. The contained subtype is helpful in forming a new subtype from the existing subtypes. In the example that follows, HouseAddress is a new subtype formed from subtype HouseNumber.

```
HouseAddress ::= INCLUDES HouseNumber
```

VALUE RANGE. Value ranges are used for INTEGER, REAL, and types obtained by tagging. As an example, assume that employee serial numbers are derived from integer values from 1000 to 20,000. A value range can be defined as follows:

```
EmployeeSerialNumber ::= INTEGER (1000..20000)
```

SIZE CONSTRAINT. A Size constraint can be used for forming subtypes and includes the keyword SIZE. SIZE mentions the length of the subtype derived from a parent.

```
LanWorkstationSerialNumber ::= OCTET STRING (SIZE (32))
```

Here, too, LanWorkstationSerialNumber is a subtype of the parent type OCTET STRING and has a length of 32 octets. Let us modify this example and assume that the workstation serial numbers are OCTET STRING with varying size anywhere from 5 to 32 octets. The modification is as follows:

```
LanWorkstationSerialNumber ::= OCTET STRING (SIZE (5..32))
```

INNER SUBTYPING. In the following example, we have made use of some of the inner subtyping keywords, such as WITH COMPONENTS, OPTIONAL, PRESENT, and ABSENT, to define subtypes of PureEther-Lan and PureTokenLan. These two subtypes are derived from the parent, LanNetwork.

```
Bandwidth ::= INTEGER (1..4096)
-- Bandwidth can be from 1 to 4096 megabits per second
MacAddresses ::= OCTET STRING (SIZE (6))
LanSegment ::= SET OF LanWorkstationSerialNumbers
EthernetNetworks ::= SET OF MacAddresses
TokenRingNetworks ::= SET OF LanSegment
FDDIBackbonenetworks ::= SET OF MacAddresses
LanNetwork ::= SET
                {networkID              GraphicString,
                networkBandwidth        Bandwidth,
                fDDIBackNet             FDDIBackbonenetworks,
                etherNet                EthernetNetworks OPTIONAL,
                tokenNet                TokenRingNetworks OPTIONAL}
PureEtherLan ::= LanNetwork (WITH COMPONENTS
                {networkID              GraphicString,
                networkBandwidth        Bandwidth,
                fDDIBackNet             FDDIBackbonenetworks,
                etherNet                PRESENT tokenNet ABSENT})
PureTokenLan ::= LanNetwork (WITH COMPONENTS
                {networkID              GraphicString,
                networkBandwidth        Bandwidth,
                fDDIBackNet             FDDIBackbonenetworks,
                etherNet                ABSENT tokenNet PRESENT})
```

5.3 X.680

ASN.1-88/90 refers to the ASN.1 notation specified in CCITT Recommendation X.208 (1988) and ISO/IEC 8824:1990. Note that a module has to use one of the notations, and the module specifications have to clearly specify whether ASN.1-88/90 ASN.1 notation or current ASN.1 notation is used. Current ASN.1 notation refers to X.680 ASN.1 specifications.

5.3.1 X.208 versus X.680

There are some differences between X.208 and X.680 ASN.1 definitions. Some of the differences are described in the following text.

ANY REMOVED. In X.208, ANY is used when specifications are defined in another place before any data transfer is done. It is mainly a placeholder for providing more details at a later time. The syntax of ANY is as given here:

```
AnyType  ::= ANY | ANY DEFINED BY identifier
AnyValue ::= Type Value
This was changed for easier parsing of ASN.1 to
AnyValue ::= Type : Value
```

AnyType has been removed from the X.680 specifications. So, for place-holders, information object classes defined in X.681 (Reference 5.5) can be used.

MACRO REMOVED. In X.208, MACRO notation is used for locally defining the types and values of variables. It is also used for extending the ASN.1 grammar using available ASN.1 definitions. Instead of MACROs, this capability is provided by an information object class defined in X.681. However, the generality that was available due to MACROs is eliminated by the removal of MACROs.

Also, MACROs are used to define expressions and this capability is provided by the parameterization enhancement provided in X.683 (Reference 5.7).

5.3.1.1 Changes to Types and Values.

In ASN.1 definitions in X.208, there are cases where there can be ambiguous definitions. So some of the definitions have been modified. Some of the changes are in the definitions of NamedType, ChoiceValue, and RealType. Let us look into each one of these.

NamedType.   The X.208 ASN.1 definition of NamedType was

```
NamedType  ::= identifier Type | Type | Selection Type
NamedValue ::= identifier Value | Value
```

In X.680, the *identifier* has been made mandatory for the NamedType and NameValue definitions. As a result, the syntax of NamedType has been changed as given below:

```
NamedType  ::= identifier Type
NamedValue ::= identifier Value.
```

ChoiceValue.   In X.208, the ASN.1 definition of ChoiceValue was

```
ChoiceValue ::= NamedValue
NamedValue  ::= identifier Value | Value
```

In X.680, the ChoiceValue has been changed to

```
ChoiceValue ::= identifier ":" Value.
```

RealType. In X.208, RealType was defined as:

```
RealType ::= REAL
RealValue ::= NumericRealValue | SpecialRealValue
NumericRealValue ::= {Mantissa, Base, Exponent} | 0
Mantissa ::= SignedNumber
Base ::= 2 | 10
Exponent ::= SignedNumber
SpecialRealValue ::= PLUS-INFINITY | MINUS-INFINITY
```

There has been a slight change in the definition of NumericRealValue in X.680 and it is defined as

```
NumericRealValue ::= SequenceValue | 0
```

SequenceValue replaces the {Mantissa, Base, Exponent}. As a result of this change, now RealValue definition can be

```
SEQUENCE {
    mantissa INTEGER,
    base INTEGER (2|10),
    exponent INTEGER
    -- real number is mantissa multiplied by base raised to the
    -- power of exponent.
}
```

ADDITIONS. In X.680, some new data types have been added over the definitions provided in X.208. Some minor additions have also been made. The additions are explained in the following text.

AUTOMATIC TAGS. In X.208, TagDefault is defined as

```
TagDefault ::- EXPLICIT TAGS | IMPLICIT TAGS | empty
```

In X.680, AUTOMATIC TAGS has been added and this is applied at the module level. Here also, if TagDefault is empty then EXPLICIT TAGS is used. The modified definition of TagDefault is

```
TagDefault ::= EXPLICIT TAGS | IMPLICIT TAGS | AUTOMATIC TAGS | empty
```

UniversalString. UniversalString, which was not available in X.208, is a new addition in X.680. In Table 5-3, UNIVERSAL 28 has been given the universal class number for UniversalString. UniversalString includes all characters available in ISO/IEC 10646-1. ISO/IEC 10646-1 has a varied range of characters such as control characters, graphic characters, and so on. For more details on the characters supported, refer to Reference 5.8. Let us take an example of UniversalString. To represent the Σ in $\Sigma stockvalue$, we can write

```
IMPORTS BasicLatin, greekCapitalSigma FROM ASN1-CHARACTER-MODULE
                                        {joint-iso-ccitt asn1(1)
specification(0) modules(0) iso10646(0)};
TotalSumOfStock ::= UniversalString {FROM (BasicLatin | greekCapi-
                                    talLetterSigma)}
myTotalSumOfStock TotalSumOfStock ::= { greekCapitalLetterSigma,
                                        "stockvalue"}
```

BMPString.   BMPString is another addition in the X.680. Universal class number of 30 has been assigned for BMPString. BMPString is a restrictive subtype of UniversalString. BMPString uses the first 64K-2 cells of the characters in ISO/IEC 10646-1. An example of a BMPString is

```
tilde BMPString ::= (0, 0, 0, 126)
```

NEW BUILT-IN TYPES.   New built-in types have been added in X.680. They are EmbeddedPDVType, ObjectClassFieldType, and InstanceOfType. EmbeddedPDVType is defined in X.680; the syntax of ObjectClassField-Type and InstanceOfType is explained in X.681.

EmbeddedPDVType has a universal class number of 11: PDV stands for presentation data value. Embedded PDV type is to be used for EXTERNAL type. This type is more suitable to model presentation layer type and data. EmbeddedPDVType type is more general in usage than EXTERNAL and there is no restriction that only ASN.1 has to be used. The data value of this type may or may not be the value of an ASN.1 type such as a value representing some item such as a graphic picture. This data type may include identification of the encoding rules used to encode the value used. The syntax of EmbeddedPDVType and values is

```
EmbeddedPDVType ::= EMBEDDED PDV
EmbeddedPDVValue ::= SequenceValue
```

An example of an EmbeddedPDVType is

```
WindowsFolder ::= SEQUENCE OF EMBEDDED PDV
```

ObjectClassFieldType **AND** **InformationObjectClass.**   ObjectClassFieldType and InstanceOfType are explained in X.681. The ObjectClassFieldType is used to define the types for information object class. Information object class contains a set of fields and these fields represent a collection of instances of the class. The syntax of ObjectClassFieldType is

```
ObjectClassFieldType ::= DefinedObjectClass"."FieldName
FieldName ::= PrimitiveFieldName"." +
```

The FieldName denotes either a type field or a variable type value field and is an open type notation. Here "+" stands for a production with a PrimitiveFieldName or an alternating series of production sequences starting and ending with PrimitiveFieldName. So, the sequence can be PrimitiveFieldName or PrimitiveFieldName.PrimitiveFieldName and so on.

```
ObjectClassFieldValue ::= OpenTypeFieldVal | FixedTypeFieldVal
OpenTypeFieldVal ::= Type ":" Value
FixedTypeFieldVal ::= Value
```

There are instances of object classes that have the values defined later or elsewhere. ANY and ANY DEFINED BY is used to define these instances in X.208. These have been replaced by information object classes in X.680 and X.681.

Let us define an information object class for ERRORS

```
ERRORS ::= CLASS
        {&OperationType        OPTIONAL,
         &Category             PrintableString (SIZE(8)),
         &ErrorCode            INTEGER UNIQUE}

WITH SYNTAX
        {[OPERATION-TYPE       &OperationType]
         [CATEGORY             &Category]
          ERROR-CODE           &ErrorCode}
```

In the preceding example, ERRORS is an object information class. ERRORS has &OperationType, a type field, and the two value fields &Category and &ErrorCode. In &OperationType the type field is undefined and is left open to be defined later by using OPTIONAL. In our example, ERRORS is the DefinedObjectClass and &OperationType is the FieldName. ERRORS.&OperationType is an example of ObjectClassFieldType.

WITH SYNTAX defines the syntax of the information object class, ERRORS. In the preceding definition, &ErrorCode is an identifier field as UNIQUE is mentioned here.

Let us define the possible categories of error codes as minor (1—5), major (6—10), critical (11—20), and failed (21—30). Each error code can be mapped to some meaningful textual description of errors. The range of possible values is in parentheses. Let us define one information object operationError1 as given in the following example:

```
operationError1 ERRORS ::= {
                    {OPERATION-TYPE      INTEGER
                     CATEGORY            "Major"
                     ERROR-CODE          8}
```

After taking the example of one information object, let us define an OperationErrorSet information object set with four information objects.

```
OperationErrorSet ERRORS ::= {
                    {INTEGER "Major" 8} |
                    {REAL "Major" 10} |
                    {CHARACTER STRING "Minor" 1} |
                    {GeneralString "Critical" 15}}
```

OperationErrorSet can be represented in the form of a table; the values of parameters are shown in Table 5-4. An object class field type can be restricted to particular types or values by defining information object set. These restrictions are called *table constraints*, as there is an associated table as in the case of OperationErrorSet. Table constraints can be applied to ObjectClassFieldType or InstanceOfType. Different kinds of constraints that can be applied to information object classes are furnished in X.682 (Reference 5.6).

Let us look into how we can extract information from the OperationErrorSet.

```
errorCategory ERRORS.&Category ({OperationErrorsSet})
```

In the preceding example, errorCategory has the values in Table 5-4 of *Major, Minor,* and *Critical.* It can be noticed that *Failed* is not there in the OperationErrorSet. So by constraining, we have restricted the errorCategory to information objects that have errorCategory values of Major, Minor, and Critical.

TABLE 5-4

OperationErrorSet
Table Value.

&OperationType	&Category	&ErrorCode
INTEGER	Major	8
REAL	Major	10
CHARACTER STRING	Minor	1
GeneralString	Critical	15

InstanceOfType. InstanceOfType has a universal class number of 8. InstanceOfType represents an instance of an information object class. The syntax of InstanceOfType is

```
InstanceOfType ::= INSTANCE OF DefinedObjectClass
```

An InstanceOfType needs an &id field, which is the OBJECT IDEN-TIFIER, and a value of &Type from an instance of the DefinedObject-Class. The InstanceOfType has an associated sequence type. The associated sequence type is used for defining the values and subtypes of InstanceOfType. The associated sequence type is defined as

```
SEQUENCE
    {
     type-id              <DefinedObjectClass>.&id,
     value                [0]<DefinedObjectClass>.&Type}
```

The syntax of InstanceOfValue is

```
InstanceOfValue ::= Value
```

Let us take an example of InstanceOfType. Going back to the example of DefinedObjectClass ERRORS, the instance of an object class, ERRORS is defined as

```
INSTANCE OF ERRORS
```

The associated sequence type is now

```
SEQUENCE {
           type-id              ERRORS.&id,
           value                [0] ERRORS.&Type}
```

As we have mentioned earlier, InstanceOfType can also be con-strained. The InstanceOfType can be constrained as follows:

```
INSTANCE OF ERRORS ({PossibleTypes})
```

And the associated sequence type now becomes

```
SEQUENCE {
          type-id ERRORS.&id ({PossibleTypes}).
          value    [0] ERRORS.&Type ({PossibleTypes}) {@.type-id})}
```

PossibleTypes is a parameter, and this may not be resolved until imple-mentation details are worked out. The type-id value is limited to one of the values permitted by PossibleTypes and value is the value of &Type

field of ERRORS. @ is used for AtNotation. AtNotation points to some other ASN.1 structure. As an example, "@" points to the ASN.1 defined within the associated SEQUENCE. So @.type-id indicates that the type-id referred means the type-id included in the innermost parent structure of SEQUENCE.

ASN.1 definitions furnished in X.681 (Reference 5.5), X.682 (Reference 5.6), and X.683 (Reference 5.7) primarily add flexibility to the definition of managed object classes and managed object instances.

PARAMETERIZATION. Parameterized definitions are used for filling holes at a later stage. There are many cases where the ASN.1 syntax cannot be fully defined. In such cases parameterized definitions can be used. ASN.1 parameterization rules are explained in X.683. Let us take a simple hypothetical example for a parameterized type. In this example, either a house name or a number can distinguish a house. For this example, the parameterized type is HOUSE-DISTINCTION {}.

```
HOUSE-DISTINCTION {ToBeDetermined} ::= CHOICE
        {houseName      ToBeDetermined,
         houseNumber    INTEGER}
```

In some other place, let us define the type as HOUSE-DISTINCTION {PrintableString}. In this case, the type notation becomes

```
CHOICE
        {houseName      PrintableString,
         houseNumber    INTEGER}
```

There are cases where extensions are required to ASN.1 definitions. Usually, software is developed in different releases. As an example, if we want to add some more features to the earlier release, we will have to change and/or add some more ASN.1 definitions to the existing ASN.1 definitions. For such cases, rules for extension of ASN.1 definitions have been added in Amendment 1 to X.680 (Reference 5.12). For more details about these rules, the reader should refer to Amendment 1.

5.4 Basic Encoding Rules (BER)

BER is used in the presentation layer, before the actual transfer of ASN.1 values, as shown in Figure 5-1. The data transfer is in the form of a stream of octets. The representation of data value as a sequence of octets is known as *encoding*. When abstract syntax data is sent, encoding is done at the sending side and decoding is done at the receiving end.

X.209 defines the encoding rules. X.690 and X.691 have extended the encoding rules defined in X.209. Basic encoding rules present a set of options for encoding the data. Of the different available encoding options provided by BER, canonical encoding rules (CER) and distinguished encoding rules (DER) use one of the encoding options, eliminating ambiguity that may arise. DER is suitable for transmitting small encoded data values, and CER is suitable for transmitting a large amount of data or partial data. DER and CER are explained in X.690 (Reference 5.10).

The structure of BER can be of the form *identifier, length,* and *contents* (ILC) when the length of the contents is known. The identifier indicates the ASN.1 data type, the length supplies the length of the contents that follow the length field, and the contents contain the ASN.1 values to be transferred. This form is shown in Figure 5-3.

5.4.1 Identifier Field

The structure of the identifier field is shown in Figure 5-3. Class consists of the 8th and 7th bits and furnishes the tag used in data. Table 5-5 supplies the values of these bits for different classes. The 6th bit stands for either *primitive* or *constructed* (see Table 5-6), and bits 5 through 1 indicate

Figure 5-3
ILC and ILCE types of encoding.

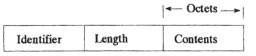

Identifier, Length, and Contents (ILC) form of Encoding

Identifier, Length, Contents, and End of Contents (ILCE) form of Encoding

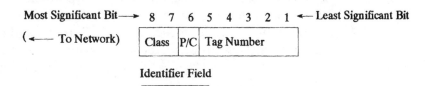

Identifier Field

TABLE 5-5

Class Bits in the Identifier Field.

Class	Bit 8	Bit 7
UNIVERSAL	0	0
APPLICATION	0	1
CONTEXT-SPECIFIC	1	0
PRIVATE	1	1

TABLE 5-6

P/C Values for Built-in ASN.1 Types.

Built-in Type	P, C, or P/C	Built-in Type	P, C, or P/C
BOOLEAN	P	CHOICE	P/C
INTEGER	P	Selection	P/C
BIT STRING	P/C	Tagged	P/C
OCTET STRING	P/C	ANY	P/C
NULL	P	EXTERNAL	P/C
SEQUENCE	C	OBJECT IDENTIFIER	P
SEQUENCE OF	C	Character String	P/C
SET	C	ENUMERATED	P
SET OF	C	REAL	P

P, primitive; C, constructed.

the ASN.1 tag number. In primitive encoding, content octets directly represent the value, whereas in constructed encoding, contents octets contain the encoding of one or more data values. In the P/C bit (Figure 5-3), a bit value of 0 indicates primitive encoding and a bit value of 1 represents constructed encoding. In Figure 5-3, bit 1 is the *least significant bit* and bit 8 is the *most significant bit*. When data is transferred, bit 8 is transferred first and bit 1 is transferred last. *Primitive* refers to simple atomic tags, while *constructed* data elements are formed from other data elements.

In tag numbers, bit 5 is the most significant bit and bit 1 is the least significant bit. Tags can be represented in two forms. If a tag number is 30 or less, then the short form with 5 bits is enough. In Figure 5-4, a tag number of 21 is shown.

Figure 5-4
Example of tag
numbers.

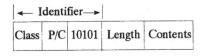

|←— Identifier—→|

| Class | P/C | 10101 | Length | Contents |

Example of Tag Number 21

| | Leading | | Last | | |
| | ←— Octet —→ | | ←- Octet-→ | | |

| Class | P/C | 11111 | 0100 1011 | Length | Contents |

Example of Tag Number 75

However, when the tag number is 31 or more, then 5 bits are not enough to represent them. In that case, the 5 bits of the leading octet are set to 1, and the tag numbers are represented by the unsigned integers in the subsequent octets. The 8th bit in each of the following octets except the last is set to 1. In the last octet, the 8th bit is set to 0 to indicate that this is the last octet to be used for calculating the tag number. In Figure 5-4, a high tag value (75) is shown.

5.4.2 Length Field

Length forms can be one of two types, *definite* or *indefinite*. The definite form, in turn, can be either *short* or *long*. This concept is depicted in Figure 5-5. In the length field, the 8th bit determines what form is used. If the

Figure 5-5
Different BER length
forms.

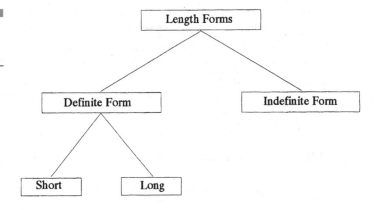

Figure 5-6
Example of short-form
and long-form
lengths.

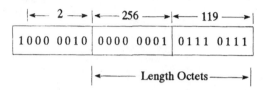

|←——— 27 ———→|

| 0001 1011 |

Length Short Form - 27 Octets of Data Contents Field

|←— 2 —→|←——— 256 ———→|←——— 119 ———→|

| 1000 0010 | 0000 0001 | 0111 0111 |

|←——————— Length Octets ———————→|

Length Long Form - 375 Octets of Data Contents Field

bit is 0, this indicates a short form. The 7 bits can hold up to a maximum of 127 octets. However, in the initial length octet, bits 7 through 1 cannot all be 1s, or "111 1111" B (127), because this is reserved for future extensions. Hence, only a maximum value of 126 can be used in the first octet that represents length. Figure 5-6 shows an example of 27 octets of data contents.

If more than 126 octets of length are to be indicated in the length field, then the long form is used. Here, the 8th bit is set to 1 in the first length octet. The subsequent bits from 7 to 1 furnish the number of length octets used.

As an example, the 375 length octets are shown in Figure 5-6. Here "000 0010" B indicates that there will be two additional octets that will have to be used for computing the length of the data octets. The bits in the subsequent two length octets represent 375.

If the length of the data contents is not known, then the *indefinite* form of encoding, also known as the ILCE form, is used. In the indefinite form, the 8th bit of the first octet of the length field is set to 1, and the rest of the bits from 7 to 1 are all set to 0. As usual, after the length field, we have data. After data, there are two octets of the end of contents field. The end of contents field is represented by "00 00" X, where X stands for a hexadecimal. We note here that because we have used "00 00" X for end of contents, we cannot have a value of "00 00" X in data.

5.4.3 Data Contents Field

Using examples, we will examine how built-in types are encoded.

BOOLEAN VALUE. A BOOLEAN value can be either TRUE or FALSE. The encoding of a BOOLEAN value of TRUE is shown in Figure 5-7. BOOLEAN belongs to the UNIVERSAL class, so bits 8 and 7 are both 0. Bit 6 is 0 because it is a primitive. The tag number for BOOLEAN from Table 5-3 is 1. Hence, the identifier field is represented as shown in Figure 5-7. The length of the data contents is one octet, so the length is shown as 1. The contents can be represented by "FF" X for the BOOLEAN value of TRUE. It may be noted that, instead of "FF" X, we can use any nonzero value in the first octet for a value of TRUE. For the BOOLEAN value of FALSE, the data contents octet is 0.

INTEGER VALUE. For the INTEGER value, the data contents field has twos complement. The INTEGER value is derived by including all bits from all octets. When computing the twos complement for a positive integer, the twos complement is the number itself. For a negative number, the ones complement is derived by reversing all the bits with 1 to 0 and bits with 0 to 1. Then the twos complement is obtained by adding 1 to the ones complement. Note that the operation is done on the binary representation of an INTEGER.

For the INTEGER value, too, we derive the identifier and length fields as described for the BOOLEAN value. For the data contents, 654 is represented as "028E" X and –654 is represented as "FD72" X, where X stands for hexadecimal representation.

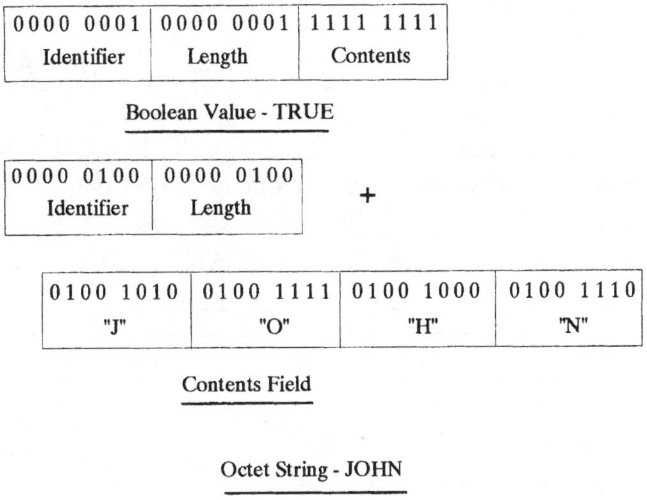

Figure 5-7
Encoding of
BOOLEAN and
OCTET STRING.

0000 0001	0000 0001	1111 1111
Identifier	Length	Contents

Boolean Value - TRUE

0000 0100	0000 0100
Identifier	Length

+

0100 1010	0100 1111	0100 1000	0100 1110
"J"	"O"	"H"	"N"

Contents Field

Octet String - JOHN

REAL VALUE. We use primitive encoding for REAL values. We use the tag nine of the UNIVERSAL class for encoding REAL values. If a REAL value is 0, then there is no contents field. A REAL value is given by:

REAL value=Mantissa(M)*Base(B)$^{\text{Exponent(E)}}$

Encoding of an AdapterCardPrice of $254.90 can be done as {25490 10–2}. Here 25490 is the mantissa, 10 is the base, and -2 is the exponent. This is one of the six encoding schemes available for encoding REAL values [see X.208 (ISO 8824), Reference 5.1].

BIT STRING VALUE. As can be seen from Table 5-5, BIT STRING can be encoded either as a primitive or constructed. When transferring data contents, if it is necessary to transfer a part of the data, the constructed form can be used.

For primitive encoding, the BIT STRING identifier and length fields are derived in the same fashion as in BOOLEAN or INTEGER encoding. The data contents are broken as shown in Figure 5-8.

In Figure 5-8, in the data contents field, the first octet is known as the *initial octet.* There are other octets numbered from 1 to 5. The last octet is known as the *final octet.* The initial octet has the same number of unused bits as the final octet. This number, represented by an unsigned binary integer, can be from 0 to 7. BIT STRING occupies one to five octets.

Let us show how a BIT STRING value can be represented, using some examples. First, a BIT STRING of "0B2FADE" X is taken. In the primitive form, it is as follows:

```
Identifier      Length      Data contents
03              05          050B2FADE0
```

In this example, because BIT STRING belongs to the UNIVERSAL class, bits 8 and 7 are each 0, the sixth bit is 0, and the other bits are set to a tag number of 3. The tag number is 3 for BIT STRING, from Table 5-3. Hence, the identifier has a value of 3. The length of the data contents is 5. In the data contents, "05" X indicates that there are 5 unused bits in the final octet of "E0" X. The initial octet of the data content field has "05" X.

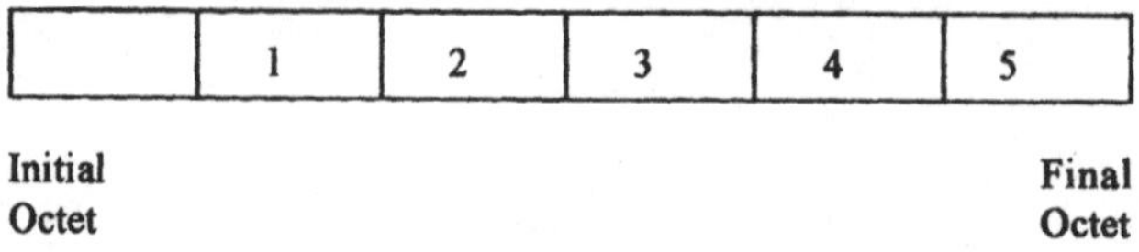

Figure 5-8

Data contents of BIT STRING values.

	1	2	3	4	5

Initial Octet   Final Octet

CONSTRUCTED FORMS. The same BIT STRING can be encoded in a constructed form as follows:

```
Identifier    Length        Data Contents
23            0A
              Identifier    Length         Data Contents
              03            03             000B2F
              03            03             05ADE0
```

This constructed string has two primitive BIT STRINGs. Here "00" (Data Contents column) in the first BIT STRING indicates that all bits in the final octet are used. However, "05" X (Data Contents column) in the second primitive BIT STRING shows that 5 bits are unused in the last octet of the data contents field. Identifier "23" X stands for "0010 0011" B. Here, bit 6 is 1, because it is a constructed string. The tag number is again 3, because it is a BIT STRING. Each primitive BIT STRING has a length of five octets. So the total length of the constructed BIT STRING comes to "0A" X.

INDEFINITE FORM. We have modified the same example to show how the BIT STRING "0B2FADE" X can be converted to BER using the indefinite form.

```
Identifier    Length    Data Contents    EOC
23            80        050B2FADE0       0000
```

In the length field, "80" X stands for the indefinite form, and it is represented as "1000 0000" B, followed by length, data in the form BIT STRING, and end of contents.

NULL VALUE. The NULL value is represented by a zero length octet, and the identifier field has "05" X.

OCTET STRING VALUE. OCTET STRING can be encoded as a primitive or constructor. The constructor form is used when we transfer data values in parts. Here all the octets are used for values, unlike the encoding of BIT STRING values. Using OCTET STRING, "JOHN" will be encoded as shown in Figure 5-7. Here, we use the primitive form, and the UNIVERSAL class number for OCTET STRING is 4.

CONSTRUCTED FORMS. As can be seen from Table 5-6, SEQUENCE, SEQUENCE OF, SET, and SET OF use constructed forms. Due to this, a P/C value of 1 is used for constructor. There are no firm rules on how different elements must be transmitted by a sender in the case of SET and SET OF. As we have seen earlier, in SET and SET OF definitions of ASN.1, no restrictions are placed on the order of elements. On the contrary, for SEQUENCE and SEQUENCE OF, the order of elements is important. So, during formation of transfer syntax, the order is preserved. The order of elements in ASN.1 is also preserved, if the values are sent for OPTIONAL or DEFAULT for all the cases. In this case, there is no distinction between SET, SET OF, SEQUENCE, and SEQUENCE OF.

OBJECT IDENTIFIER AND OBJECTDESCRIPTOR. In the case of OBJECT IDENTIFIER, we encode it after we make a conversion of the first two elements into one by using the first element, × 40, plus the next element. Each element uses bits 7 to 1 of an octet. If an element cannot be represented by 7 bits of an octet, more octets are used. Bit 8 of the first octet and each subsequent octet except the last one is set to 1. Bit 8 of the last octet is set to 0, indicating that it is the last octet used for calculating the value of an element. Let us return to our example of lanNetwork and see how an OBJECT IDENTIFIER is encoded.

```
lanNetwork OBJECT IDENTIFIER ::= {1 3 6 1 4 1 140 85}
```

The lanNetwork is encoded as shown in Figure 5-9. Because OBJECT IDENTIFIER falls under the UNIVERSAL class, bits 8 and 7 are both set to 0. Because it is primitive, bit 6 is 0. OBJECT IDENTIFIER has a value of 6 in the UNIVERSAL class, and so the tag number is 5. The first element of OBJECT IDENTIFIER for encoding is $1 \times 40 + 3$ or 43, so for encoding we use {43 6 1 4 1 140 85}. Each element is encoded using one or more octets. In Figure 5-9, we have used two octets to encode the value of 140.

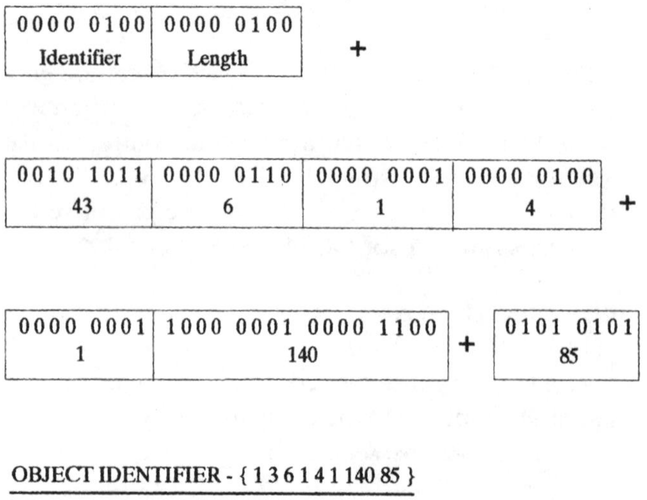

Figure 5-9
Example of encoding
of OBJECT
IDENTIFIER.

0000 0100	0000 0100
Identifier	Length

+

0010 1011	0000 0110	0000 0001	0000 0100
43	6	1	4

+

0000 0001	1000 0001 0000 1100	0101 0101
1	140	85

+

OBJECT IDENTIFIER - { 1 3 6 1 4 1 140 85 }

Note that, in the first octet, in order to represent 140, the 8th bit is set to 1 and in the second octet the 8th bit is set to 0.

ObjectDescriptor is encoded as an OCTET STRING and the UNIVERSAL class value of 7 is used.

EXTERNAL. EXTERNAL has relevance if it is defined, since data types other than ASN.1 may be used. There must be agreement on the encoding between the sending and receiving sides for the data to be useful.

CANONICAL ENCODING RULES (CER). CER places some restrictions on the BER. If the encoding is constructed, the indefinite length form (Figure 5-5) is used. However, if the encoding is primitive, then fewest length octets are used.

Bit string, octet string, and restricted character string use primitive encoding if there are 1000 or less octets in the contents field. However, when there are more than 1000 octets, constructed encoding is used.

For encoding set component values, canonical order of tagging is used. In a canonical order of tags, elements with universal class tags appear first, followed by application tags, context-specific tags, and finally private class tags. Additionally, within a class of tags, the elements appear in the ascending order of their tag numbers.

Component values of a set value are encoded in order of their tags; the order of encoding is from the lowest tag to the highest, and the encoding of tags follow the canonical order of tagging. An untagged choice is treated as having the lowest tag.

DISTINGUISHED ENCODING RULES (DER). DER also uses the encoding rules used in BER with some restrictions, just like CER. In DER, a definite length form of encoding is used. For bit string, octet string, and restricted character string types, only primitive encoding is used, and encoding of component values of a set value follows the canonical order of tagging.

In addition to these specific rules, CER and DER follow some more rules. If the BOOLEAN value is TRUE, then all bits of contents of a single octet are set to 1 as shown in Figure 5-7. When encoding set or sequence values, component values set to default values are not encoded. For more details on the encoding CER and DER, refer to Reference 5.10.

When we encode and decode the abstract syntax, we need to know which encoding rules we are using. To identify whether BER, CER, or DER encoding is used, unique object identifiers and object descriptors have been assigned. The object identifiers and object descriptors are:

- *BER:* {joint-iso-itu-t asn1(1) basic-encoding (1)} and "Basic Encoding of a single ASN.1 type"
- *CER:* {joint-iso-itu-t asn1(1) ber-derived (2) canonical-encoding (0)} and "Canonical encoding of a single ASN.1 type"
- *DER:* {joint-iso-itu-t asn1(1) ber-derived (2) distinguished-encoding (1)} and "Distinguished Encoding of a single ASN.1 type"

5.5 Notes on the Use of ASN.1 and BER

In some cases, the encoding of ASN.1 types is not efficient. As an example, to encode a BOOLEAN value, three octets are required. Such lacunas can be overcome by using *Packed Encoding Rules* (PER). The PER compact encoding scheme enables us to represent the values by eliminating the use of identifier, length, or both, depending on the situation. For more details on PER refer to X.691, Specification of Packed Encoding Rules (PER) (Reference 5.11).

The use of ASN.1 and BER is not mandatory in applications for transferring data between application entities by OSI standards. It may or may not be used, depending on the applications.

One disadvantage of ASN.1 and BER is that they are difficult to understand. There are encoders that convert ASN.1 values to BER. The encoded data can be converted back to ASN.1 values using decoders. These encoders and decoders are commercially available. Note that encoder and decoder terms have become common in the industry and they are used for conversions from one format to another, but in this book they specifically refer to the data conversions from ASN.1 to BER and from BER back to ASN.1. These encoders and decoders add complexity and extra processing and code. Extra processing has an effect on performance and should be avoided as much as possible.

Encoders and decoders simplify the coding aspect, but they do not eliminate the extra steps involved in encoding and decoding. So, why do we need these transformations if both the ends speak the same language? A partial solution is to use the transformation only where needed. There may be cases in which the application entities span different languages and continents. In such cases, encoding and decoding may be useful.

5.6 Summary

In this chapter, we have investigated ASN.1, used for communicating between application entities. We have discussed both X.208 and X.680. ASN.1 concepts have been explained with examples. We also looked at the BER, used for transferring data between presentation layers. After the discussion of BER (X.209), we have also examined CER and DER. Finally, we have discussed the practical aspects of using ASN.1 and BER.

5.7 References

5.1. ITU-T Recommendation X.208 (ISO/IEC 8824), Information Processing Systems, Open Systems Interconnection, Specification of Abstract Syntax Notation One (ASN.1), 1988.

5.2. ITU-T Recommendation X.680 (ISO/IEC 8824-1), Information Technology, Abstract Syntax Notation One (ASN.1), Specification of Basic Notation, 1994.

5.3. ITU-T Recommendation T.61, Character Repertoire and Coded Character Sets for the International Teletex Service, 1992.

5.4. ITU-T Recommendation T1.101, Data Syntax 1 for International Interactive Videotex Service, 1992.

5.5. ITU-T Recommendation X.681 (ISO/IEC 8824-2), Information Technology, Abstract Syntax Notation One (ASN.1), Information Object Specification, 1994.

5.6. ITU-T Recommendation X.682 (ISO/IEC 8824-3), Information Technology, Abstract Syntax Notation One (ASN.1), Constraint Specification, 1994.

5.7. ITU-T Recommendation X.683 (ISO/IEC 8824-4), Information Technology, Abstract Syntax Notation One (ASN.1), Parameterization of ASN.1 Specifications, 1994.

5.8. ISO/IEC 10646-1, Information Technology, Universal Multiple-Octet Coded Character Set (UCS): Architecture and Basic Multilingual Plane, 1993.

5.9. ITU-T Recommendation X.209 (ISO/IEC 8825), Open Systems Interconnection, Specification Basic Encoding for Abstract Syntax Notation (ASN.1), 1988.

5.10. ITU-T Recommendation X.690 (ISO/IEC 8825-1), Information Technology, ASN.1 Encoding Rules, Specification of Basic Encoding Rules (BER), Canonical Encoding Rules (CER), and Distinguished Encoding Rules (DER), 1994.

5.11. ITU-T Recommendation X.691 (ISO/IEC 8825-2), Information Technology, ASN.1 Encoding Rules, Specification of Packed Encoding Rules (PER), 1995.

5.12. ITU-T Recommendation Amendment 1 to X.680 (ISO/IEC 8824-1), Information Technology, Abstract Syntax Notation One (ASN.1), Specification of Basic Notation, Amendment 1: Rules of Extensibility, 1995.

5.8 Further Reading

Hebrawi, B., *OSI Upper Layer Standards and Practices*, New York: McGraw-Hill, 1993.

ISO 6093, Information Processing Systems, Representation of Numerical Values in Character Strings for Information Interchange Version, 1985.

Rose, M. T., *The Open Book, A Practical Perspective on OSI*, Englewood Cliffs, NJ: Prentice Hall, 1990.

CHAPTER 6

Structure of Management Information and TMN Information Model

6.1 Introduction

We have seen in earlier chapters that for a resource to be managed, it must be represented as a managed object class. When representing a new resource, the inheritance hierarchy defined by the X.721, Definition of Management Information (Reference 6.2), is very useful. The new resource must be appropriately made a subclass of the managed object class, which it closely resembles. All the characteristics, such as attributes, operations, notifications, and behaviors, of the superclasses are inherited. Sometimes an inheritance property reduces the process of defining a managed object class to a minor tweaking of characteristics.

It is also useful to understand how a managed object class is defined, which makes it essential that the concepts involved in the definitions of managed object classes be understood. We have investigated the meaning of a managed object class in Chapter 1. The present chapter will extend the concepts explained earlier by further examining how a managed object class is defined.

The most important activity in TMN is appropriate modeling of the telecommunications resources as managed object classes. From this point of view, we need to take a close look at how to define the managed object classes. Guidelines for the definition of managed objects (GDMO) are used for defining the managed object classes. We first look into the concepts used in defining the managed object classes. As M.3100, Generic Network Information Model (Reference 6.10), is specifically devoted to the generic TMN-related managed object classes, we will also look into the different managed object classes defined in M.3100.

6.2 Overview of the Structure of Management Information (SMI) Documents

ITU-T X.720, Management Information Model (Reference 6.1), primarily furnishes basic building blocks for the definition of a managed object class. The X.721 contains the following:

- Concepts of managed object classes and how they are defined
- Explanations of how managed object classes should be defined for purposes of compatibility and interoperability

■ Descriptions of management operations that can be done on attributes and managed objects

■ Descriptions of filter operations that can be done on managed object classes, because filters are widely used in CMIP

■ Descriptions of notifications that must be emitted by managed objects

■ Discussion of the issues involved in the naming of managed objects—including the concept of containment—which are very important for consistency in implementation

X.721, Definition of Management Information (Reference 6.2), defines the managed object classes required for systems management functions. The most important standard, X.722, Guidelines for the Definition of Managed Objects (Reference 7.3), specifies rules and provides templates for defining managed object classes. This document is popularly known as *Guidelines for the Definition of Managed Objects* (GDMO).

X.723, Generic Management Information (Reference 7.4), defines managed object classes that can be used in different layers. This document also provides definitions of resource-specific managed object classes such as ports. X.724, Requirements and Guidelines for Implementation Conformance Statement Proformas Associated with OSI Management, relates to the conformance testing of managed objects and systems management functions. To those involved in the TMN area, it is useful to know what is in each document; thus, we have furnished further details on these documents in Section 6.5.

6.3 Managed Object Class

The definition of a managed object class needs the following:

■ An *identifier* of the managed object class

■ An *allomorph attribute* that identifies the managed object classes that are allomorphic to the managed object class defining the allomorph attribute

■ A *name binding attribute*, used to uniquely identify a managed object of the managed object class, that states the relationship of a managed object to its superior

■ A *package attribute*, which is a conditional attribute and contains a list of object identifiers of the packages used

6.4 Guidelines for the Definition of Managed Objects (GDMO) Templates

To avoid confusion in defining managed object classes, a formal GDMO format for definitions must be used. This standard format is known as a *template*. These templates are used for the definitions of components of managed object classes such as packages, parameters, attributes, attribute groups, behaviors, actions, or notifications. GDMO provide the following templates:

■ *Managed object class:* In this template, inheritance relationships, which are central to the reuse of characteristics with other managed object classes, are defined. Managed object classes contain packages of behavior, attributes, attribute groups, actions, and notifications. Also, additional templates can be included or borrowed from other managed object classes. Figure 6-1 details the contents used in the definition of a managed object class.

■ *Package:* Attributes, attribute groups, operations, notifications, behavior definitions, and parameters are collected to form an identifiable template. A package template can be inserted in managed object class templates.

Figure 6-1

Managed object class definition.

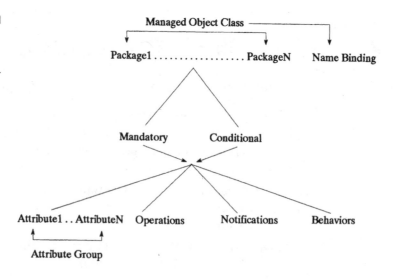

- *Attribute:*   This template is used for providing attribute syntax, and includes attribute syntax, rules to test the attribute values, behaviors, the attribute identifier, and parameters.

- *Attribute group:*   When attributes are grouped for convenience, they form attribute groups. Attribute group templates indicate the set attributes comprising the group, and an identifier value to identify the attribute group.

- *Action:*   This template is used to define the behavior and syntax of action types, which are carried in CMIS M-ACTION.

- *Behavior:*   This template is used to extend the semantics of previously defined templates. It is helpful in further explaining managed object classes, name bindings, attributes, parameters and actions, and notifications that have been defined elsewhere.

- *Notification:*   Notifications carried in CMIS M-EVENT-REPORT are defined in this template.

- *Parameter:*   Parameters used in defining attributes, operations, and notifications are defined in this template. Specifications and parameter syntaxes are also listed along with the behaviors.

- *Name binding:*   This template is used for uniquely naming a managed object. It specifies the naming attribute used for naming and identifies the superior object.

We have used a bottom-up approach in furnishing the details of these templates, starting with the explanation of attributes (Section 6.4.1) and proceeding to the managed object classes (Section 6.4.10). When using templates for defining managed object classes, certain conventions are followed; these are furnished in X.722. The important ones are:

- A semicolon (;) marks the end of each construct and the end of a template.

- All symbols and keywords are case-sensitive. That means lower- and uppercase letters indicate different things. For example, "A" is different from "a."

- Comments start with a double hyphen (--) and end with a double hyphen or the end of a line.

- Spaces, the end of a line, a blank line, or comments are valid delimiters.

- Whenever text is used in a template, one of the text-delimiter characters is used. These are: ! " # $ ^ & * ' ` , ? @ \. However, the same text delimiter should be used at the start and end of the string representing the text. For example, if we use an exclamation point (!), then the text should also end with an exclamation point.

■ The template label must be unique to a document. When defining templates, the syntax is <template-label> Template Name.

Strings included within square brackets ([]) may be present or absent in each instance of a template; these strings delimit parts of the template definition. If the square brackets are followed by an asterisk (*), as in the case of []*, the contents within the square brackets may appear zero or more times.

6.4.1 Attribute

A managed object class must have properties to be meaningful. These properties are known as *attributes*. An attribute must have a value: For example, the definition of a managed object class, tokenRing, can have an attribute such as tokenRingBandwidth. When defining this attribute, tokenRingBandwidth=16 indicates a token ring with a bandwidth of 16 Mbits.

Attributes can be single-valued or set-valued. *Single-valued* attributes have only one value. *Set* is a mathematical concept. *Set-valued* means that there can be more than one value of the same type. In sets, ordering is not important, and there is no repetition of values.

An attribute may have more than one value. For example, assume that the managed object class tokenRing has an attribute tokenRingBand-width. We model bandwidth as an attribute, because bandwidths can vary. In tokenRingBandwidth=4,16,100, the attribute tokenRingBand-width has different values, namely 4, 16, and 100 Mbits.

Attribute values are visible at the boundary of a managed object class. When we perform certain operations on a managed object class, these values can be retrieved or modified. For example, a GET on the attribute tokenRingBandwidth will retrieve the values of 4, 16, or 100. Similarly, when we do a SET on the attribute tokenRing Bandwidth, we can modify a value from 16 to 4.

When an object is identified, the managed object class must have at least one attribute used for naming. This is a mandatory attribute. This attribute identifier and its value uniquely identify a managed object. The attribute is read-only. If this attribute can be deleted, then it is necessary to define an additional unique identification attribute.

6.4.2 Attribute Template and Definition

Let us define an attribute template for the managed object class token-Ring.

```
tokenRingBandwidth ::= INTEGER
tokenRingCardPrice ::= SET OF INTEGER
tokenRingID ::= tokenRingAddress
tokenRingAddress ::= OCTET STRING SIZE (4)
tokenRingBandwidth              ATTRIBUTE
    WITH ATTRIBUTE SYNTAX INTEGER;
REGISTERED AS                      {1 3 5 8 9 2};
tokenRingCardPrice             ATTRIBUTE
    WITH ATTRIBUTE SYNTAX SET OF INTEGER;
REGISTERED AS                      {1 3 5 8 9 3};
tokenRingID                    ATTRIBUTE
    WITH ATTRIBUTE SYNTAX tokenRingAddress;
REGISTERED AS                      {1 3 5 8 9 4};
```

In the preceding definition of attributes for the managed object class tokenRing, observe the following interesting points:

- For defining the attributes, ASN.1 notations are used.

- tokenRingBandwidth is the template label, and ATTRIBUTE is the template name. The ATTRIBUTE template starts with tokenRing-Bandwidth and ends with ";" for REGISTERED AS.

- REGISTERED AS {1 3 5 8 9 2} is a *construct;* REGISTERED AS is the *construct name* and {1 3 5 8 9 2} is the *construct argument.*

- Formats for defining attributes follow a definite pattern, starting with the data type. This is followed by the definition of each attribute. Each attribute name has the keyword ATTRIBUTE. Then the data type of the attribute is defined by WITH ATTRIBUTE SYNTAX. The definition of the attribute ends with REGISTERED AS. These values are obtained either by internally defining the attributes or by following the guidelines of standards bodies. However, the values must be unique and are indicated by the last numbers within the braces: 2, 3, or 4. Note that the registration numbers used are arbitrary; these are used just for explanation purposes.

- The attribute identifier values given by REGISTERED AS are used to identify the attribute, and they are in addition to the managed object class identifiers.

- Notice that tokenRingID is defined in terms of another data type, tokenRingAddress. We again define the data type of tokenRing-

Address. Thus, the data type of tokenRingID is defined by the data type of tokenRingAddress.

An attribute template has some additional keywords, which will be explained next. Examine the attribute counter1.

```
counter1                ATTRIBUTE
    WITH ATTRIBUTE SYNTAX INTEGER;
    MATCHES FOR EQUALITY, ORDERING;;
REGISTERED AS           {1 3 5 8 9 5};
```

MATCHES FOR defines tests that can be performed on values of attributes for filter operation. If this is not indicated, then the tests on the values cannot be done, and they are not defined. Any specific attribute characteristics or indications of how attributes behave under matching rules are provided by MATCHES FOR or other behaviors. Behaviors that are specific to a managed object class are defined in the managed object class definition template.

The attribute counter1 is defined as an INTEGER that can take only a single value. MATCHES FOR is then defined; it means that we can test this counter for equality, that is, whether the counter value has reached or is equal to 30. By having the qualifier ORDERING, we can also test whether the present counter value is greater than or less than 30. There are two semicolons because there are two qualifiers, EQUALITY and ORDERING.

```
tokenRingCounter        ATTRIBUTE
    DERIVED FROM counter1;
REGISTERED AS           {1 3 5 8 9 6};
```

In the preceding definition of the attribute tokenRingCounter, attribute characteristics are derived from another attribute, counter1. Here, counter1 is defined in a different place. Note that DERIVED FROM is absent if the WITH ATTRIBUTE SYNTAX is present. DERIVED FROM helps us to make use of attribute definitions already made. By defining new rules, we can further extend or restrict the definitions derived from another attribute.

Let us proceed in our definition of counter by adding a new keyword, BEHAVIOR.

```
counter2            ATTRIBUTE
    WITH ATTRIBUTE SYNTAX INTEGER;
    MATCHES FOR EQUALITY, ORDERING;;
    BEHAVIOR
        counterBehavior  BEHAVIOR
        DEFINED AS "Tests for equality and greater than values
        are permitted.";
REGISTERED AS   {1 3 5 8 9 7};
```

DEFINED AS is used along with BEHAVIOR. DEFINED AS is followed by a string, and it supplies further meaning for the behavior of the managed object class, name bindings, parameters, attributes, actions, or notifications. Here, note that we have used quotes (" ") as text delimiters.

An attribute template uses the keyword PARAMETER. When an extension is required for the syntax of attributes, operations or notifications, PARAMETER is used to provide extensions. To define PARAMETER, we reference the label defined in a PARAMETER template (see Section 6.4.7).

```
counter3              ATTRIBUTE
     WITH ATTRIBUTE SYNTAX INTEGER;
     MATCHES FOR EQUALITY, ORDERING;;
     BEHAVIOR
        counterBehavior          BEHAVIOR
        DEFINED AS "Tests for equality and greater than values
        are permitted.";
     PARAMETER counterThresholdDetails;
REGISTERED AS                    {1 3 5 8 9 8};
```

In the preceding definition of the counter3 attribute template, we have added counterThresholdDetails along with the keyword PARAMETER. PARAMETER counterThresholdDetails is defined outside the counter3 attribute, and it is defined in the parameter template.

An attribute can have a single value. For TokenRingBandwidth, it may be 4. It can also have values of 16 and 100. Here we need to use the data type SET OF. Types can also be SEQUENCE and SEQUENCE OF.

The attribute values can be a set of values of the same data type. These are restricted to a *permitted set*. The permitted value set mentions the values that an attribute can take. They may also be called *allowed values*. When being modified, the value of an attribute cannot cross the limits of a permitted value set. A permitted value set can be further restricted to a *required value* set. This set can be empty if no values are required; otherwise, it mentions the values an attribute is required to have.

When a managed object class has many attributes, it may be better to subdivide it into subordinate classes. This will improve the efficiency of operations that are performed on it.

6.4.3 Attribute Group

A managed object class may have many attributes. For convenience and ease of operations, we can combine attributes into an *attribute group*. However, this restricts the operations we can perform on an attribute group. An attribute group has no value; hence, only those operations that do not require values can be performed on it.

Attribute groups are of two types: *fixed*, in which a collection of attributes is defined and more attributes cannot be added; and *extensible*, in which attributes can be added. Extensible attributes are defined in mandatory or conditional packages.

Attributes can be part of different attribute groups. In the following example, the attribute tokenRingID can be part of another attribute group in addition to the tokenRingGroup.

```
tokenRingGroup            ATTRIBUTE GROUP
GROUP ELEMENTS            tokenRingBandwidth, tokenRingCardPrice,
                         tokenRingID;
FIXED;
DESCRIPTION     "This includes tokenRingID of lanNet managed object
                class.";
REGISTERED AS            {1 3 5 8 9 6};
```

In the preceding definition of the attribute group tokenRingGroup, the attributes tokenRingBandwidth, tokenRingCardPrice, and tokenRingID are grouped together. By adding the keyword FIXED, we have ensured that no more attributes can be added to the tokenRingGroup. If FIXED was not there, we could add one or more attributes, such as tokenRingBridge. Note that individual attributes such as tokenRingBandwidth, tokenRingCardPrice, and tokenRingID can be single-valued or set-valued attributes.

6.4.4 Action Template

The *action template* is used in the definition of a managed object class. It maps to the action type parameter of CMIS M-ACTION service. For example, in a token ring, a ring station may have errors. When errors are hard errors or errors that must be rectified before a ring station becomes operational, there is no option but to bypass the ring station. When the errors are rectified, the ring station can be brought back into the token ring network. To bypass the ring station, a new action, tokenRingBypass, is defined as follows:

```
tokenRingBypass                   ACTION
     BEHAVIOR                     ringStationBypass;
     MODE CONFIRMED;
     WITH INFORMATION SYNTAX CHARACTER STRING SIZE (128);
     WITH REPLY SYNTAX        CHARACTER STRING SIZE (128);
REGISTERED AS                    {1 3 5 8 9 6};
ringStationBypass                BEHAVIOR
     DEFINED AS "When a ring station is to be bypassed on hard
                errors, this message is sent.";
```

The preceding definition of tokenRingBypass furnishes some interesting details. tokenRingBypass is the name of the action defined. For details of the behavior of this action, we must go to the behavior template labeled "ringStationBypass." Because it contains the keyword MODE CONFIRMED, Action will have a confirmed message or reply after sending ACTION. If MODE CONFIRMED is not there, then ACTION is confirmed or unconfirmed as decided by the managing station.

WITH INFORMATION SYNTAX furnishes details of the information carried by Action. It is defined here as a string of messages which can be up to 128 octets. However, if this keyword is absent, then there is no information carried by Action.

The keyword WITH REPLY SYNTAX carries details of reply information that is sent as a result of Action. WITH REPLY SYNTAX is also defined as a string of messages with a maximum length of 128 octets. If this keyword is absent, then there is no reply associated with Action. Finally, REGISTERED AS is our usual identifier of the Action template.

6.4.5 Behavior Template

When a managed object is defined, it must be specified how attributes, operations on attributes, notifications, and name bindings behave. These details are explained in a behavior template. Behavior should be an extension of the earlier aspects of behaviors, to which it should not add new semantics or meanings.

```
tokenRingBridgeError        BEHAVIOR
     DEFINED AS "When a token ring bridge encounters errors, this
               message is sent.";
```

In the definition of managed object classes, behavior is a text description that is prone to ambiguous interpretations and is not parsable by a machine. To overcome this limitation, formal languages such as Z, object Z, and specification and description language (SDL) can be used. As some of the languages are complex and their use involves placing an additional burden on modelers, the methodology of describing behavior using formal languages is not unanimously agreed upon (Reference 6.14).

6.4.6 Notification Template

A managed object sends notifications when a certain internal or external event occurs. The notification must contain information to be useful.

The kind of notification and the information it contains are defined when defining a managed object class. The notification type defined in the notification template is carried in the Event Information or Event Reply parameters of CMIS M-EVENT-REPORT.

For example, when a token ring adapter is about to fail, it may provide an indication or emit a message saying that it is going to be "dead." This can be defined as follows:

```
tokenRingBeaconing              NOTIFICATION
REGISTERED AS                   {1 3 5 8 9 7};
```

Whether these notifications are logged internally or forwarded externally depends upon the *event forwarding discriminators* (EFDs). EFDs also determine whether these notifications generate confirmed or unconfirmed event reports. Refer to Table 6-1 for more explanation of EFD.

6.4.7 Parameter Template

Parameters can be associated with attributes, operations, and notifications. They can be included in package, attribute, action, and notification templates. A parameter can define CMIS processing failures, notification requests and responses, or action requests and responses.

Referring to the example of counterThresholdDetails, a parameter template is defined as follows:

```
counterThresholdDetails         PARAMETER
        CONTEXT                 ACTION-REPLY;
        WITH SYNTAX             CHARACTER STRING (40);
REGISTERED AS                   {1 3 5 8 9 14};
```

After a threshold value of 30 is reached for soft errors in the network, the error message SoftErrors Threshold is exceeded by x number of errors, where x is any number from 0 to 29. However, when we reach the number 30 again, our counter wraps around. Soft errors are errors in ring stations in a token ring network where the ring station need not be bypassed.

In the preceding example, CONTEXT references conditions defined externally to this parameter template. As an example, CMIS parameters are defined in another place. The error message is carried in the CMIS M-ACTION Action Reply parameter. This parameter will be a Character String with a maximum of 40 octets.

6.4.8 Package Template

The *package template* is used for grouping many characteristics of a managed object class. If we look from the top of a managed object class template down, the package template is one hierarchy below the managed object class template. In managed object class templates, package templates can be included using CHARACTERIZED BY or CONDITIONAL PACKAGES.

A managed object class consists of package templates. These package templates can be *mandatory* or *conditional.* Mandatory packages (as the name suggests) are required. However, the attributes in conditional packages will be present depending on the conditions spelled out in the definitions. For example, if a printer is the managed object class, the toner package will be present if it is a laser printer.

These packages, in turn, consist of attributes visible at our conceptual boundary, operations on a managed object, behavior of a managed object, and the notifications emitted by a managed object class.

In packages, we have to consider the following key points:

- The rules regarding the creation and deletion of managed objects must be spelled out. The way managed object class instances relate to each other must be specified. If there is any relationship with other managed object class instances, these must be specified, too. Initial value managed object (IVMO) values are also outlined.

- The attributes and operations that can be done on these attributes should be indicated.

- Attributes have a property list that defines operations that can be done on them. The list can also supply details such as default values, initial values, permitted values, and required values. For example, the attribute tokenRingBandwidth can have a default value of 4 Mbits, if the network has 4 Mbits as the most common value. However, the permitted value can be anywhere from 0 to 100. The required values can be in the range of 1 to 16 Mbits. When there is a default value of 4 Mbits, we can set the initial values to 1 Mbit in another token ring that has mostly adapters with values of 1 Mbit.

- The operations and notifications of managed object class instances are specified. As noted earlier, operations on attributes are Get, Replace Attribute Values, Replace with Default Value, Add Member, and Remove Member. However, the operations on a managed object class, such as Create and Delete, are part of the name binding template. Actions are defined in action templates.

Now, let us define a package by combining the concepts we introduced earlier.

```
tokenRingLan          PACKAGE
    BEHAVIOR          tokenRingLanBeh
    ATTRIBUTES        tokenRingBandWidth    REPLACE-WITH-DEFAULT,
                      tokenRingCardPrice    GET,
                      tokenRingID           PERMITTED VALUES
                                            000000-XXXXXXX,
                      tokenRingCounter      INITIAL      VALUE 0;
    ATTRIBUTE GROUPS  tokenRingGroup;
    ACTION            tokenRingBypass;
    NOTIFICATION      tokenRingBeaconing;
tokenRingLanBeh       BEHAVIOR
    DEFINED AS        "This LAN segment connects token ring";
```

In the preceding template, we have left out REGISTERED AS. If CONDITIONAL PACKAGES is to be used, then REGISTERED AS is required.

6.4.9 Name Binding Template

Name binding template is useful for defining the life cycles of managed objects. It defines the rules for creating, deleting, copying, and naming managed objects. Principles involved in naming are explained in X.720. Each instance of a managed object class needs to have a unique name. This is formed by concatenating the relative distinguished names (RDNs) indicated in the naming tree. An RDN is unique with respect to its superiors. The RDN consists of the naming attribute used in the name binding template and the value associated with it.

Return to the example of tokenRing. In the naming tree, lanNetwork (Chapter 4, Figure 4-9) is the superior managed object class, if we consider the tokenRing managed object class. To make up the name of a managed object instance, we concatenate RDNs. It is necessary for one attribute, known as a *distinguishing attribute*, to be unique in the managed object class tokenRing, and this is used to distinguish each instance.

Previously, we assumed that workstationIDs are uniquely assigned IDs for identification purposes in the tokenRing network. This enables the naming relationship of instances formed by using either networkAddress or workstationID.

```
tokenRingNaming                        NAME BINDING
    SUBORDINATE OBJECT CLASS           tokenRing AND SUBCLASSES;
    SUPERIOR OBJECT CLASS              lanNetwork;
    WITH ATTRIBUTE                     workstationID;
    BEHAVIOR                           workstationIDnaming;
    CREATE                             WITH-AUTOMATIC-INSTANCE-NAMING;
    DELETE                             ONLY-IF-NO-CONTAINED-OBJECTS;
    REGISTERED AS                      {1 3 5 8 9 20};
workstationIDnaming                    BEHAVIOR
    DEFINED AS                         "This is unique identifier";
```

In the preceding name binding template, there are many interesting issues. The distinguishing attribute is workstationID. It is used for forming the RDN of lanNetwork. However, for forming a unique name or a distinguished name, name binding of the superior managed object class lanNetwork is used. SUBORDINATE OBJECT CLASS is actually the label of the managed object class template. AND SUBCLASSES here states that workstationID can be used for naming of subclasses of the managed object class tokenRing. BEHAVIOR should specify the choices that must be made if there is more than one name binding relationship.

When creating an object instance, one need not specify a name for the Create object operation. In Delete, by specifying ONLY-IF-NO-CONTAINED OBJECTS, the Delete operations are limited or restricted. A managed object that is being deleted may have zero or more objects contained in it, so all the contained objects must be deleted before a Delete operation is performed; otherwise, there will be an error.

With another option, DELETES-CONTAINED-OBJECTS, it doesn't matter whether there are contained objects. They are deleted, too.

6.4.10 Managed Object Class Template

The definition of a managed object class is uniformly done in a standard template to avoid the confusion that might result from different people defining objects in different manners. This ensures that a managed object class defined in place A can be interpreted easily in place B. The good news is that we make use of templates we have previously defined. The managed object class template is at the top of the definitions hierarchy.

One of the important keywords is DERIVED FROM, which indicates that all the characteristics of the superclasses in the inheritance hierarchy will be inherited. The highest superclass is *top*. In other words, all managed objects are derived from the managed object class *top*. Also, all characteristics of superclasses are inherited, and none can be excluded. We can add more characteristics by including mandatory and conditional packages.

However, while defining managed object classes, one can develop one's own inheritance hierarchy instead of specializing from *top*. Notice that this may lead to the problem of interoperability with other systems.

The presence of mandatory packages is indicated by the keyword CHARACTERIZED BY. As seen earlier, packages may have behavior, attributes, attribute groups, operations, and notifications. The presence of conditional packages is identified by the keyword CONDITIONAL PACKAGES.

Making use of earlier definitions, a managed object class, tokenRing, is defined.

```
tokenRing                      MANAGED OBJECT CLASS
    DERIVED FROM               lanNet;
    CHARACTERIZED BY           tokenRingLan;
    CONDITIONAL PACKAGE        tokenRingRouter PRESENT IF "connected
                               to an FDDI backbone LAN";
    REGISTERED AS              {1 3 5 8 9 2};
```

In the preceding definition of the tokenRing managed object class, the superclass is lanNet, which, in turn, may have its own superclasses. The mandatory package is tokenRingLan, which has already been explained. There is, however, one more conditional package of tokenRingRouter. It specifies that this conditional package will be present only if the token ring network is connected to an FDDI backbone. In this case, definitions of tokenRingRouter will also be included. As mentioned earlier, REGISTERED AS gives the unique identifier for a managed object class.

Compilers are available for managed object class definitions. These compilers do the syntax checking on whether the managed objects defined follow the Guidelines for the Definition of Managed Objects (GDMO) format. These compilers furnish outputs in GDMO and ASN.1 formats. Some front-end editors take the user-friendly screen inputs for the definition of managed object classes in GDMO format. These editors do the syntax checking and provide definitions of managed object classes in GDMO format. This can be used as input to GDMO compilers.

We have already alluded to the possible ambiguities in the definition of managed object classes due to BEHAVIOR. Some more limitations/constraints of GDMO are:

- The informational model cannot be refined beyond a certain stage because of the object sizes and complexity of the object definitions.
- Interactions between objects are difficult to model. As a result, it is difficult to combine different views of an object.
- Modeling of same resources by different experts may result in different managed object class definitions. There are also cases where some prefer small managed object classes as compared to large complex managed object classes. Some ambiguities in design will occur, as the design of managed object classes is still an art.

6.5 Notes on the ITU-T SMI Documents

Important managed object classes are defined in X.721, Definition of Management Information. Refer to Table 6-1 for an explanation of the MOCs defined in X.721. This is a core group of MOCs, and they can be used for defining other managed object classes used in TMN. Note that for explanation of the syntax of some of the MOCs defined in X.721, we have to further refer to other ITU recommendations furnished in references 6.5, 6.6, 6.7, 6.8, and 6.9. As an example, while discriminator and event forwarding discriminator MOCs are defined in X.721, their syntax and event report processing models are explained in X.734, Event Report Management Function (Reference 6.7). X.721 also defines attribute types, name bindings, packages, attributes, action types, parameter types, and notification types. In addition, conventions for conformance and templates for compliance testing are specified in this document.

Packages defined in X.721 are presented in Table 6-4. This document has attribute types such as counter, gauge, counter-Threshold, gauge-Threshold, and tideMark. These are useful for performance management. Twenty-five EVENT-REPORT—related attributes are also defined in this document; these are useful for different systems management functions. In addition, state and relationship attributes are defined in this document. X.721 is quite useful for defining our own managed object classes. It is, however, better to reuse definitions furnished in the document.

X.723 defines managed object classes that can be used as superclasses for defining the managed object classes of individual layers. These managed object classes, which are listed in Table 6-2, are known as *generic managed object classes*. Name bindings to be used are furnished in this document. These managed object classes can use inheritance and extend the definitions of managed object classes defined in X.723. Some of the objectives is to reduce duplication of efforts and inconsistencies in the definition of managed object classes.

In addition, 28 attributes used in the definition of managed object classes have been defined in document X.723. One attribute group (Counters), three Actions (activate, deactivate, and deactivateWhenNoUsers), and one notification (communicationsInformation) have been defined. Note that clProtocolMachine can be used by an entity using a connectionless mode communications function. Similarly, coProtocolMachine refers to a connection-oriented communication function.

TABLE 6-1

Managed Object Classes Defined in X.721 and Their Descriptions.

Managed Object Class	Description
alarmRecord	Used to define the format of logs for storing alarm notifications or alarm reports. alarmRecord is a subclass of eventLogRecord.
attributeValueChangeRecord	Defines the format of logs for storing notifications or event reports due to attribute value change. The attributeValueChangeDefinition attribute is a SET OF identifier of the attribute whose value has changed, the old attribute value, and a new attribute value. Note that these values are read-only. The conditional package sourceIndicatorPackage indicates whether the attribute value change is due to an internal operation, a management operation, or an unknown source. Also, the conditional package attributeIdentifierListPackage provides the set of attribute Ids of attributes whose value are being changed. This MOC is a subclass of eventLogReport.
discriminator	A superclass MOC introduced to control event reporting to external systems. The attribute discriminatorConstruct furnishes the logical operations, which should be evaluated to TRUE, to forward event reports. discriminatorConstruct functions as a filter and determines which event reports are to be forwarded. Conditional scheduling packages are used to control the scheduling of the event reports.
eventForwardingDiscriminator	A subclass of discriminator. As this MOC is inherited from discriminator MOC, eventForwardingDiscriminator sets conditions that should be satisfied before event reports are sent to one or more destinations. If the active destination/ destinations fail, then a backup destination list is used to forward the event reports. The attribute confirmedMode indicates whether the receipt of event report has to be acknowledged or not.
eventLogRecord	A subclass of logRecord. This MOC defines the log records in a log due to event reports or notifications. The log records can be classified by event types.
log	Derived from top; used to control the logging of information. Log is a collection of records. The logging behavior is controlled by the discriminatorConstruct attribute. logFullAction attribute states whether the oldest log record is deleted (wrap) or to halt logging when the maximum log size is reached. Conditional scheduling packages control the duration and start time of logging. The logging may be done by an external system, if the externalScheduler conditional package is present. maxLogSize attribute specifies the size of the log in octets. current-LogSize attribute indicates the current size of a log.
logRecord	A subclass of top. logRecord managed objects are created for event reports or notifications and represent the information stored in logs. loggingTime indicates the time when a log record was stored in the log. logRecordId is a unique integer to identify a log record.
objectCreationRecord	A subclass of eventLogRecord. This MOC defines the format of logs for storing object creation notifications or event reports. The conditional package sourceIndicatorPackage indicates whether the managed object has been created due to an internal operation, a management operation, or an unknown source. Also the conditional package attributeIdentifierListPackage provides the list of attributes and values when a managed object is created.

TABLE 6-1 (Continued)

Managed Object Classes Defined in X.721 and Their Descriptions.

Managed Object Class	Description
objectDeletionRecord	Similar in functionality to objectCreationRecord, except that this notification or event report is received when a managed object is deleted instead of during creation of a managed object.
relationshipChangeRecord	Derived from eventLogRecord. This MOC is used for defining format of logs for relationship change notifications or relationship change event reports. This MOC also includes the conditional packages sourceIndicatorPackage and attribute-IdentifierListPackage. We have discussed the functions of these packages in attributeValueChangeRecord. The attribute relationshipChangeDefinition has a similar syntax to that of attributeValueChangeDefinition.
securityAlarmReportRecord	Used for the specific purpose of logging when security alarm notifications or security alarm reports are received. The security alarm cause and severity, and the system that detects the alarm, are logged. Also, the alarm service requester and service provider are logged.
stateChangeRecord	Derived from eventLogRecord. This MOC is used for representing log records due to state changes such as object creation, object deletion, relationship change, or attribute value change log records. This MOC has also the conditional packages sourceIndicatorPackage and attributeIdentifierListPackage. The syntax of the attribute stateChangeDefinition is similar to that of the attribute ValueChange-Definition.
system	Used to represent hardware or software used in information processing or information transfer. This MOC can be used for naming other managed objects. The mandatory attribute systemId, which can be used for uniquely identifying the system managed objects, can be a graphic string, integer, or NULL. Another mandatory attribute, systemTitle, which can also be used for identifying the system managed object, can be a distinguished name, object identifier, or NULL. The value of NULL is used when the system managed object is not configured or when the attribute is not to be used for naming.
top	The ultimate superclass in the class hierarchy of MOCs. Other MOCs involved in information processing or information transfer hardware or software are specialized from the top or MOCs specialized from top. top cannot be instantiated.

TABLE 6-2

Packages Defined in
ITU-T X.721.

additionalInformationPackage	notificationIdentifierPackage
additionalTextPackage	dailyScheduling
attributeIdentifierListPackage	duration
attributeListPackage	externalScheduler
availabilityStatusPackage	sourceIndicatorPackage
correlatedNotificationsPackage	weeklyScheduling

6.6 TMN Information Model

Managed object classes for telecommunications resources such as telecommunications equipment and telecommunications services are defined in ITU-T Recommendation M.3100, Generic Network Information Model (Reference 6.10). M.3100 contains MOCs defined for physical resources and logical resources. Physical resources can be PBXs, digital cross-connect systems, cards, and shelves. These are usually represented as NEs. Logical resources can be communication protocols, logs, and network services. The MOCs in M.3100 are defined using the GDMO. The MOCs, which are similar, are grouped into different groups for convenience; these groups are known as *fragments*. The MOCs defined in M.3100 are explained in Table 6-3.

TABLE 6-3

Generic Managed
Object Class Defini-
tions in X.723.

applicationProcess	port
communicationsEntity	sap1
communicationsInformationRecord	sap2
clProtocolMachine	singlePeerConnection
coProtocolMachine	subSystem
physicalMedia	

TABLE 6-4

M.3100 Managed Object Classes and Their Descriptions.

Managed Object Class	Description
Network Fragment	
network	Represents a collection of telecommunications and management managed objects associated with a single administrative entity. May be owned by a single customer or provider, or associated with a specific service network.
networkR1	A subclass of network MOC.
Managed Element Fragment	
circuitPack	Used to model a plug-in replaceable unit that can be inserted or removed from an equipment holder. Line cards, processors, or power supply units are examples of resources that can be modeled as circuitPacks. The attributes associated with the MOC, such as availabilityStatus, indicate whether the correct circuit pack is installed. Similarly, administrativeState attribute is used to control the operation of a circuitPack, and operationalState attribute permits us to know whether an instance of the circuitPack is working or not. In addition to the attributes, there are notifications for changes such as creation or deletion of circuitPack instances. These are some of the basic principles of MOC manipulation.
equipment	Represents physical components including replaceable units. An equipment MOC may be nested within another equipment MOC.
equipmentHolder	Used to represent resources that can hold physical resources.
equipmentR1	A subclass of equipment MOC.
managedElement	Represents a network element. A managed element communicates with a manager/OS using Q interfaces.
managedElementR1	A subclass of managed element.
managedElementComplex	Represents a collection of NEs. This grouping facilitates easy management of NEs by an OS.
software	Used to represent logical information stored in equipment. Can represent software or firmware used in equipment and data tables.
softwareR1	A subclass of software.
Termination Point Fragment	
connectionTermination-PointBidirectional	Managed object originates and terminates a link connection.
connectionTermination-PointSink	Managed object terminates a link connection.
connectionTermination-PointSource	Managed object originates a link connection.
terminationPoint	Represents termination of a transport entity such as a trail or connection. One or more connections, when linked together, form a trail. A trail includes two trail termination points, one or more connections, and associated connection termination points. A trail can be either unidirectional or bidirectional.

TABLE 6-4 (Continued)

M.3100 Managed Object Classes and Their Descriptions.

Managed Object Class	Description
trailTerminationPoint-Bidirectional	Used to represent a termination point where one trail terminates and another trail originates.
trailTerminationPointSink	Represents a termination point where a trail terminates.
trailTerminationPointSource	Used to model a termination point where a trail originates.
Switching and Transmission Fragment	
circuitEndPointSubGroup	Represents a circuit end point that connects one exchange to another.
connectionR1	Represents a connection used to transparently transfer infromation between connection termination points. Connection is a component of a trail.
pipe	Represents managed objects responsible for transfer of information between termination points. The information transfer is between a trail and connection. Trail and connection have a client-server relationship.
trialR1	A subclass of pipe. Managed objects of this MOC are responsible for the integrity of information transfer in a trail.
Cross-Connection Fragment	
crossConnection	Used to represent a connection that connects two termination points. Different types of cross-connections are furnished in Appendix I of M.3100.
fabric	Manages establishing and releasing of cross-connections. Also, managed objects belonging to the fabric MOC are responsible for creating, removing, and modifying termination points available in termination point pools and group termination points (GTPs).
fabricR1	A subclass of fabric.
gtp	Represents a group of termination points managed as a single entity.
mpCrossConnection	Assigns relationship between termination points or group termination points. From termination is furnished by the fromTermination attribute and to termination is indicated by the toTermination attribute in the contained crossConnection managed objects.
namedCrossConnection	A subclass of crossConnection. Used for managing sensitive cross-connections. An example is the line to the President of the United States.
namedMpCrossConnection	A subclass of mpCrossConnection. This MOC is also used for managing sensitive multiple cross-connections.
tpPool	Represents a set of termination points or GTPs.
Functional Area Fragment	
alarmRecord	Defined in X.721.
alarmSeverity-AssignmentProfile	Specifies the alarm severity assigned to managed objects.

The MOCs defined in M.3100 are generic and support a broad behavior. MOCs required for specific telecommunications resources have to be specialized from the MOCs defined in M.3100. Many TMN application-specific managed object classes are defined in ITU-T recommendations such as Q821, Alarm Surveillance (Reference 6.11); Q822, Performance Management (Reference 6.12); and Q823, Traffic Management (Reference 6.13). In addition to these, standards bodies such as ANSI and ETSI have defined their own managed object classes for specific purposes. Table 6-5 furnishes summaries of the MOCs defined in Q821 and Table 6-6 provides explanations of MOCs defined in Q822.

As a rule of thumb, before defining new managed object classes, examine the availability of standard managed object classes. As an example, to define performance managed object classes, use standard managed object classes, such as scanner, defined in X.739, Metric Objects and Attributes. However, if the standard managed object classes do not satisfy your specific needs, then specialize the managed object class from the standard managed object classes.

Note that managed object classes use CMIP as the management protocol. FTAM can also be used in some cases.

TABLE 6-5	Managed Object Class	Description
Description of Managed Object Classes in Q.821, Alarm Surveillance.	currentAlarm-SummaryControl	Used for the generation of current alarm summary reports. This MOC is a subclass of top. The attribute objectList provides the list of managed objects for which current alarm summaries have to be generated. The type of current alarm summary can be controlled on the basis of the alarm status, perceived severity, and probable cause. The scheduling of the current alarm summary reports is done by the managementOperationsSchedule managed object class.
	managementOperations-Schedule	Provides the functionality to schedule periodic management services on specified managed objects. The starting and ending times of the scheduling activity are furnished by the beginTime and endTime attributes, respectively. Attribute interval provides the time between the occurrences of scheduling activities.

TABLE 6-6

Description of
Managed Object
Classes in Q.822,
Performance
Management.

Managed Object Class	Description
currentData	Contains current performance data. This MOC is derived from scanner MOC defined in X.739. To create current performance data, the currentData managed object is assumed to be contained in a managed object such as circuitPack. Attributes monitored are in the form of counters or gauges. currentData has conditional packages to ensure creation of history data and to send scan report notifications. History data are formed from current performance data at the end of each performance reporting interval as furnished by granularityPeriod. If conditional package thresholdPkg is included, then quality of service alarm notifications are sent to managing systems when threshold limits are crossed.
historyData	Derived from top. At the end of each current performance data collection interval, a copy of the current data is stored in an instance of the historyData. Note that the creation of the historyData managed object is optional and a historyData managed object is created if discriminatorConstruct in the conditional package, filterSuppressionPkg, evaluates to TRUE. filterSuppressionPkg is a conditional package in currentData MOC.
thresholdData	Specialized from top. Contains values of counter or gauge threshold settings.

6.7 Example of GDMO and ASN.1 Definitions

Here we furnish an example of how GDMO and ASN.1 definitions for managed object classes are made. The primary motivation for this example is to define a managed object class showing the steps involved in the definitions of a MOC. The syntax checking can be performed with GDMO and ASN.1 compilers.

In this simplistic example, managedElementDiagnosticTest is the MOC designed to perform diagnostic test on an NE. This test is performed from an OS. Note that we have deliberately borrowed the ASN.1 definitions from X.721 and other standard documents. In real life, it is not necessary to include those definitions, which are defined in other modules. Instead, while performing ASN.1 compilations, the modules are imported.

Basically, managedElementDiagnosticTest includes only one package—managedElementDiagnosticTestPkg. This package includes the attribute diagnosticTestDestination, which indicates the NE on which the diagnostic test has to be performed.

This package also includes two ACTIONS—performDiagnosticTest and abortDiagnosticTest. ACTION performDiagnosticTest is used to initiate the diagnostic test on the destination indicated by the attribute diagnosticTestDestination. ACTION abortDiagnosticTest aborts a diagnostic test in progress. Usually, it is essential to have a mechanism to end an ACTION, which performs starting of some actions. These two ACTIONS perform the functions required, and the replies sent do not contain much information except whether ACTION command has been accepted or not and the reasons for accepting or rejecting the ACTIONs. The detailed results of ACTION performDiagnosticTest are sent in the notification diagnosticTestResult. Notice that values in REGISTERED AS are arbitrary.

Notice that in the example furnished below, module definitions for GDMO and ASN.1 are not furnished.

6.7.1 GDMO Definitions

```
managedElementDiagnosticTest MANAGED OBJECT CLASS
      DERIVED FROM Recommendation X.721 | ISO/IEC 10165-2: 1992"
      :top;
      CHARACTERIZED BY
            managedElementDiagnosticTestPkg;
      REGISTERED AS {2 9 3 4 3 0}


managedElementDiagnosticTestPkg PACKAGE
      BEHAVIOR managedElementDiagnosticTestBeh;
      ATTRIBUTES
            diagnosticTestDestination
                  GET-REPLACE;
      ACTIONS
            performDiagnosticTest,
            abortDiagnosticTest;
      NOTIFICATIONS
            diagnosticTestResult;
REGISTERED AS {2 9 3 4 4 1}


managedElementDiagnosticTestBeh        BEHAVIOR
      DEFINED AS
            "This package is defined to perform and abort
            diagnostic tests on a managed element or NE. This test
            is run from an OS."

diagnosticTestDestination ATTRIBUTE
      WITH ATTRIBUTE SYNTAX DiagnosticTestDestination;
MATCHES FOR EQUALITY, ORDERING, SUBSTRINGS;
BEHAVIOR diagnosticTestDestinationBeh;
REGISTERED AS {2 9 3 4 7 1}

diagnosticTestDestinationBeh BEHAVIOR
      DEFINED AS
            "This attribute identifies a network element and has
            the syntax of NameType. NameType is defined in M.3100."
```

```
abortDiagnosticTest          ACTION
     BEHAVIOR                abortDiagnosticTestBeh;
     WITH INFORMATION SYNTAX AbortDiagnosticTestInfo;
     WITH REPLY SYNTAX       AbortDiagnosticTestReply;
REGISTERED AS {2 9 3 4 9 1}


abortDiagnosticTestBeh       BEHAVIOR
     DEFINED AS
          "This action is used for aborting a diagnostic test on
          a NE which has been started by performDaignosticTest
          ACTION."


performDiagnosticTest        ACTION
     BEHAVIOR                performDiagnosticTestBeh;
     WITH INFORMATION SYNTAX PerformDiagnosticTestInfo;
     WITH REPLY SYNTAX       PerformDiagnosticTestReply;
REGISTERED AS {2 9 3 4 9 0}


performDiagnosticTestBeh     BEHAVIOR
     DEFINED AS
          "This action is used for performing diagnostic tests on
          a NE."


diagnosticTestResult         NOTIFICATION
     BEHAVIOR                diagnosticTestResultBeh;
     WITH INFORMATION SYNTAX DiagnosticTestResultInfo;
REGISTERED AS {2 9 3 4 10 0}


diagnosticTestResultBeh      BEHAVIOR
     DEFINED AS
          "This notification is used to send the results of a
          diagnostic test on a NE."


managedElementDiagnosticTest-managedElement             NAME BINDING
     SUBORDINATE OBJECT CLASS      managedElementDiagnosticTest and
     SUBCLASSES NAMED BY SUPERIOR OBJECT CLASS      managedElement;
     WITH ATTRIBUTE                                 managedElementId;
     BEHAVIOR        managedElementDiagnosticTest-managedElementBeh;
     CREATE;
DELETE ONLY-IF-NO-CONTAINED-OBJECTS;
REGISTERED AS {2 9 3 4 6 0}


managedElementDiagnosticTest-managedElementBeh BEHAVIOR
     DEFINED AS
          "This is for name binding of the managed objects diag-
          nostic tests. Diagnostic test objects can be created
          and deleted if there are no contained objects. man-
          agedElementId is defined in M.3100."
```

6.7.2 ASN.1 Definitions

```
AbortDiagnosticTestInfo ::=    SEQUENCE {
     diagnosticTestDestination      [0] DiagnosticTestDestination,
     additionalInformation          [1] AdditionalInformation}
```

```
AbortDiagnosticTestReply ::=      SEQUENCE {
     acceptedOrRejectedReason          [0] AcceptedOrRejectedReason,
     additionalInformation             [1] AdditionalInformation}


AcceptedOrRejectedReason           ::= ENUMERATED {
                                   accepted (0),
                                   rejected (1),
                                   notAllowedInCurrentState (2),
                                   diagnosticTestInProgress (3),
                                   diagnosticTestIsNotBeingDone (4),
                                   diagnosticTestNotSupported (5)}


AdditionalInformation ::= SET OF ManagementExtension


DiagnosticTestDestination ::= NameType


DiagnosticTestResultInfo ::=  SEQUENCE {
     acceptedOrRejectedReason     [0] AcceptedOrRejectedReason,
     additionText                 [1] GraphicString,
     additionalInformation        [2] AdditionalInformation
                                      OPTIONAL

}


ManagementExtension ::= SEQUENCE {
                    identifier       OBJECT IDENTIFIER,
                    significance     [1] BOOLEAN DEFAULT FALSE,
                    information      [2] ANY DEFINED BY Identifier }


NameType ::= CHOICE { numericName     INTEGER,
                      pSting       GraphicString}


PerformDiagnosticTestInfo ::=  SEQUENCE {
     diagnosticTestDestination    [0] DiagnosticTestDestination,
     additionalInformation        [1] AdditionalInformation }


PerformDiagnosticTestReply ::= SEQUENCE {
     acceptedOrRejectReason       [0] AcceptedOrRejectReason,
     additionalInformation        [1] AdditionalInformation}
```

6.8 Summary

In this chapter, we have discussed how a managed object class is defined using templates. This information is furnished in ITU-T X.722, Guidelines for the Definition of Managed Objects (GDMO). Along with this, we have examined the different templates, such as attribute, action, attribute group, notification, and behavior. An overview of ITU-T X.721 and X.723 has also been presented. We have discussed M.3100, as it is an important part of the TMN information model. We have ended the chapter by providing an example of defining a hypothetical managed object class to explain the processes and steps involved in defining a managed object class.

6.9 References

6.1. ITU-T Recommendation X.720 (ISO 10165-1), Information Technology, Open Systems Interconnection, Structure of Management Information, Part 1: Management Information Model, 1992.

6.2. ITU-T Recommendation X.721 (ISO 10165-2), Information Technology, Open Systems Interconnection, Structure of Management Information, Part 2: Definition of Management Information, 1992.

6.3. ITU-T Recommendation X.722 (ISO 10165-4), Information Technology, Open Systems Interconnection, Structure of Management Information, Part 4: Guidelines for the Definition of Managed Objects, 1992.

6.4. ITU-T Recommendation X.723 (ISO 10165-5), Information Technology, Open Systems Interconnection, Structure of Management Information, Part 5: Generic Management Information, 1993.

6.5. ITU-T Recommendation X.730 (ISO 10164-1), Information Technology, Open Systems Interconnection, Systems Management: Object Management Function, 1992.

6.6. ITU-T Recommendation X.733 (ISO 10164-4), Information Technology, Open Systems Interconnection, Systems Management: Alarm Reporting Function, 1992.

6.7. ITU-T Recommendation X.734 (ISO 10164-5), Information Technology, Open Systems Interconnection, Systems Management: Event Report Management Function, 1992.

6.8. ITU-T Recommendation X.735 (ISO 10164-6), Information Technology, Open Systems Interconnection, Systems Management: Log Control Function, 1992.

6.9. ITU-T Recommendation X.736 (ISO 10164-7), Information Technology, Open Systems Interconnection, Systems Management: Security Alarm Reporting Function, 1992.

6.10. ITU-T Recommendation M.3100, Generic Network Information Model, 1995.

6.11. ITU-T Recommendation Q821, Stage 2 and Stage 3 Description for the O3 Interface—Alarm Surveillance, 1993.

6.12. ITU-T Recommendation Q822, Stage 1, Stage 2, Stage 3 Description for the O3 Interface—Performance Management, 1994.

6.13. ITU-T Recommendation Q823, Stage 2 and Stage 3 Functional Specifications for Traffic Management, 1996.

6.14. Raman, L., Information Modeling and Its Role in Network Management. In *The Telecommunications Network Management, Technologies and Implementations*, Aidarous, S. and Plevyak, T. (eds.), New York: The Institute of Electrical and Electronics Engineers, Inc., pp. 1—62, 1998.

CHAPTER 7

ACSE, ROSE, CMISE, and CMIP

7.1 Introduction

In Chapter 1, Section 1.8, we discussed important concepts such as managers and agents. Management information must be communicated between a manager and agents. Without this, a manager cannot know what is happening in the objects under the control of agents. To build any useful system management functional application, a manager needs to gather management information on objects and, sometimes, store it. For gathering this management information, we will examine how associations between managers and agents are made.

Also, there are management protocols between manager and agents that must be explored. How frames are formed and carried between a manager and agents is examined in this chapter. We must note here that ITU-T recommendations furnish generic descriptions of services and protocols and rules for communications between peer systems. It is up to users to interpret these services and protocols and package them into meaningful profiles of management protocols between manager and agents. ITU-T recommendations also furnish generic definitions, such as those for service providers and service users. However, these terms have to be tailored to suit the TMN and system management requirements.

7.2 Application Layer Component Concepts

The topmost layer of the OSI reference model is the *application layer.* The application layer functions and the functions below it are used by the *application process* (AP). Figure 7-1 illustrates the concept of an AP. An AP combines all the information processing and communication aspects that are grouped together and given a single name for remote reference. An example of an AP is the retrieval of information from a database. This database may be in another open system, so retrieval will include different aspects such as establishing an association and communicating the command, in turn consisting of querying, receiving the response, and processing and presenting the response.

One AP may use one or more *application entities* (AEs) to represent its communications aspects. The application layer appears as a collection of AEs, each of which includes information for communicating with another peer AE. AEs use the immediate lower layer of presentation services

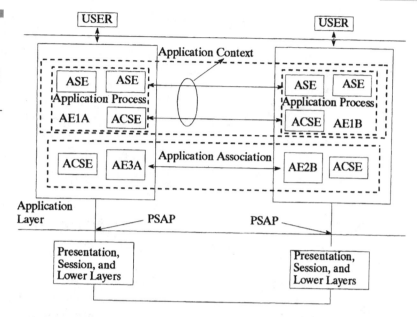

Figure 7-1

Concepts of application process, application entity, application context, and application association.

to communicate with each other. A cooperative logical connection between two AEs is known as an *application association* (AA). See Figure 7-1 for a depiction of an AA.

Functions of AEs required for cooperative processing are broken down further into *application service elements* (ASEs). These ASEs represent a collection of communication capabilities packaged into a module. One ASE may communicate with another ASE in the same application layer or with ASEs in other peer open systems using lower layers. These have their own service definitions and protocol specifications.

There are generic ASEs such as the *association control service element* (ACSE) and the *remote operations service element* (ROSE), as well as specialized ASEs such as the *common management information service element* (CMISE), the *systems management application service element* (SMASE), and *file transfer, access, and management* (FTAM). The *reliable transfer service element* (RTSE) is used for bulk data transfers. Because RTSE is not much used in TMN, we will not discuss it here. For details on RTSE refer to X.218, Reliable Transfer: Model and Service Definition (Reference 7.9) and X.228, Reliable Transfer: Protocol Specification (Reference 7.10).

There are advantages to classifying functions into generic ASEs. For example, if the establishment of an association for the transfer of messages such as in e-mail or a message handling system (MHS) is required, an ACSE can be used to establish the connection instead of "reinventing the wheel." Then, for any specific portion of the MHS, an MHS ASE can be used.

For a manager and agents to communicate, each must know about the other; thus the application context (AC) must be known. AC refers to the ASEs used between a manager and agents and the protocols used. For interoperability, ASEs and the rules for using them are grouped into identifiable ACs (see Figure 7-1). This application context is identified by an *application context name*, which is an object identifier. An application context assists in the cooperative working of AEs. This is one of the important parameters used during association or connection establishment. A run-time instance of an ASE is known as an *ASE invocation*. A collection of these invocations is known as a *control function* (CF).

7.3 Systems Management Service Elements

As we will refer to protocol data unit (PDUs) often, let us investigate what a PDU is. A PDU is a unit of data associated with a protocol. A PDU has protocol control information (PCI), which contains information to coordinate operation between two N entities, and possibly user data as shown in Figure 7-2. In the case of service data unit (SDU), the data are preserved during data transfer between peer (N + 1) entities and are not interpreted by the N entities.

When PDUs are associated with a particular protocol, they are given unique names. As an example, when PDUs are associated with application layer, these PDUs are known as application protocol data units (APDU).

ASEs such as ACSE, ROSE, CMISE, and SMASE are used by a systems management application entity (SMAE), as shown in Figure 7-3. SMASE is used to form *management application protocol data units* (MAPDUs). These

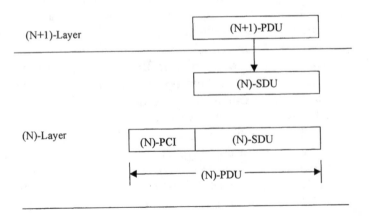

Figure 7-2
Concepts of a PDU.

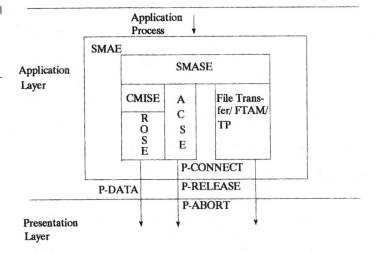

Figure 7-3
Relationship between
systems management
service elements.

MAPDUs as well as pass-through CMIP APDUs carry management information from one SMAE to another. The communication of management information between SMAEs is carried out by the *common management information protocol* (CMIP), or possibly by means of other communication services provided by ASEs such as *file transfer* or *transaction processing* (TP).

In TP, the key concept is *transaction*. The properties of a transaction are atomicity, consistency, isolation, and durability. *Atomicity* means that either all operations of a unit of work are performed or none of the operations are performed. *Consistency* refers to the units of work being performed accurately, correctly, and with validity. By *isolation,* we mean that partial results of a unit of work are not available. *Durability* represents the characteristic whereby a failure or any other action does not affect the results of the unit of work performed.

SMASE uses CMIS services. This frame is formed in CMISE, then transformed into the CMIP protocol frame in the *common management information protocol machine* (CMIPM). Here CMIPM is a *finite state machine* (FSM). The CMIP APDU has the appropriate ROSE headers to form the frame suitable for transfer of management data via underlying presentation services to another SMAE.

However, initially, for communication to take place between SMAEs, an association must be formed. This is a rather complex operation. The two SMAEs involved in forming an association must support similar *functional units.* A functional unit is an abstract concept used for combining service options. These functional units assist in providing systems management services. It may be noted here that there are functional units for the presentation layer as well as for the session layer. If functional units between two SMAEs are similar, there is not much of a problem. But there may be cases where functional units supported by SMAEs are not similar. For this reason, during association, the characteristics of the association need to be negotiated. This is done with the help of ACSE services. Successful interoperability is improved by the use of a standardized application context and standard profile that specifies common application, presentation, and session layer options.

7.4 ACSE Services

For systems management purposes, management information needs to be transferred between a manager and agents. For data transfer between a manager and agents, a connection or association must be established initially. In addition, there should be the ability to release the connection when a manager and an agent do not want to communicate any longer. The ACSE services used for establishing an association and, subsequently, releasing the association formed are shown in Table 7-1. Release of an association means orderly closing and, in some cases, aborting the association. The prefix A- is added to ACSE services to distinguish them from other application layer services.

ACSE protocols are described in X.217, Service Definition for the Association Control Service Element (Reference 7.1). Authentication for connectionless ACSE was not available in X.217 service definitions; therefore, it was added in Amendment 1 to X.217 (Reference 7.2). Connection-oriented ACSE protocols are described in X.227 (Reference 7.3) and the connectionless ACSE protocols are explained in X.237 (Reference 7.5). In ASN.1 definitions some holes are left to provide for the possible extensions to the connection-oriented and connectionless ACSE protocols; these are provided by amendments to X.227 (Reference 7.4) and X.237 (Reference 7.6). Also, the amendment to X.237 (Reference 7.6) includes authentication parameters.

TABLE 7-1

Application Control Element (ACSE) Services.

Communication Mode	Service	Type
Connection-oriented	A-ASSOCIATE	Confirmed
	A-RELEASE	Confirmed
	A-ABORT	Nonconfirmed
	A-P-ABORT	Provider-initiated
Connectionless	A-UNIT-DATA	Nonconfirmed

ACSE services have the following two modes of operation:

- *Normal mode:* Used in OSI management and TMN. In normal mode, ACSE services use presentation and session services, and A-ASSOCIATE services furnish the parameters of both presentation and session services. In normal mode, session services layer restrictions such as length must also be taken into consideration.

- *X.410-1984 mode:* Originally used with the MHS for ACSE. This mode uses a null presentation layer, and A-ASSOCIATE services do not provide presentation and session services parameters. There may be applications using the X.410-1984 mode, so it has been provided for backward compatibility with ACSE service of applications that require the X.410-1984 mode. This mode is not used in OSI management and TMN..

ACSE services subsequently explained assume underlying connection-oriented services. Connection-oriented ACSE services support the following three functional units:

- *Kernel functional unit:* Is always present and includes the services A-ASSOCIATE, A-RELEASE, A-ABORT, and A-P-ABORT.

- *Authentication functional unit:* Supports authentication while establishing association. Password verification is one of the commonly used methods for authentication. Authentication rules are negotiated while establishing the association. To support authentication, additional parameters are added to the A-ASSOCIATE and A-ABORT services. A-ASSOCIATE includes Authentication-mechanism name, Authentication value, and ACSE requirements. Authentication-mechanism name indicates the authentication function/mechanism used. If there is no authentication-mechanism name, then the authentication mechanism used is implicit. Authentication value includes the authentication value generated by the authentication function used. We will look into the parameter, ACSE requirements, later. A-ABORT has one additional parameter, diagnostic, included for authentication. Diagnostic includes the reasons related to authentication failures.

- *Application context negotiation functional unit:* Is used to negotiate application contexts while establishing association. If this functional unit is included, the acceptor has to select one or more application contexts mentioned in the Application Context Name or Application Context Name List. This functional unit is supported by adding the Application Context Name List and ACSE requirements parameters in the A-ASSOCIATE service. If the acceptor accepts the list of application contexts, then the list of application contexts is not included in the response from the acceptor. However, if the list of application contexts are not acceptable to the acceptor, then the acceptor includes its own list of application contexts it can support.

7.4.1 ACSE Application Protocol Data Units (APDUS)

ACSE uses the following APDUs:

- *A-ASSOCIATE-REQUEST (AARQ):*   A-ASSOCIATE.req is mapped to AARQ by the ACSE service provider.
- *A-ASSOCIATE-RESPONSE (AARE):*   A-ASSOCIATE.rsp is converted to AARE.
- *A-RELEASE-REQUEST (RLRQ):*   A-RELEASE.req becomes RLRQ.
- *A-RELEASE-RESPONSE (RLRE):*   A-RELEASE.rsp is converted to RLRE.
- *A-ABORT (ABRT):*   A-ABORT.req or A-P-ABORT.ind becomes ABRT. This and the preceding four APDUs are used with connection-oriented establishing and releasing of application associations in normal mode.
- *A-UNIT-DATA (AUDT):*   A-UNIT-DATA.req is mapped to AUDT APDU and is used for connectionless application associations.

7.4.2 A-ASSOCIATE

During the connection establishment phase, each side must agree on how information will be exchanged. This phase is done by A-ASSOCIATE. It is during this phase that the application context and the rules for coordinating different ASEs are made. Negotiations on the functional units are also done. One of the functional units is the *negotiated release* functional unit. A-ASSOCIATE is a confirmed service, indicating that a reply is required.

A requestor sends its list of parameters and, on the other end, the acceptor may agree to the list furnished. Or, the acceptor may send its own list of rules for communicating. If the requestor can use this list, there is no problem. If the requestor cannot communicate with the list of the acceptor, it can send an ABORT.req.

In the following explanations, the terms *Calling, Called,* and *Responding* are used. *Calling* refers to the requestor of A-ASSOCIATE. *Called* corresponds to the intended acceptor of A-ASSOCIATE, while *Responding* is the actual receiver of A-ASSOCIATE. This distinction between Called and Responding is made because the actual receiver and intended acceptor of A-ASSOCIATE can be different in some cases. For example, there can be an alternate receiver of A-ASSOCIATE if the original A-ASSOCIATE fails for some reason or if the called address is a generic one. A-ASSOCIATE parameters for the X.410-1984 mode are as follows:

■ *Mode:*   This can be X.410-1984. Normal mode is the default mode.

■ *User Information:*   This can be used by the requestor and acceptor to carry information to either end. One such example is forwarding passwords or keys to the other end. The AC may specify how this field is used and how the ASEs included are used in the AC.

■ *Result:*   The result of the association negotiation from the other (acceptor) side is provided in this field. It has three values: accepted, rejected (permanent), or rejected (transient). We have seen the action when an association and its terms are accepted. What happens when the other side is not able to accept the association and its associated terms? In this case, either *rejected (permanent)* or *rejected (transient)* is in the Result parameter, and the association is not established.

■ *Result Source:*   If an association is accepted by the acceptor, then this parameter has the value of the acceptor. On the other hand, if the association is rejected, then it will have the value of the service user, service provider, or presentation service provider.

■ *Diagnostic:*   This parameter can be used for providing diagnostic information, including specifically the reasons for rejecting an association.

■ *Presentation Address (Calling, Called, and Responding):*   These are respective presentation service access point (PSAP) addresses of the supporting presentation layer.

■ *Quality of Service:*   This indicates characteristics of services provided by the sessions layer, such as error rates, throughput, and others.

■ *Session Requirements:*   These provide for the negotiation of functional units.

■ *Initial Synchronization Point Serial Number:*   When we restart a session, it is resumed from this point.

■ *Initial Assignment of Tokens:*   This can be used for token assignments for purposes such as synchronization.

■ *Session-Connection Identifier:*   This is used to distinguish one connection from another.

In Normal mode, A-ASSOCIATE has the following additional parameters:

- *Application Context Name:* This is a mandatory parameter and specifies the AC name chosen by the requestor. The acceptor on the other end may return the same AC name, indicating that it agrees with the AC that will be used. The acceptor may also suggest a different AC. If the requestor agrees, then there is no problem; otherwise, the requestor will issue an A-ABORT.req.

- *AP Title (Calling, Called, and Responding):* This field has a string associated with an AP. Usually, AP titles are stored in an application title directory from which addressing information of the entities is retrieved using the AP title. The AP title can be either the directory name where AP titles are stored or an object identifier.

- *AP Invocation Identifier (Calling, Called, and Responding):* Each AP invocation is provided with a unique integer value to clearly differentiate one AP invocation from another AP invocation.

- *AE Qualifier (Calling, Called, and Responding):* Identifies an AE within an AP. The AE qualifier can be a relative distinguished name or an integer.

- *Presentation Context Definition List:* This provides abstract syntaxes and their presentation context identifier (PCI) values.

- *Presentation Context Definition Result List:* This refers to the abstract syntaxes and PCI values of the responding presentation service provider from the acceptor.

- *Default Presentation Context Name:* The abstract syntax name is provided for default conditions.

- *Default Presentation Context Result:* This is, again, the abstract syntax name of the responding service provider.

- *Presentation Requirements:* Functional units that may be used by the user of presentation services such as an AE are indicated in this parameter.

- *ACSE Requirements:* Used to indicate whether authentication or application context negotiation functional units are used. The ASN.1 for this parameter is a BIT STRING. A value of 0 indicates that an authentication functional unit is being used, and a value of 1 shows that an application context negotiation functional unit is being used. As mentioned earlier, the kernel functional unit is always present. If the ACSE requirements parameter is not present, then only the kernel functional unit is available.

In the preceding explanations, presentation parameters are governed by X.216, Presentation Service Definition. Similarly, X.215, Basic Connection-Oriented Service Definition, describes the session layer parameters. Let us examine further how the associations between two AEs are formed. These AEs can be between a manager and an agent or two managers acting as peers. A user of an ACSE sends an A-ASSOCIATE.req to the ACSE. This A-ASSOCIATE.req gets converted to AARQ and is wrapped with the headers of P-CONNECT. AARQ becomes user data in the P-CONNECT.req presentation protocol data unit (PPDU). This becomes user data for the S-CONNECT.req session protocol data unit (SPDU) in the session layer. In the transport layer, it becomes T-DATA.req. T-DATA.req, and similarly, other lower layers such as network, data link and physical layers, add their own layer headers. Then A-ASSOCIATE APDU is sent to the other end. In Figure 7-4, OSI lower layers refer to the layers below the session layer of the OSI seven-layer model. In other words, it includes layers such as the transport layer, network layer, data link layer, and physical layer. In Figure 7-4, there is no presentation layer for the X.410-1984 mode.

On the other end, another ACSE service user receives the frame as A-ASSOCIATE.ind. If the ACSE and AE are able to accept the terms of the association, the receiver of the ACSE forms A-ASSOCIATE.rsp, and the ACSE service provider converts to AARE and packages it with the header of P-CONNECT. Here we are making the assumption that we are in normal mode and are using presentation services. The AARE goes all the way down again, picking the necessary headers, and reaches the other end. The requesting ACSE service provider receives the AARE and converts it to A-ASSOCIATE.conf.

Figure 7-4
Functioning
of A-ASSOCIATE
(normal mode).

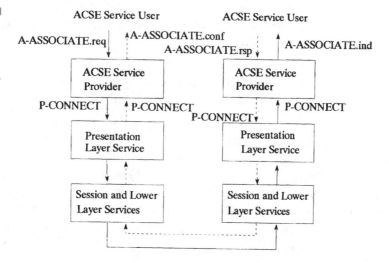

After having sent an A-ASSOCIATE.req, an AE cannot send another service request, such as another A-ASSOCIATE.req, to the same recipient. It can send only an A-ABORT.req to stop the association establishment procedures. The A-ABORT.req is turned into A-ABORT.ind on the other end of ACSE, and the association is, naturally, not established.

7.4.3 A-RELEASE

Once an association is established, obviously there is also a need to end the association when it is no longer needed. For this purpose, A-RELEASE is used. The key here is that no data or information in transit is lost. This is an orderly release. A-RELEASE can be sent from either the AE in a manager or the AE in an agent. This is a confirmed service, indicating that a reply is required. However, if a negotiated functional unit has been agreed upon during association, then the session layer takes over the release of the connection.

A-RELEASE has the following parameters:

■ *Reason:* In A-RELEASE.req, this indicates how an association must be terminated—as normal, urgent, or user-defined. In turn, the acceptor on the other end states in the Reason parameter of A-RELEASE.rsp one of the three values: normal, not finished, or user-defined. The acceptor may indicate that this has been accepted or that there are data remaining, and there is flexibility on the part of an acceptor to define its own values for the user-defined values. This parameter is used in normal mode only.

■ *User Information:* As is obvious from the name of the parameter, this consists of user data permitted within the rules set down by the AC and the ASEs used. This parameter is used in normal mode only.

■ *Result:* This is a mandatory parameter in response and confirm. Result is used by the acceptor to indicate whether or not the acceptor has accepted the request to release the association.

The A-RELEASE function is illustrated in Figure 7-5. The first thing to remember is that A-RELEASE.req can be sent from either AE. The functioning of A-RELEASE is similar to that of A-ASSOCIATE. One major difference is that we use the RLRQ APDU as user data for the P-RELEASE PPDU. The responder service provider provides the RLRE APDU to the presentation layer below it. When an association is released, then lower-level presentation and session services connections are also released. Here also we assume normal mode operation.

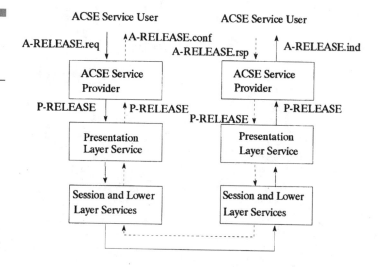

Figure 7-5
Functioning
of A-RELEASE
(normal mode).

7.4.4 A-ABORT

A-ABORT comes in handy when there have been errors, such as users no longer being able to communicate. The procedure followed by A-ABORT can be compared to a fire alarm drill: Leave everything as it is and rush to the fire exit! A-ABORT is a nonconfirmed service, indicating that a reply is not expected. The important points to note are that it is an abnormal release and that data or information in transit may be lost. Receiving an A-ABORT will stop everything, including data transfer related to the association. A-ABORT.req is sent by an AE if there are problems. Also, an ASE can send A-ABORT.ind to an AE. A-ABORT can be sent by the AEs in a manager or an agent. A-ABORT has the following parameters:

■ *Abort Source:* This indicates who initiated the A-ABORT. It can be a service user (AE) or a service provider (ACSE). Abort Source is used only in normal mode and is mandatory in A-ABORT.ind.

■ *User Information:* This has the provision to include user information by the acceptor of an A-ABORT service. In the original version of session service standards, user information could be only nine octets in length. However, if we use the addendum to the original version, Unlimited User Data, this restriction is not there and we can use any length to explain to the other end the reason for A-ABORT.

How the A-ABORT service functions is shown in Figure 7-6. The APDU used here is ABRT. The corresponding presentation service used here is P-U-ABORT. As we have seen, A-ABORT may be sent either by a

Figure 7-6
Functioning
of A-ABORT
(normal mode).

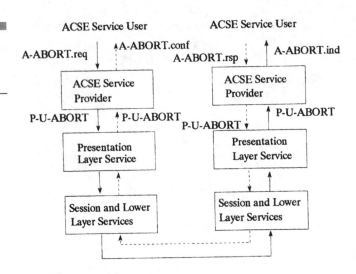

user of an ACSE service, which is an AE, or by the ACSE service provider itself.

7.4.5 A-P-ABORT

A-P-ABORT.ind is sent by an ACSE service provider to an AE. The errors involved may be the result of internal errors in an ACSE or errors in layers such as the presentation layer and other layers below it. In such a case, a service provider uses A-P-ABORT to terminate the association. As with A-ABORT, there is also a possibility of loss of information in transit. Reason is the only parameter associated with A-P-ABORT. Reason Included is related to presentation-layer reasons. Because the functioning of A-P-ABORT is similar to that of other ACSE services, we have not repeated the steps involved in A-P-ABORT. In the presentation layer, we use P-P-ABORT instead of P-U-ABORT as used in A-ABORT. Here, too, the APDU used is ABRT as in A-U-ABORT.

7.4.6 Connectionless ACSE

ACSE services have also been defined for the connectionless mode of transmission. The major difference is that, in the connectionless mode of transmission, the presentation and session layer parameters must be specified in each service primitive. In connection-oriented transmission, once a connection is established, we need not provide all the presentation and session layer parameters all over again. We can reuse the knowledge of the connection already made.

Connectionless mode of ACSE has only A-UNIT-DATA service and uses the connectionless presentation service, P-UNIT-DATA. Connectionless mode of service supports only authentication functional unit. If authentication functional unit is included in the connectionless mode, then two additional parameters—authentication mechanism name and authentication value—are included. The parameter, ACSE requirements, is not required in A-UNIT-DATA, as the presence of the authentication mechanism name and authentication value parameters implicitly indicates the presence of the authentication functional unit.

The parameters included along with A-UNIT-DATA are Protocol Version, Application Context Name, AP Title (Calling and Called), AE Qualifier (Calling and Called), AP Invocation Identifier (Calling and Called), AE Invocation Identifier (Calling and Called), Implementation Information, and User Information. As we have already discussed these parameters in the connection-oriented ACSE, we will not discuss these parameters again.

While it is the normal practice for a manager to initiate an association with an agent, there is no rule that it should always be so. It is possible for an agent to initiate an association with a manager. Also, there is no restriction stating there should be only one association between a manager and an agent. There are cases where a manager and agent can have more than one association. It can also help balance the workloads. As an example, it may be a good idea to do Gets and process the Gets, say, for configuration management on one association, and to process the event reports due to threshold crossing for fault management on another association.

7.5 Remote Operations Service Element (ROSE)

An illustration best explains remote operations. In Figure 7-7, an application entity AE1 requests an operation to be performed on another application entity AE2. The outcome of the operation is reported back. The operation performed on AE2 is known as a *remote operation*. Here AE1 is known as the *invoker* and AE2 is termed the *performer.* ROSE primitives are listed in Table 7-2. Except for RO-REJECT, all are nonconfirmed services. ROSE services are analogous to *remote procedure calls* (RPCs). RPCs are sim-

Figure 7-7
ROSE concepts.

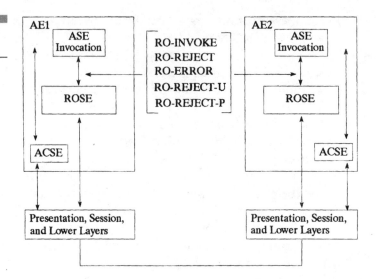

ilar to the subroutine calls found in programming languages, except that RPC are made to processes in another system.

At first, an association is formed between the invoker (AE1) and performer (AE2) AEs, using the association service A-ASSOCIATE. After an association is formed for data transfer, ROSE interacts with the presentation service. These concepts are illustrated in Figure 7-7.

ROSE APDUs—ROIV, RORS, ROER, and RORJ—are formed in a *remote operation protocol machine* (ROPM), as shown in Figure 7-8. ROPM, just like CMIPM, is a finite-state machine. ROIV is used for invoking an operation on another system (performer). If there are no errors, then the results of the operation are conveyed back to the invoker using RORS. However, if there are errors, then the ROER APDU is used by the performer to report the errors to the invoker. If the invoker or performer cannot process an APDU, then the RORJ APDU is used. The correspondences between ROSE services and the APDU are provided in Table 7-3.

TABLE 7-2

Remote Operation
Service Element
(ROSE).

Services	Type
RO-INVOKE	Nonconfirmed
RO-RESULT	Nonconfirmed
RO-ERROR	Nonconfirmed
RO-REJECT-U	Nonconfirmed
RO-REJECT-P	Provider-initiated

Figure 7-8
ROSE APDUs.

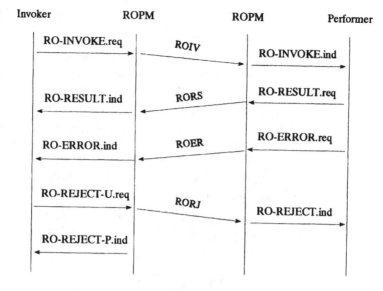

7.5.1 RO-INVOKE

The first service primitive of ROSE is *Invocation.* Here RO-INVOKE is used by AE1 to request that AE2 perform an operation. This operation may be a manager requesting an agent to create an object instance. The result of an operation by AE2 is transferred back to AE1 by RO-RESULT. RO-INVOKE has the following parameters:

- *Invoke-ID:*   This is the identifier value of the RO-INVOKE.req and is a mandatory parameter.
- *Linked-ID:*   This is an identifier of the parent invocation. If the ROSE invocation is child of another invocation, then this value is used.
- *Operation Value:*   This is a mandatory parameter, containing the operation number, which is mutually agreed on between the invoker and the performer.

TABLE 7-3

Mapping ROSE
Services and
APDUs.

ROSE Services	APDU
RO-INVOKE.req/ind	ROIV
RO-RESULT.req/ind	RORS
RO-ERROR.req/ind	ROER
RO-REJECT-U.req/ind	RORJ
RO-REJECT-P.ind	RORJ

- *Argument:* This contains the argument for the operation stated in the Operation Value parameter.

- *Operation Class:* This can be synchronous or asynchronous operations. In synchronous operations, we wait for the reply to come before sending another operation, whereas in asynchronous operations we need not be concerned about receiving replies right away, and we can invoke other operations. ROSE has five class operations: Class 1 (synchronous with replies involving results and errors), Class 2 (asynchronous with results and errors), Class 3 (asynchronous with only errors), Class 4 (asynchronous with only results), and Class 5 (asynchronous with no results or errors).

- *Priority:* This states the priority of the invocation. Smaller numbers indicate a higher priority.

7.5.2 RO-RESULT

The result of a successful operation of a performer is included in the RO-RESULT.req parameter. Parameters used are Invoke-ID, Result, Operation Value, and Priority. Here Invoke-ID is the identifier of RO-RESULT.req and is the only mandatory parameter. If the Result parameter is present, then the Operation Value parameter is also present.

7.5.3 RO-ERROR

There is always the possibility of error while performing some processing. In the application entity AE2, if there is an error during performance of an operation, RO-ERROR is used to report the errors. RO-ERROR's parameters are Invoke-ID, Error Value, Error, and Priority. Of these four parameters, Invoke-ID and Error Value are mandatory parameters. Here, too, Invoke-ID is the invoke identifier of RO-INVOKE.req for which the error is being reported. Error data is placed in the Error parameter, and it is given a value that is placed in Error Value.

7.5.4 RO-REJECT

If there are problems in accepting an invocation as a result of error by the user of ROSE, such as AE1 or AE2, then RO-REJECT-U is used. Here the user includes the Invoke-ID of the ROSE service from which the RO-REJECT-U has been generated. Invoke-ID is a mandatory parameter. Another parameter is Problem, which is mandatory and can include Invoke Problem, Return Result Problem, or Return Error Problem parameters. Priority is an optional parameter.

RO-REJECT-P is used to inform a ROSE user if a problem is detected in the ROSE service provider. The Invoke-ID is that of the invocation which encounters the problem. This may be due to unrecognized fields, unacceptable structure, or badly structured PDUs. It may be noted that these problems can be in either the ROSE invoker or the ROSE performer.

ROSE protocols are described in X.219, Remote Operations: Model, Notation, and Service Definition (Reference 7.7) and X.229, Connection-mode Protocol Specifications (Reference 7.8).

7.6 Common Management Information Service Element (CMISE)

The common management information service element (CMISE) provides the management operations and notification used by CMIP and services defined by CMIS. The services provided by CMISE are shown in Table 7-4. Management information may be in the form of operations or notifications. Those processes that use these services are known as CMISE service users. The CMISE service provider provides the CMISE services.

TABLE 7-4

Common Management Information Service Element (CMISE) Services.

Service	Type
M-GET	Confirmed
M-SET	Confirmed/nonconfirmed
M-CREATE	Confirmed
M-DELETE	Confirmed
M-CANCEL-GET	Confirmed
M-EVENT-REPORT	Confirmed/nonconfirmed
M-ACTION	Confirmed/nonconfirmed

From Table 7-4, we notice that M-GET, M-CREATE, M-CANCEL-GET, and M-DELETE are confirmed services. That means the responses have to be sent when these services are used. The remaining CMISE services such as M-EVENT-REPORT, M-SET, and M-ACTION can be either confirmed or nonconfirmed. The implication of a nonconfirmed service is that no reply is sent. However, the confirmed responses can be linked together if required. As an example, if a scope request selects multiple managed objects, then the response consists of responses from each of the managed objects selected. The Linked Identifier parameter is used to assemble the responses by the requestor of CMISE services. The prefix M- used in CMISE services stands for management, and it indicates that these services are used for management-related operations and notifications.

For establishing associations prior to the use of CMISE services, A-ASSOCIATE is used. The initiating CMISE service user includes the CMIS-specific parameters Functional Units, Access Control, and User Information in the User Information parameter of A-ASSOCIATE. Here, additional functional units that can be supported are negotiated. Additional functional units refers to the functional units related to CMIS; these functional units are explained in Section 7.7. If a Functional Unit parameter is not mentioned, then only the kernel functional unit is supported. The set of additional functional units, if agreed on by both the user and the provider, will be used for management operations and notifications.

Access Control establishes all the access control privileges for associations. However, if Access Control is mentioned as a parameter in a service request, it will be valid only for the invocation and not for other management operations. Any user information that must be exchanged between a user and a provider can be included in the User Information parameter.

Finally, when connections are formed there should also be a means to break them. Usually, A-RELEASE is used for releasing the association between a user and a provider. However, when the situation is hopeless and nothing else works, then A-ABORT can be used. A CMISE service user or CMISE service provider can use A-ABORT. The A-ABORT user information parameter includes the Abort Source and User Information parameters. The Abort Source parameter indicates whether the CMISE service user or CMISE service provider initiated the A-ABORT. Context-specific user information, if any, is included in the user information by service user or service provider that initiates the abort.

Some parameters are common to all the CMISE services (see Table 7-5). Some of these parameters are required, but the use of some is optional.

TABLE 7-5	**Services**	**Parameters**
CMISE Services and Parameters.	M-EVENT-REPORT.req/ind	Invoke-ID (M), Mode (M), Managed Object Class (M), Managed Object Instance (M), Event Type (M), Event Time, Event Information
	M-EVENT-REPORT.rsp/conf	Invoke-ID (M), Managed Object Class, Managed Object Instance, Event Type, Current Time, Event Reply, Errors
	M-GET.req/ind	Invoke-ID (M), Base Object Class (M), Base Object Instance (M), Scope, Filter, Access Control, Synchronization, Attribute Identifier List
	M-GET.rsp/conf	Invoke-ID (M), Linked-ID, Managed Object Class, Managed Object Instance, Current Time, Attribute List, Errors
	M-CANCEL-GET.req/ind	Invoke-ID (M), Get Invoke-ID (M)
	M-CANCEL-GET.rsp/conf	Invoke-ID (M), Errors
	M-SET.req/ind	Invoke-ID (M), Mode (M), Base Object Class (M), Base Object Instance (M), Scope, Filter, Access Control, Synchronization, Modification List
	M-SET.rsp/conf	Invoke-ID (M), Linked-ID (M), Managed Object Class, Managed Object Instance, Attribute List, Current Time, Errors
	M-ACTION.req/ind	Invoke-ID (M), Mode (M), Base Object Class (M), Base Object Instance (M), Scope, Filter, Access Control, Synchronization, Action Type, Action Information
	M-ACTION.rsp/conf	Invoke-ID (M), Linked-ID, Managed Object Class, Managed Object Instance, Action Type, Current Time, Action Reply, Errors
	M-CREATE.req/ind	Invoke-ID (M), Managed Object Class (M), Managed Object Instance, Superior Object Instance, Access Control, Reference Object Instance, Attribute List
	M-CREATE.rsp/conf	Invoke-ID (M), Managed Object Class, Managed Object Instance, Attribute List, Current Time, Errors
	M-DELETE.req/ind	Invoke-ID (M), Base Object Class (M), Base Object Instance (M), Scope, Filter, Access Control, Synchronization
	M-DELETE.rsp/conf	Invoke-ID (M), Linked-ID, Managed Object Class, Managed Object Instance, Current Time, Errors

M, mandatory parameter (for parameters column only).

Invoke-ID is one of the required parameters. Each CMIS operation is given a unique identifier to distinguish one CMIS operation from the other. This parameter is necessary because many CMIS operations or only one particular kind of operation can be performed. Whenever any management operation or notification is done, there is always a possibility of errors. So Errors is a conditional parameter used when sending a response or confirmation.

Another CMISE parameter is Managed Object Class. It identifies the managed object class on which an operation is performed. Managed Object Instance refers to a specific object instance in a possible set of instances of a managed object class. These two parameters are not included in M-CANCEL-GET. Table 7-5 lists the parameters of the CMISE services.

7.6.1 M-EVENT-REPORT

When an object instance has something to report, such as a change of state or errors, then M-EVENT-REPORT is used. Naturally, the parameters must include various details, such as the type of information, when the information was generated, when notification occurred, when response to a notification was generated, and details of the information.

M-EVENT-REPORT is important and is widely used for reporting notifications emitted by managed objects. Managed objects can generate notifications, which the agents send as an M-EVENT-REPORT to managers.

When an M-EVENT-REPORT is sent, there is a possibility of errors, which are included in M-EVENT-REPORT.conf. These are included in the Errors service parameter. Figure 7-9 illustrates how M-EVENT-REPORT is used. In the figure, *invoking* and *performing service users* refer to the services, which may be a process in an agent or a manager. Because there is no response in the nonconfirmed mode, the figure is applicable only to the confirmed mode.

7.6.2 M-GET

It is possible to retrieve values from managed objects. For this purpose, the M-GET CMIS primitive is used. It is a confirmed service and can be canceled by an M-CANCEL-GET service. Here, too, the parameters supported must be able to retrieve the information from the object instances.

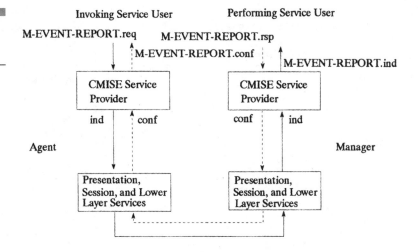

Figure 7-9
Working of
M-EVENT-REPORT.

There may be more than one object instance, so the parameters of scoping and filter are used to select a group of managed objects. In such a case, there is also the possibility of more than one reply. To handle this situation, the Linked-ID parameter is used. Figure 7-10 depicts M-GET without linked replies. Figure 7-11 illustrates the functioning of M-GET if linked replies are used. The synchronization parameter indicates how to retrieve the values. When an object instance value is retrieved, it may be important to limit the access to managed objects. For this purpose, the Access Control parameter is used. An example of how the M-GET functions is shown in Figure 7-12.

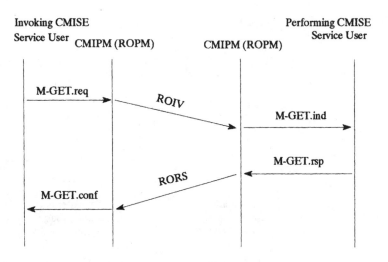

Figure 7-10
Functioning of M-GET
without linked replies.

Figure 7-11
Functioning of M-GET
with linked replies.

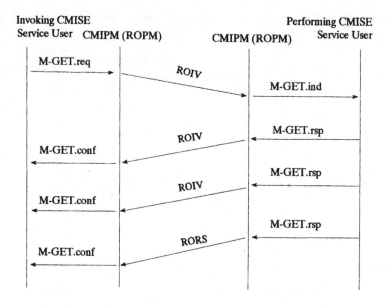

7.6.3 M-CANCEL-GET

As mentioned earlier, M-CANCEL-GET is used to abort any M-GET service that is pending. This service is useful when the amount of information being returned is unexpectedly large. The M-GET service may lead
to long multiple replies. Besides, most of the information may be useless
and, in some cases, it may be a duplicate of information already received.
M-CANCEL-GET is very useful in such cases. Here, Get Invoke-ID refers
to the identifier of the M-GET operation to be canceled.

Figure 7-12
Functioning of
M-GET.

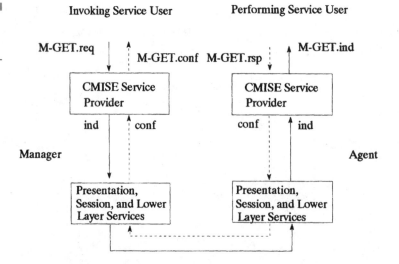

7.6.4 M-SET

The attribute values of managed objects may need to be changed to control the resource represented by a managed object. For this, the M-SET CMISE service is used. It has parameters such as Linked-ID, Scoping, Filter, Synchronization, and Access Control to control the operations performed on an object instance or instances. The parameter list is similar to that of M-GET. While M-GET is used to retrieve the values of the object instances, M-SET is used to modify the values that have been assigned. M-SET can be a confirmed or nonconfirmed service.

7.6.5 M-ACTION

M-ACTION is used to perform management action on managed objects. This operation may be confusing. Why do we need it, and where do we use it? Let us look at a special case in which some operation such as EXECUTE must be performed on an object instance or a set of object instances. In this case, EXECUTE can be packed in M-ACTION in Action Type and Action Information parameters. Except for M-ACTION, there is no other CMISE service that can be used to carry the operation EXECUTE. Hence, M-ACTION provides the escape mechanism to accommodate any operation that must be defined for a managed object class but that cannot be accurately modeled with a standardized attribute-oriented operation, M-CREATE, or M-DELETE.

When defining managed objects, we must clearly spell out the operations that can be performed on them. M-ACTION, like M-GET and M-SET, has parameters to identify a set of object instances and how they can be handled by the Scoping, Filter, Synchronization, and Access Control parameters. They also have linked identifiers to receive multiple replies from more than one object instance. The definer of M-ACTION can specify request/response syntaxes, the number of responses, and any other behavior required.

7.6.6 M-CREATE

When managed object classes are defined, instances of managed object classes must be created. For this purpose, the M-CREATE CMISE service is used. Managed objects that are created should subsequently be clearly identifiable. Thus, the reply should contain attribute values, the managed object class identifier that is the registered value, details on how to access the object instance, the superior object instance, and other details. The parameters of the superior object instance are optional, because the object instance's superior is obvious from that object's distinguished name.

7.6.7 M-DELETE

The reverse action of Create is Delete. For this purpose, the M-DELETE CMISE service is provided; it is a confirmed service. M-DELETE has parameters to do the scoping and filtering to select a set of object instances. The method of deleting these object instances is furnished by the Synchronization parameter. Using M-DELETE deregisters the object instance or instances involved. Some of the parameters, such as managed object classes and object class instances, are similar to those of the M-CREATE CMISE service.

7.7 Functional Units

For negotiating the CMISE services during association establishment, CMISE services are grouped into different functional units, which makes it easy to negotiate which services are to be included. Let us examine each of the functional units.

7.7.1 Kernel Functional Unit

The kernel functional unit provides the basic CMISE services such as M-EVENT-REPORT, M-GET, M-SET, M-ACTION, M-CREATE, and M-DELETE. However, it does not include specialized functions such as multiple replies, scoping, filtering, and synchronization capabilities. The parameters relevant to these services are included if functional units providing the specialized functions are included.

7.7.2 Multiple Object Selection Functional Unit

The multiple object selection functional unit is used for specifying the scoping and synchronization capabilities. These two capabilities are not applicable to M-EVENT-REPORT and M-CREATE. When this functional unit is specified, then the multiple reply functional unit is also required.

7.7.3 Multiple Reply Functional Unit

The multiple reply functional unit makes use of the Linked-ID parameter in different CMISE services. This parameter is not used in M-EVENT-REPORT and M-CREATE. Combining multiple replies is a powerful concept and is very useful when a large amount of data has to be sent in replies. Some common scenarios for obtaining a large amount of data in replies occur during operations involving multiple managed objects or due to M-ACTION, which can result in a large amount of data. These large, continuous streams of replies may sometimes pose problems, in which case M-CANCEL-GET can be used to stop the further flow of data.

7.7.4 Filter Functional Unit

The filter functional unit makes use of the Filter parameter. As we have seen earlier, the Filter operation can be used along with scoping to select managed objects. The Filter parameter is not available in M-EVENT-REPORT and M-CREATE.

7.7.5 Extended Service Functional Unit

Availability of P-DATA is assumed for the CMISE services. To make use of the additional presentation layer services, the extended service functional unit was anticipated. However, no one has attempted to standardize any use of this functional unit.

7.7.6 Cancel Get Functional Unit

We have seen earlier that the kernel functional unit does not include M-CANCEL-GET CMISE service. So, to provide M-CANCEL-GET service, we must include this functional unit at the time of negotiating the establishment of the association.

7.8 Common Management Information Protocol (CMIP)

CMIS primitives (e.g., M-GET.req) are used by the CMISE users. These CMIS primitives are conceptually converted to CMIP PDUs in CMIPM, as shown in Figure 7-13. These PDUs are used to exchange management information between two peer open systems. CMIP operations, which are part of the CMIP PDUs, are listed in Table 7-6.

Basically, CMIPM converts a CMIS primitive to the equivalent CMIP PDU and uses one of the appropriate ROSE PDUs, such as RO-INVOKE, RO-RESULT, or RO-ERROR, to transfer the CMIP PDU to the lower presentation layer. As an example, CMIS M-GET.req maps to the CMIP m-Get operation, and this m-Get operation becomes a part of the RO-INVOKE PDU. It will be necessary to envelop this RO-INVOKE PDU with the parameters of P-DATA of presentation services.

On the other end, CMIPM also converts the PDU containing CMIP operation to a CMIS primitive and passes the CMIS primitive to the CMISE service user. One example of the conversion is that the CMIP m-EventReport operation gets mapped to the CMIS M-EVENT-REPORT.ind. Note that the terms CMIPM or ROPM can be misleading because of the M. These are mainly FSMs, which can be software modules or microcode, and the term *machine* should be not interpreted beyond this in its scope.

CMIS is explained in X.710, Common Management Information Service Definition for CCITT Applications (Reference 7.11), and CMIP is

Figure 7-13

Relationship between CMIPM and presentation services.

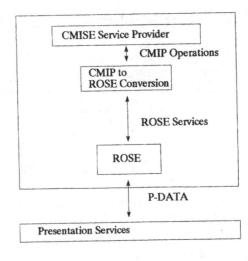

TABLE 7-6

Mapping of CMISE Services and CMIP Operations.

CMISE Services	CMIP Operation	Notes
M-EVENT-REPORT	m-EventReport	—
M-GET	m-Get	m-Linked-Reply for rsp/conf.
M-CANCEL-GET	m-Cancel-Get	—
M-SET	m-Set	m-Linked-Reply for rsp/conf.
M-ACTION	m-Action	m-Linked-Reply for rsp/conf.
M-CREATE	m-Create	—
M-DELETE	m-Delete	m-Linked-Reply for rsp/conf.

defined in X.711, Common Management Information Protocol Specification for CCITT Applications (Reference 7.12). Note that the X.710 and X.711 standards only mention connection-oriented management data transfers between a manager and agent.

7.9 Systems Management Operations on Objects and Attributes

There are two kinds of operations on managed objects. One kind can be done on attributes; the other can be on managed objects of a managed object class. These operations are shown in Figure 7-14. Get, Replace Attribute Value, Replace With Default Value, Add Member, and Remove Member operations can be done on attributes. These are used as explained in the following:

■ For retrieving values of attributes of a managed object, a Get operation can be done.

■ To set the values of one or more attributes of a managed object to specified values, a Replace Attribute Value operation is done.

■ If the value or values of attributes are to be set to default values, a Replace With Default Value operation is used.

■ For adding or removing members in the case of set-valued attributes, an Add or Remove Member operation can be used.

Figure 7-14
Managed object and attribute-related mangement operations.

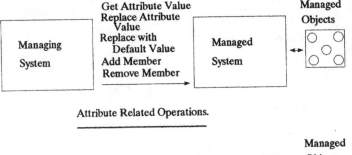

Attribute Related Operations.

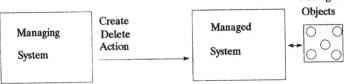

Managed Object Class Related Operations.

When defining a managed object class, the operations that can be done by a managed system on managed objects must be included and the semantics of each operation must be described. Delete and Action are operations that can be performed on a managed object, as explained in the following:

- If an object instance can be created by a management operation, then a Create operation of an instance of the specified managed object class must be supported by the managed system for at least one name binding.

- If an object instance is to be deleted, then a Delete operation is done. However, it is not necessary that all managed objects support this. Here also, support for Delete is specified in the name binding.

- The Action operation is defined for use when none of the preceding operations can be done. If we want to perform operations such as EXECUTE on a managed object class, Action can be used. These operations are packaged in the Action operation.

7.10 Pass-through Services

Pass-through services (see Figure 7-15) can be used by layer management, (N) layer operations, or those cases that do not cover the OSI. Pass-through

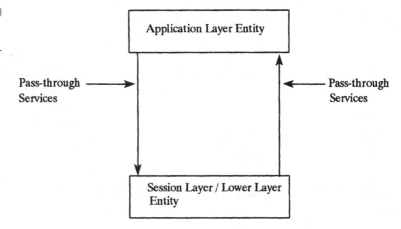

Figure 7-15
Pass-through services.

services can be mapped to management operations as shown in Table 7-7. Pass-through services provide the following:

■ *Object-related operations:*   Managed objects can be created and deleted, and actions can be performed on managed objects. This is done by using the primitives PT-CREATE, PT-DELETE, and PT-ACTION, respectively. Here, PT stands for pass-through services.

■ *Attribute-related operations:*   These include changing the value of one or more attributes to default values using PT-SET, reading the values of attributes via PT-GET, replacement of the value of one or more attributes with the help of PT-SET, and addition or removal of one or more members of sets using PT-SET.

■ *Notifications:*   These are sent for changes in attributes or managed objects. For this, PT-EVENT-REPORT is used.

TABLE 7-7

Mapping of Pass-through Services and Management Operations.

Pass-through Services	Management Operations
PT-CREATE	Create
PT-DELETE	Delete
PT-ACTION	Action
PT-SET	Replace, Add, Remove, and Replace with Default
PT-GET	Get
PT-EVENT-REPORT	Notification

7.11 Summary

In this chapter, we have discussed what ACSE, ROSE, CMISE, and CMIP mean. We have examined these important ITU-T functions from the perspective of TMN and systems management and have discussed how they can be grouped to support TMN and systems management functions. We have also briefly discussed the topics of pass-through services.

7.12 References

ACSE

7.1. ITU-T Recommendation X.217 (ISO 8649), Information Processing Systems, Open Systems Interconnection, Service Definition for the Association Control Service Element, 1995.

7.2. ITU-T Recommendation X.217 Amendment 1 (ISO 8649 AM 1), Information Processing Systems, Open Systems Interconnection, Service Definition for the Association Control Service Element, Amendment 1: Support of Authentication Mechanisms for the Connectionless Mode, 1996.

7.3. ITU-T Recommendation X.227 (ISO 8650-1), Information Processing Systems, Open Systems Interconnection, Connection-oriented Protocol for the Association Control Service Element: Protocol Specification, 1995.

7.4. ITU-T Recommendation X.227 Amendment 1 (ISO 8650-1 AM 1), Information Processing Systems, Open Systems Interconnection, Connection-oriented Protocol for the Association Control Service Element: Protocol Specification. Amendment 1: Incorporation of Extensibility Markers, 1996.

7.5. ITU-T Recommendation X.237 (ISO 10035-1), Information Processing Systems, Open Systems Interconnection, Connectionless Protocol for the Association Control Service Element: Protocol Specification, 1995.

7.6. ITU-T Recommendation X.237 Amendment 1 (ISO 10035-1 Amd. 1), Information Processing Systems, Open Systems Interconnection, Connectionless Protocol for the Association Control Service Element: Protocol Specification. Amendment 1: Incorporation of Extensibility Markers and Authentication Parameters, 1996.

ROSE

7.7. ITU-T Recommendation X.219 (ISO 9072-1), Open Systems Interconnection, Service Definitions, Remote Operations: Model, Notation, and Service Definition, 1988.

7.8. ITU-T Recommendation X.229 (ISO 9072-2), Open Systems Interconnection, Connection-mode Protocol Specifications, 1988.

RTSE

7.9. ITU-T Recommendation X.218 ((ISO 9066-1), Open Systems Interconnection—General Service Definitions, Reliable Transfer: Model and Service Definition, 1993.

7.10. ITU-T Recommendation X.228 (ISO 9066-2), Open Systems Interconnection, PICS Proformas, Reliable Transfer: Protocol Specification, 1988.

CMIS AND CMIP

7.11. ITU-T Recommendation X.710 (ISO 9595), Information Technology, Open Systems Interconnection, Common Management Information Service Definition for CCITT Applications, 1991.

7.12. ITU-T Recommendation X.711 (ISO 9596-1), Information Technology, Open Systems Interconnection, Common Management Information Protocol Specification for CCITT Applications, 1991.

7.13 Further Reading

ITU-T Recommendation, X.650, Information Technology, Open Systems Interconnection, Basic Reference Model, Naming and Addressing, 1996.

ITU-T Recommendation, X.660, Information Technology, Open Systems Interconnection, Procedures for the Operation of OSI Registration Authorities, General Procedures, 1992.

ITU-T Recommendation, X.660, Amendment 1, Information Technology, Open Systems Interconnection, Procedures for the Operation of OSI Registration Authorities, General Procedures, Incorporation of Object Identifiers Components, 1996.

CHAPTER 8

Internet Network Management: SNMPv1, SNMPv2, and SNMPv3

■■ ■■ 8.1 Introduction

In the Internet arena, the management of networks, devices, and hosts is referred to as *network management,* in contrast to the terms used in TMN. To closely reflect the protocols and to be consistent with the terms used in the Internet community, we prefer to retain the term *network management* rather than *systems management.*

Originally, Internet network management was done using the *simple gateway monitoring protocol* (SGMP). Then the *simple network management protocol* (SNMP) was defined for the management of networks and network devices. However, the syntax and semantics of SNMP are different from those of SGMP. The protocol stack of SNMP is shown in Figure 8-1.

The objects to be managed are defined in the *management information base* (MIB). These objects must follow a certain set of rules as mentioned in the *structure of management information* (SMI) such that an object defined by the X group is compatible with the definition of the object by the Y group.

Note that objects in the Internet and those in TMN are different. Internet objects are similar to attributes in a TMN managed object, and an Internet object group can best be described as analogous to a TMN managed object class. In the Internet, an object is more like a variable found in programming languages; it has a syntax and semantics. Each object can have one or more object instances, each of which, in turn, has one or more values. In the following text, the terms *object* and *variable* are used interchangeably because of the closeness in the semantics of the two terms.

Figure 8-1
SNMP management protocols.

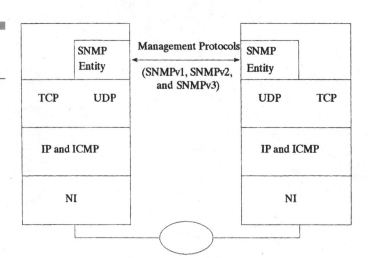

The documentation on SNMP is vast. In addition to SNMPv1 we have different versions of SNMPv2, and SNMPv3 has been introduced. So in this chapter we will cover only the important points regarding each of these SNMP versions. For details, readers should look into the Requests for Comments (RFCs) mentioned in the references.

The network management system consists of one or more *network management stations* (NMSs) and one or more *network elements* (NEs) with network management functions, management information, and management protocols. The network management system is shown in Figure 8-2. An NMS is analogous to a manager in concept, and the network management functions of NEs are rolled into agents. NMSs have the following primary functions:

- Retrieve values of objects in NEs using agents. This management operation is done by a GetRequest. A GetReguest is similar to a Get of CMIP.

- Change or alter the values of objects in NEs using agents. This can be done by a SetRequest. A SetRequest is similar to a Set of CMIP.

- Process the notifications or traps received from NEs.

Network management functions are responsible for monitoring and controlling the managed nodes. SNMP provides the management protocol for network management in the Internet world. The application entities, which can be managers or agents, exchange management information. These application entities are known as SNMP application entities. An NMS sends requests and receives responses from the agents. The NMS can also receive asynchronous reports on events, known as *traps*. A trap is an

Figure 8-2
Internet network management.

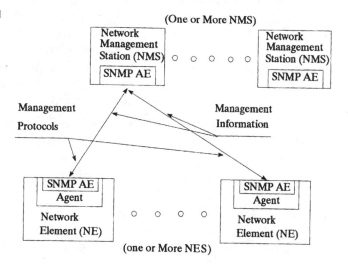

unsolicited and unconfirmed message sent from an agent. Agents reside in NEs, which are also sometimes referred to as *managed nodes.* These managed nodes are devices such as hosts, routers, LAN adapters, modems, multiplexers, hubs, and printers. Agents have the following important functions:

- They are instrumented to retrieve management information from the objects, which represent the resources.
- They alter the values of objects.
- They receive responses and traps and send these, in turn, to network management stations.

SNMP is used to communicate management information between a management station and the agents. The management applications are built on the top of network management stations. Some key philosophies involved in the design of SNMP are as follows:

- The management protocol should be as simple as possible and must be provided at the lowest cost. The management protocols should have bare minimum operations.
- Network management must be robust and able to provide services, even when the state of the network is not quite reliable or when there are too many errors. SNMP must be able to handle the worst-case scenarios.
- The standard MIB will have core objects defined, and new objects to cover managed devices or managed nodes should be added to the MIB as needed. This extensibility should be easy.
- In the workload distribution between the NMS and the agents in the managed nodes, the major workload will be off-loaded to the NMS, such that it will be easy to add new managed nodes to the network. In other words, SNMP uses the *minimalist* approach. As per this approach, most of the network management functions are centralized in an NMS and the agents are kept simple. Reducing the workload in agents minimizes the need for processing power in the devices. This will also aid in the easy extensibility of the managed nodes supported.
- The transport used for carrying management protocols is connectionless User Datagram Protocol (UDP). It is not necessary to have the facilities provided by a connection-oriented transport, because they add complexity to the transport.
- The initial objective was to ensure easy migration to the OSI/ITU-T network management. Now, due to the popularity of SNMP, this objective is in question. Some proponents of SNMP support abandon-

ing the ultimate migration to OSI/ITU-T and instead favor the independent growth of Internet network management.

8.2 Internet Network Management Framework (SNMPv1)

The original network management framework consisted of RFC 1155 (Reference 8.1), RFC 1157 (Reference 8.2), and RFC 1212 (Reference 8.3). This is known as SNMP Version 1 (SNMPv1) (see Figure 8-3). The syntax and semantics used for the definition of objects for network management are furnished in RFC 1155, and are known as the structure of management information (SMI). SMI primarily states how to define objects and how to access them. RFC 1157 furnishes the SNMP management protocol used for accessing the objects. This management protocol is used for monitoring and controlling objects. RFC 1212 furnishes guidelines for defining new MIB modules. RFC 1213 (Reference 8.4) furnishes the definitions of a core set of objects that are known as MIB-II and that provide the base set for network management.

SNMP needs the support of the transport and network layers below it. The transport layer provides multiplexing and demultiplexing of services. This can result in many-to-many relationships that are possible between SNMP entities. Also, transport protocols provide for the end-to-end checksum, thus improving the reliability of data transfer.

Figure 8-3
SNMPv1 network
management
framework.

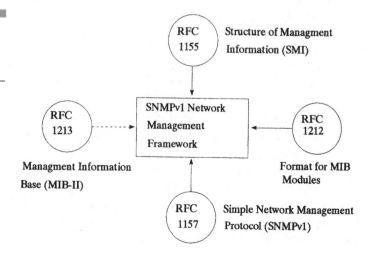

The network layer provides for the routing capabilities between networks. Also, this layer shields the SNMP entities from differences in the media. In addition, the fragmentation and reassembly of packets of different sizes transmitted across the networks are provided by this layer. However, to reduce the possibility of fragments being lost, it is better to send small packets.

In some cases, it may not be necessary to use the transport and network layers. The network management functions may be provided directly over data link layers, as in the case of network management for point-to-point or out-of-band (OOB) management directly to the managed devices. In OOB, connections are sometimes made from management stations to the managed devices directly via dial-ups.

However, sometimes the network layer will be required. When management must be done over devices across networks, then it may be necessary to use the routing capabilities of the network layers. Skinny UDP/IP stacks may also be required in some cases. So, ultimately, these decisions must be made while designing management functions for networks.

Because much overhead is involved in maintaining one or more connections or establishing a connection and tearing it down for each SNMP entity operation on an object, a connectionless transport layer is preferred. This is one of the reasons for choosing UDP. UDP provides unreliable datagram service as a trade-off to keep the protocol simple. Every piece of management information is supposed to be carried in a single and independent transport datagram. This way, the complexity involved in assembling frames and in recovery after failures, such as frames not being received in order or lost frames being retransmitted, is avoided.

Internet network management operations are kept simple by limiting the operations to retrieve the value of a variable or set the value of a variable. Also, the traps sent from agents are very limited so as to reduce network traffic. Imperative commands, or commands that trigger some other action, are avoided. The Internet network management functions can be part of the network operations center (NOC). The NOC is usually a central location for monitoring the operation of a network and rectifying network problems.

The exchange of management information between an NMS and an NE is done by SNMPs. Each NE has a set of objects also known as the SNMP MIB view. We will discuss the SNMP MIB in detail in a later section. When an SNMP AE in an agent is associated with a set of SNMP AEs in one or more managers, this pairing is known as a *community* (Figure 8-4). Each com-

Figure 8-4

SNMPv1 community.

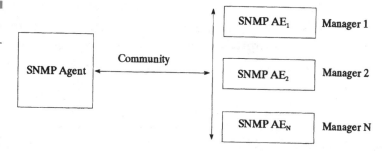

munity has an identifier known as the *community name*. The data type of the community name is OCTET STRING of a size from 0 to 255 octets. Only printable ASCII characters are allowed.

An SNMP message consists of a version identifier, an SNMP community name, and an SNMP PDU. The messages exchanged between an NMS and agents are independent of each other. Assume that we are keeping count of messages sent from an NMS to an agent. We have sent 15 messages, and message 16 is sent from the management station to the agent. Now, message 16 does not have any dependency on message 15. Also, in the SNMP implementation, it is recommended that message length not exceed 484 octets.

The SNMP community authentication scheme, defined by a set of rules, determines whether the messages sent between AEs are authentic. One example is that of an SNMP agent. It is possible that this agent would not send a trap to one particular manager, in which case checking whether the agent is really allowed to send the trap must be done by the authentication scheme.

8.3 Internet Objects

SNMP uses ASN.1 for defining objects and PDUs exchanged by the management protocol. However, all data types defined in ITU-T ASN.1 are not used. It was thought that by using a subset of data types, other data types could be constructed. ASN.1 data types used are INTEGER, OCTET STRING, OBJECT IDENTIFIER, NULL, SEQUENCE, and SEQUENCE OF. The data types not used in SNMP are BOOLEAN, OBJECT DESCRIPTOR, EXTERNAL, REAL, ENUMERATED, SET, and SET OF. Object types also must be encoded to be sent across a network. To keep the network management process simple, SNMP uses only a subset of the

BER of ITU-T for transfer syntax. Definite length form and noncon-
structor encodings are used (see Chapter 5 for a discussion of these terms).
SMI permits two kinds of constructor types:

- *list* has the following syntax:

```
list ::= SEQUENCE { <type1>,      <typeN>}
```

"type1" stands for one of the ASN.1 primitive types defined in SMI.
DEFAULT and OPTIONAL clauses are not allowed within the
SEQUENCE of a list. We can imagine "list" as being analogous to a one-
dimensional row or a column.

- *table* is defined as

```
table ::= sequence of <entry>
```

Here "entry" corresponds to the list constructor. "table" is two-
dimensional and has one or more rows, with each row having one or
more columns.

RFC 1155 states how the objects are to be defined. The syntax of an
object is as follows:

- *Object name:* Should consist of the textual name along with the
  OBJECT IDENTIFIER. The textual name is known as OBJECT
  DESCRIPTOR. An example is sysLocation {system 6}. Here, sysLocation is the OBJECT DESCRIPTOR, and {system 6} is the OBJECT
  IDENTIFIER. In the Internet, the conventions for naming objects are
  similar to those used in ITU-T; however, the object name must be
  unique and easily identifiable, and it must be a printable string. {sys-
  tem 6} states that sysLocation is a child under "system" and is the sixth
  node in the object registration hierarchy. Note here that the object
  registration hierarchy in the Internet is similar to that of ITU-T.

- *Syntax:* Refers to the syntax used by the object type and should map
  to one of the permitted ASN.1 data types. sysLocation object type
  syntax is DisplayString (SIZE (0..255)), for example, DURHAM2154.

- *Definition:* Contains an unambiguous description of the object type.
  This description is useful for instantiating object types.

- *Access:* States how the object can be accessed by management operations and is the minimum level of support for an object type. The values are read-only, read-write, write-only, and not accessible. With
  read-only we cannot change the value using the SNMPv1 operation
  SetRequest. The operations that can be performed for read-only are

GetRequest and GetNextRequest. The access right of write-only enables the SetRequest operation to be done on an object. With read-write, GetRequest, GetNextRequest, and SetRequest operations can be performed. We will examine the SNMPv1 operations in detail later in this chapter.

■ *Status:* Refers to the implementation support to the object type. The values are mandatory, optional, or obsolete.

SMI standard RFC 1155 also defines the following object types:

■ *Network address:* Presents options for stating addresses in different protocols. At present, only the Internet family of network addresses is allowed.

■ *IP address:* Represents a 32-bit Internet address and is represented using OCTET STRING. For BER, only primitive encoding is allowed.

■ *Counter:* A nonnegative integer value that increases from 0 to the maximum value of $2^{32}-1$. After reaching the maximum value, the counter becomes 0 and increases in value. This is also known as *wrapping around.*

■ *Gauge:* A nonnegative integer that can increase or decrease in value. The maximum value allowed for a gauge is $2^{32}-1$. One difference between a counter and a gauge is that in a gauge no wrapping around is allowed.

■ *TimeTicks:* A nonnegative integer that represents elapsed time, in hundredths of a second, since a particular action. The description of the object type must clearly state the particular action, such as the last update of an object.

■ *Opaque:* Permits an object to transmit any data as an OCTET STRING. It is similar to the ASN.1 EXTERNAL type. Note here that an NMS and agents must have previous knowledge of the data type to parse the data.

SMI document RFC 1155 covers the object information model and a set of generic types used to describe management information. To extend the ASN.1 grammar in SMI definitions, the OBJECT-TYPE MACRO is included.

Let us take an arbitrary example of an object to illustrate the meanings of the different terms used.

```
tokenRingPrice OBJECT-TYPE
        SYNTAX INTEGER
        ACCESS read-write
        STATUS optional
        ::= {enterprises 100}
```

In the preceding object definition, tokenRingPrice is the OBJECT DESCRIPTOR, and the syntax of this object is INTEGER. {enterprises 100} is the OBJECT IDENTIFIER. ACCESS is read-write, stating that the values can be read or changed. STATUS optional states that this is an optional object.

For more details on SMI, refer to RFC 1155 (Reference 8.1).

8.4 Management Information Base (MIB-II)

In Internet, as with the ITU-T, the details of objects are stored in a database called the management information base (MIB). MIB is an abstract concept applied to storing data. In the MIB, object types are described by the OBJECT DESCRIPTOR along with OBJECT IDENTIFIER. MIBs are defined by different RFCs. The earlier MIB versions followed RFC 1065, Structure and Identification of Management Information for TCP/IP-based Internets, and RFC 1066, Management Information Base Network Management of TCP/IP-based Internets. RFC 1065 specified how the objects were to be defined and has been superseded by RFC 1155. RFC 1066 defined the objects, but was made obsolete by RFC 1156.

RFC 1155, Structure and Identification of Management Information for TCP/IP-based Internets, specified how the objects were to be defined. This RFC attempted to structure the definition of objects more in the manner of the ITU-T managed object class definitions. RFC 1156, known as MIB-I, contained the definition of objects. This became the Full Standard Protocol. Extensions were added to MIB-I in RFC 1158, and this version is known as MIB-II. This RFC added new objects to different groups and deprecated (i.e., marked for removal from the next versions) some objects. The idea behind these changes was to provide support for multiprotocol entities, as well as readability, clarity, and cleaning up.

RFC 1212, Concise MIB Definitions, provided methods to clean up and remove the redundant object descriptions. RFC 1213, MIB-II for Network Management of TCP/IP-based Internets: MIB II, is yet another improvement over RFCs 1156 and 1158. It adds and refines objects defined in RFCs 1156 and 1158, and also makes use of RFC 1212.

However, readers should consult the latest IAB Official Protocol Standards, published often, for information about the current standardization maturity and requirement levels. Changes are frequently being made to accommodate new requirements and compatibility with OSI/ITU-T systems management.

8.4.1 Internet Registration Hierarchy

Objects must be uniquely identified for manipulation for management purposes: This is accomplished by using OBJECT IDENTIFIERs. OBJECT IDENTIFIERs are a series of identifiers derived by tagging the numbers attached to the nodes from the root in the registration hierarchy. These numbers are separated by periods.

In the registration tree shown in Chapter 4, Figure 4.7, the registration tree at the starting point has three children with labels of itu-t(0), iso(1), and joint-iso-iut-t(2). Here, itu-t stands for the textual description of the International Telegraph and Telephone Consultative Committee, and 0 stands for the position within the root. Similarly, iso(1) stands for the ISO, and joint-iso-itu-t(2) indicates joint administration by ISO and ITU-T.

The administrative control of each of the subtrees for assigning the numbers below them is the responsibility of the nodes. However, this may be delegated as we go down the tree. Under iso(1), org(3) is assigned to national standards organizations. The two nodes below org(3) have been assigned to the U.S. National Institute of Standards and Technology (NIST). Of the two, one node, dod(6), has been assigned to the Department of Defense (DOD), U.S. Here, internet(1) is a child under dod(6).

There are four children under internet(1), as shown in Figure 8-5: directory(1), mgmt(2), experimental(3), and private(4). The child directory(1) is reserved for the future use of OSI directory services. The Internet MIB-II is defined as a first child under mgmt(2). The IAB has delegated the authority to assign numbers in this subtree to the Internet Assigned Numbers Authority. Thus, the object identifier would be 1.3.6.1.2.1. Here, 1 is from iso; 3 is from org; 6 is from dod; 1 is from internet; 2 is from mgmt; and the final 1 is from MIB-II.

The experimental(3) subtree is meant for objects used in Internet experiments. As an example, if an experimenter gets a number, 12, then the object identifier is 1.3.6.1.3.12. Here, except for the last two numbers, the registration numbers are the same. The next-to-last number, 3, is from the experimental node, and 12 is the number that has been assigned to the experimenter by the Internet Assigned Numbers Authority.

However, the private(4) subtree is used for numbering the objects registered by private bodies. For example, the ABCD Company may ask for a number for registering objects. If it receives a number of 100 from the

Figure 8-5
Internet registration
hierarchy.

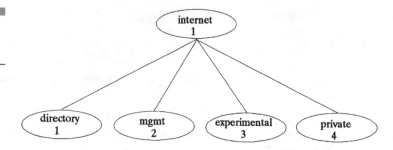

Internet Assigned Numbers Authority, it will be under the private(4) sub-tree. The ABCD Company can define its own objects under this registration number of 100; for example, it may define an adapter for token ring as 25. Then the object identifier for token ring is 1.3.6.1.4.–.100.25. Here, the first four numbers are as explained earlier. The registration number of 4 indicates private, and 100 is the number for the ABCD Company. As already mentioned, the Internet Assigned Numbers Authority assigns these private numbers.

8.4.2 Object Instance Identification

To know the value of an instance of an object, it is necessary to identify the instance. This is done using the OBJECT IDENTIFIER. The following conventions apply for identifying object instances:

■ *Scalar objects:* These have only one instance associated with an object. An example of a scalar object is snmpInBadValues. For snmp group, the OBJECT IDENTIFIER for the snmp subtree is 1.3.6.1.2.1.11. By extending the snmp subtree, the snmpInBadValues OBJECT IDENTIFIER is 1.3.6.1.2.1.11.10. We have concatenated the subidentifier of 10 to the snmp subtree to get the OBJECT IDENTIFIER of snmpInBad-Values. For each scalar object of snmpInBadValues, there is only one instance, and this instance is identified again by concatenating a value of 0 to the OBJECT IDENTIFIER of snmpInBadValues. So an instance identifier for the instance of snmpInBadValues is 1.3.6.1.2.1.11.10.0. The same procedure for deriving an instance identifier is shown as follows:

```
                                    OBJECT IDENTIFIER
snmp subtree                        1.3.6.1.2.1.11
snmpInBadValues                     1.3.6.1.2.1.11.10
An instance of snmpInBadValues      1.3.6.1.2.1.11.10.0
```

- *Columnar objects:* Only objects in a table, known as columnar objects (Figure 8-6), can be manipulated by SNMP. Tables in SNMP are two-dimensional. Instances of objects in tables are identified by the INDEX clause or the AUGMENTS clause. The INDEX clause refers to a row in a table. Note that the AUGMENTS clause is an addition in SNMPv2. Let us take the example of ipAdEntIfIndex in ipAddrTable and see how an instance identifier is formed. The OBJECT IDENTIFIER of the ip subtree is 1.3.6.1.2.1.4. The OBJECT IDENTIFIER of ipAddrEntry is obtained by concatenating subidentifiers 20.1 to the ip OBJECT IDENTIFIER. Hence, the OBJECT IDENTIFIER of ipAddrEntry is 1.3.6.1.2.1.4.20.1. ipAddrTable has a value of 20 in the IP group and ipAddrEntry has a value of 1 in ipAddrTable. The INDEX clause for ipAddrEntry has ipAdEntIfIndex (RFC 1213). The OBJECT IDENTIFIER of ipAdEntIfIndex is derived by concatenating the column number of 2 to the OBJECT IDENTIFIER of ipAddrEntry, which is 1.3.6.1.2.1.4.20.1.2. Now any row of ipAdEntIfIndex is indexed by the INDEX clause subidentifiers associated with ipAdEntIfIndex.

```
                                       OBJECT IDENTIFIER
ip subtree                             1.3.6.1.2.1.4
ipAdEntIfIndex                         1.3.6.1.2.1.4.20.1.2
Fifth instance of ipAdEntIfIndex       1.3.6.1.2.1.4.10.1.2.(fifth
                                       row value of ipAdEntIfIndex)
```

- *Conceptual rows and tables:* When the object types are just rows and tables, they are known as *conceptual rows* and *conceptual tables*. There are no instance identifiers associated with the conceptual rows and tables, and they are not accessible by SNMP operations.
- *Lexicographic ordering:* *Webster's New Collegiate Dictionary* defines *lexical* as "of or relating to words or the vocabulary of a language as distinguished from its grammar or construction." OBJECT IDENTIFIERs are arranged in increasing value in SNMP MIBs. Referring to the previous example of the ip subtree, the OBJECT IDENTIFIER of ipAdEntIfIndex is lexicographically greater than the OBJECT IDENTIFIER of ip. This lexicographic ordering is useful for traversing a table without a management station actually knowing the OBJECT IDENTIFIER of an entry. For example, to retrieve the fifth instance of ipAdEntIfIndex, four GetNextRequest PDUs will be enough to obtain the value of the fifth instance.

The following rules are used for instance identification using the INDEX clause:

- *Integer-valued:* Has a single-value subidentifier to identify an object instance. These are nonnegative integers. The value of ifIndex, which can take any value ranging from 1 to the value of ifNumber, is an example of an integer-valued INDEX clause.

- *String-valued (fixed-length strings):*   Has *n* octet length with *n* subidentifiers.

- *String-valued (variable-length strings):*   Has *n* + 1 octet length with *n* subidentifiers. The first octet has the value of *n*, which indicates the number of subidentifiers.

- *Object-identifier-valued:*   Used with object identifiers. The first value is the number *n* of subidentifiers used along with the *n* subidentifiers.

- *IpAddress-valued:*   Associated with four subidentifiers familiar in the IP address of the type a.b.c.d.

- *NsapAddress-valued:*   Uses syntax similar to a fixed-length string with the length of the string as *n*.

8.4.3 Table Manipulation

In MIB-II tables (Figure 8-6), each object is represented by a column; the value of each object instance is represented in a row. The way to retrieve values from a table is somewhat nonintuitive. The length of each column is traversed in its entirety, and then one moves on to the next column. To add the value of an object instance, the value is entered in a row with a SetRequest operation. To delete an entry, again using the SetRequest operation, the value is set to invalid.

Whether or not to remove the invalid entries is left as an implementation option. It is better to remove invalid entries when storage is a constraint; traversing the table will be faster with fewer entries. But this involves extra work—now and then, some sort of cleanup of the table to remove invalid entries must be done. If it is decided to do this cleaning,

Figure 8-6
Concept of tables.

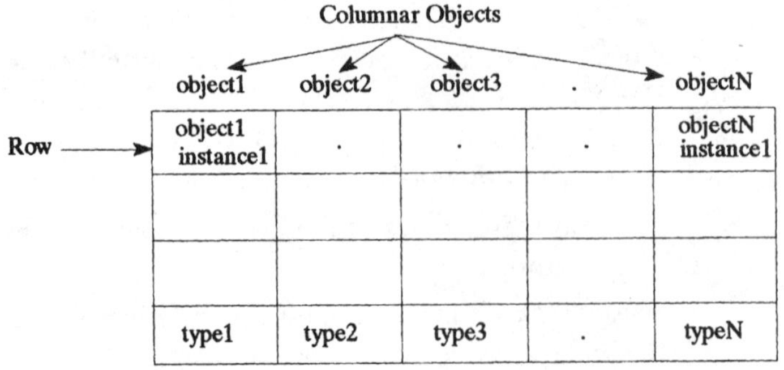

then it must also be determined how frequently to remove the invalid entries. Ultimately, these decisions involve trade-offs that should be examined during the design stage.

8.4.4 MIB-II Details (RFC1213)

It is necessary to follow rules when defining new MIBs. Old object types are not deleted, but they may be deprecated. The semantics of old object types should not be changed between versions: if it is necessary to change the semantics, new object types must be formed. Some of these rules are formulated because of the coexistence of multiple versions of MIB.

In MIB, only the essential objects are defined. This has been done to make the implementations simple. However, there is enough flexibility to define the implementation of specific objects. The guidelines for defining new objects are provided by SMI. New objects can be added under the experimental subtree or under the enterprises subtree. Also, new versions of MIB can be released for the new standard objects, by which the definition of objects is sufficiently flexible in Internet.

MIB-II has added the data type, DisplayString. DisplayString is defined as an OCTET STRING, and is a printable ASCII character string ranging in size from 0 to 255 octets. Another data type of PhyAddress is again an OCTET STRING used to represent media addresses. As an example, a token ring address can be represented in binary in six octets.

Objects in the Internet are classified into different groups. These groups are under {mgmt 2}, as shown in Figure 8-7, and the classification into groups assists in easily assigning object identifiers to the groups. Also, the objects under these groups must be implemented as a group. For example, if the TCP group is implemented, then all objects under the TCP group, such as tcpRtoAlgorithm and tcpRtoMin, must be implemented. For more details, MIB-II objects, refer to RFC 1213 (Reference 8.4).

8.5 SNMPv1 Protocol and Protocol Details

SNMPv1 PDUs are furnished in Table 8-1. Note that these PDUs use a similar data format. When one protocol entity sends a GetRequest, GetNextRequest, or SetRequest PDU, the response is a GetResponse PDU

Figure 8-7
MIB-II objects group.

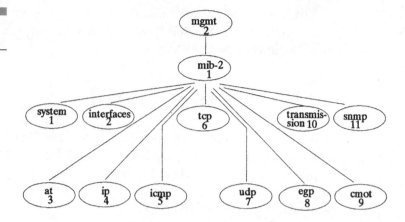

(Figure 8-8). When there are errors or special cases, traps are sent from one protocol entity to another one. An SNMPv1 trap is used for reporting an asynchronous occurrence of an event such as a serious error, important state change, or crossing of a threshold. It is usually reported from an agent to a manager, and is not confirmed. Event types are defined in TRAP-TYPE. In SNMP especially, GetNextRequest assumes that object values in the MIB are arranged in a tabular form.

The PDUs GetRequest, GetNextRequest, SetRequest, and GetResponse have request-id, error-status, error-index, and variable-bindings. Values for error status and error index for GetRequest, GetNextRequest, and SetRequest PDUs are always taken as 0. Request-id is used as an identifier for correlating the responses or for identifying duplicate responses. error-status indicates the kind of error. These are listed in Table 8-2. error-index gives the position of the variable which was responsible for the error. Variable refers to an instance of an object, and variable-binding refers to the combination of a variable name and value. There can also be a list of variable names and values.

TABLE 8-1

SNMPv1 Protocol
Data Units.

GetRequest

GetNextRequest

GetResponse

SetRequest

Trap

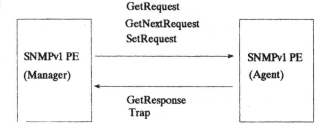

Figure 8-8

SNMPv1 management
protocol PDUs.

SNMP uses a combination of traps and polling for retrieving management information. Traps are expected to be sparingly used. When there is an error, a trap is sent from an agent to the NMS. Once this trap is received, the NMS must send a response. Further management information is retrieved using polling.

8.5.1 Functioning of SNMPv1 PDUs

As mentioned earlier, SNMP is used for carrying messages from one *protocol entity* (PE) to another. A PDU is constructed in ASN.1 form and is then sent to an authenticator, along with the community name and source and transport addresses. The authenticator checks whether the sending and receiving protocol entities can really exchange messages. The result of the check, which can be an authentication failure or an ASN.1 object, is sent back to the PE. If the message has passed the authenticator check, it is formatted using BER and sent by the transport mechanism to the receiving PE. Generating an SNMPv1 message is shown in Figure 8-9.

On the receiving side, the PE parses the data received and checks for version numbers. If the PDU fails during this action, then the datagram is

TABLE 8-2

SNMPv1 Protocol
Errors.

noError

tooBig

noSuchName

badValue

readOnly

genErr

Figure 8-9
Generating an
SNMPv1 message.

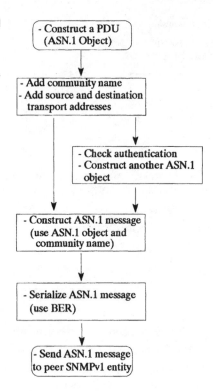

discarded. After this operation, user data, community name, and source and destination addresses go to the authenticator. The authenticator checks whether the receiving PE can actually receive data from the sending PE. The result can be authentication failure. In such a case, a trap may be generated and sent to the sending PE. However, sometimes this trap is just logged and a record is maintained for any remedial action to be taken. On the other hand, if the authenticator passes the authentication process, the receiving PE processes the message, takes the appropriate action, and sends the response back to the sending PE. The steps involved in the receiving end are shown in Figure 8-10.

Here we must note that some management applications may not need the security provided by authentication. In such implementations, the authentication steps may be skipped altogether for management applications. Also, in some cases, additional security steps such as extra access control functions, may be needed. Thus, the level of authentication required is guided by implementation considerations.

When SNMPv1 protocols are used, errors such as those listed in Table 8-2 can be generated. The value of noError is 0; from there, values pro-

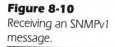

Figure 8-10
Receiving an SNMPv1
message.

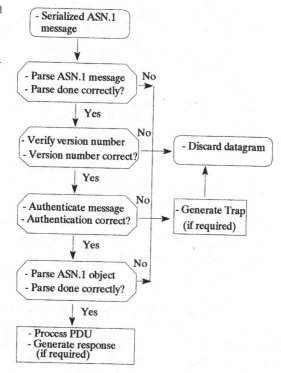

gressively increase by 1. Thus, badValue has a value of 3. Let us examine the individual SNMPv1 PDU function. When a GetRequest PDU is sent, the receiving PE checks whether the object name is correct. If the object name is not correct, then the error status is noSuchName. Afterward, a check is made as to whether the object type is aggregate. Because SNMP does not allow aggregate object types, the error status of noSuchName is set for the aggregate object type cases.

A response for GetRequest must be within the capacity of the local PE. If it is not possible to generate responses, then the error status is set to tooBig. When processing a GetRequest, there may be errors. In such a case, the error status is set to genError. When there are no errors, the error status is set to noError. Responses in all cases are sent in the form of a GetResponse PDU.

GetNextRequest is similar to GetRequest except that we retrieve the next value instead of the one furnished, and the PDU type is different. Here, the assumption is that MIB has object names arranged in a lexicographical order. However, if a lexicographical successor is not available, then error status is set to genErr.

In SetRequest, too, if a variable name is not available, then the error status is set to noSuchName. If the value of a variable whose value must be changed to that furnished in SetRequest is not in conformity with ASN.1 language, type, length, or variable, the error status is set to badValue. The case of error status set to tooBig is similar to that explained earlier. If the value of a variable cannot be changed, it is classified under genError. However, if the value of a variable is changed to the value mentioned in SetRequest, then the reply PDU of GetResponse has its error status set to noErr.

A trap is used to present problems or changes in the Internet. A trap PDU consists of the object type generating the trap; the address of the object generating the trap, the generic trap type, the time stamp when the trap was generated, and any variable binding carrying relevant information. If the enterpriseSpecific trap is present, the specific trap field is present. Generic traps are listed in Table 8-3. In this table, just as in Table 8-2, coldStart has a value of 0 and the values for other traps increase by 1. Hence, linkUp has a value of 3 associated with it.

Let us briefly review the meanings of different generic traps. The first trap is coldStart, which implies that an agent is reinitializing and the configuration and implementation details might have changed. Thus, the station receiving this trap will have to reset itself, whereas in the case of warmStart, there are no changes in the configuration and implementation details when reinitializing.

The traps linkDown and linkUp are used when the communication links used are affected, and the affected link name and value are furnished in variable bindings. When a protocol message fails authentication, then the authenticationFailure trap is generated. egpNeighborLoss is generated when an EGP neighbor is no longer available. When traps can-

TABLE 8-3	
SNMPv1 Traps Generated.	coldStart
	warmStart
	linkDown
	linkUp
	authenticationFailure
	egpNeighborLoss
	enterpriseSpecific

not be specifically classified into any one of these categories, the enter-priseSpecific trap comes in handy. This trap can also be used to convey any specific trap that may be implementation-specific. This is carried in the specific trap field.

8.6 Proxy

The *proxy* concept is very popular. It is possible that a management station may not be able to manage a device such as a modem, bridge, or router because the device responds to proprietary commands. In such a case, a proxy agent is used, as shown in Figure 8-11. Between a management station and a proxy agent, standard protocols are used. However, between the proxy agent and the managed devices, proprietary protocols are used. The proxy assumes the role of an agent with respect to the manager and acts as a manager for managed devices.

One of the main functions of a proxy agent is protocol conversion. As an example, the standard command from the management station is converted or mapped to the semantically equivalent proprietary command and sent to the managed devices. As mentioned earlier, managed devices understand these proprietary commands. Similarly, responses to the commands sent to managed devices are mapped back to standard responses in the proxy agent.

The conversion from standard protocols to proprietary protocols can be achieved by two methods. One is the mapping or translation of each field of standard protocols to each field of proprietary protocols. However, in some cases, one-to-one mapping of fields may not be possible,

Figure 8-11
The proxy concept.

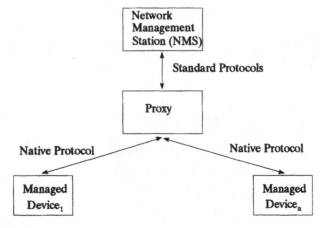

because there may not be similar, functionally equivalent fields. In such cases, the best possible assumptions will have to be made.

Another method involves encapsulating the standard protocols within the data fields of the proprietary protocols. This information will have to be retrieved by the software or hardware in the managed devices, but the managed devices will have the added responsibility of interpreting standard protocol fields. In some cases, the information carried in standard protocols may prove redundant or not amenable for proper interpretation. In either case, it is possible that some information will be lost due to the inability to use one-to-one mapping or the inability to retrieve all the information. To overcome this, the proprietary protocols are normally continuously modified to keep abreast of the standards.

Furthermore, the introduction of a proxy agent adds complexity. The mapping of standard protocols to the proprietary protocol requires resources. Note that we are adding one more level to the communication between the management station and managed devices. Also, if the proxy is in a separate workstation, there are considerations such as additional backup in case of the failure of the backup. All these add to the complexity.

Also, a proxy agent provides the flexibility to enforce "under-the-cover" access policies. The SNMP MIBs do not have to bother about them. The access policy can be for managed devices represented as objects, and it will be handled between the proxy agent and the managed devices.

A proxy can also be used for selectively forwarding information to a management station. It may log the information it receives from managed devices, and may maintain details of aggregate objects. Aggregate objects are defined for combining the details on more than one object. The management system may ask the proxy to send the details on aggregate objects. The aggregate objects may also be defined for summary statistics, configuration details, and so on.

8.7 SNMP over Different Protocols

SNMP has been defined over different popular protocols. Some of these are:

- SNMP over IPX (RFC 1420)
- SNMP over Ethernet (RFC 1089)
- SNMP over AppleTalk (RFC 1419)
- SNMP over OSI (RFC 1418)

8.8 SNMPv2

The original SNMP did not have elaborate security arrangements. To overcome this major weakness, SNMP version 2 (SNMPv2) was released. Accordingly, the original SNMP is known as SNMP version 1 or SNMPv1.

After SNMPv2 was released, there was much controversy on the administrative and security frameworks. One of the primary complaints on administrative and security frameworks was that they were complex, and it was difficult for the network administrators to use the administrative and security frameworks. As a result, SNMPv2 work got bogged down in controversies for some time.

The SNMPv2 security model was based on the concept of *parties*. Because of the disagreements on SNMPv2 security, two different approaches to security were taken in SNMPv2u and SNMPv2*. SNMPv2u advocated minimum standardization and was primarily focused on providing solutions to small agents. Security issues involving large networks were left open to be solved later.

In contrast, the SNMPv2* approach suggested standardization of security such that large networks were also covered. SNMPv2* also addressed remote configuration of security as well as scalability issues. SNMP version 3 or SNMPv3 started from these two approaches. We will look into SNMPv3 later. Those interested in the discussion on some of the controversies on SNMPv2 should consult Reference 8.21.

It was felt that the good work done in SNMPv2 should be reused. So, the least controversial RFCs in the SNMPv2 documents were accepted as draft standards. SNMPv2 documents from RFC 1902 through RFC 1908 (Table 8-4) are draft standards. RFC 1901, Introduction to Community-based SNMPv2; RFC 1909, An Administrative Infrastructure for SNMPv2; and RFC 1910, User-based Security Model for SNMPv2, were changed to the status of experimental. RFC 2089, Mapping SNMPv2 onto SNMPv1 within a Bilingual SNMP Agent, was given the status of informational. All these RFCs were part of the original SNMPv2.

We will discuss only the salient points of SNMv2 and the RFCs in the draft standard status. Bearing this point in mind, SNMPv2 has the following enhancements over SNMPv1:

- There have been major enhancements to the structure of management information of SNMPv1. MIB-II has been extended to include managed objects for SNMPv2. The syntax and semantics of managed objects have been refined. Also textual conventions have been

TABLE 8-4

SNMPv2 Draft
Standard
Documents.

RFC Number	Title of RFC
1902	Structure of Management Information for Version 2 of the Simple Network Management Protocol (SNMPv2)
1903	Textual Conventions for Version 2 of the Simple Network Management Protocol (SNMPv2)
1904	Conformance Statements for Version 2 of the Simple Network Management Protocol (SNMPv2)
1905	Protocol Operations for Version 2 of the Simple Network Management Protocol (SNMPv2)
1906	Transport Mappings for Version 2 of the Simple Network Management Protocol (SNMPv2)
1907	Management Information Base for Version 2 of the Simple Network Management Protocol (SNMPv2)
1908	Coexistence between Version 1 and Version 2 of the Internet-standard Network Management Framework

enhanced to extend the semantics of the standard object types defined in SMI.

- More operational PDUs are added. GetBulkRequest has been added to retrieve a large amount of management information. InformRequest has been added for communication between managers in a distributed environment. Though InformRequest was proposed for communication between managers, in SNMPv2 and SNMPv3 it is popular for sending notifications.

- Conformance statements have been added and a strategy for the migration of SNMPv1 to SNMPv2 has been provided.

- The transport used for carrying SNMPv2 protocols has been made more flexible and defined for different environments.

8.8.1 SNMPv2 Structure of Management Information (SMI)

The Structure of management information for SNMPv2 RFC 1902 (Reference 8.5) describes rules for defining modules, objects, and traps. Note that module is a collection of related objects. SMI provides the following definitions:

- *Module definitions:* The ASN.1 macro MODULE-IDENTITY is used to provide the syntax and semantics when defining a module.

- *Object definitions:* The ASN.1 macro OBJECT-TYPE provides the syntax and semantics to define an object.

- *Notification definitions:* The ASN.1 macro NOTIFICATION-TYPE is used to describe a *notification.* A notification is an unsolicited confirmed message of an event within an InformRequest-PDU.

8.8.1.1 Information Module. An *information module* is an ASN.1 module and provides information for network management. An information module is identified by a MODULE-IDENTITY macro. It provides the contact and revision history of the information modules. There are three types of information modules:

- *MIB modules:* Contain information on related objects.

- *Compliance statements:* Provide compliance requirements for MIB modules.

- *Capability statements:* Contain information on the capabilities of the agent implementation.

An information module need not have all the three modules. Compliance and capability statements will be discussed in Section 8.8.2.

8.8.1.2 Explanation of New Terms. Many new terms have been added in RFC 1902 (Reference 8.5) over the SNMPv1 SMI. Some of the new terms that need explanation are:

- *BITS:* Used for enumeration of named bits; starts from a value of 0.

- *Unsigned32:* Represents an integer value from 0 to $2^{32} - 1$.

- *Counter64:* A wraparound counter with a maximum value of $2^{64} - 1$.

- *UNITS:* Has textual definition of the units of measurements, such as hours and minutes, associated with an object.

- *MAX-ACCESS:* Relates to the maximum level of access allowed for an object. Note the distinction between the access rights of read-write and read-create. read-create is the maximum level of access allowed. With the read-create access right, an object instance can be created in addition to the read-write permission.

- *INDEX:* Used for object instance identification in a conceptual row. A new keyword, IMPLIED, is used for objects with variable-length syntax.

- *AUGMENTS:* An alternative to an INDEX clause, it extends the conceptual row with reference to a base conceptual row provided by an INDEX clause. AUGMENTS is useful for extending the definitions of tables. As an example, if Table 2 is a logical extension of Table 1, then the AUGMENTS clause may be used to connect these two tables.

The use of the Opaque data type (Section 8.3) is retained in RFC 1902 for backward compatibility reasons and should not be used for defining new object types. Reference 8.20 explains well the changes made to RFC 1902, RFC 1903, and RFC 1904.

8.8.1.3 Naming of Objects. The naming hierarchy is shown in Figure 8-12. The snmpV2 object subtree is contained in the internet subtree. We have already discussed mgmt(2), experimental(3), and private(4) in Section 8.4.1.

Under the snmpV2 subtree are snmpDomains(1), snmpProxys(2), and snmpModules(3). snmpDomains is used for transport mapping, snmpProxys is for transport proxies, and snmpModules is for the module identities.

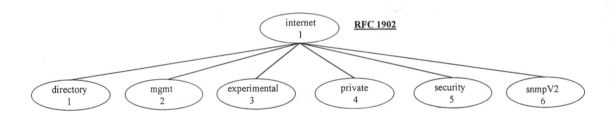

SNMPv2 Naming Hierarchy

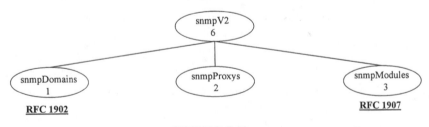

SNMPV2 Definitions

Figure 8-12
SNMPv2 naming hierarchy and object definitions.

8.8.1.4 SNMPv2 Textual Convention. The SNMPv2 textual convention is used for extending the semantics of standard data types in SMI. With this provision, SMI need not be modified often. RFC 1903 (Reference 8.6) defines a base set of textual conventions that use the conventions of the TEXTUAL-CONVENTION ASN.1 macro.

- *DisplayString (OCTET STRING (SIZE(0..255))):* Represents the textual convention using the ASCII character set. It is used for easy readability. The length of DisplayString should not exceed 255 octets.

- *PhysAddress (OCTET STRING):* Used to indicate the media address.

- *MacAddress (OCTET STRING (SIZE(6))):* Represents the MAC address as defined by IEEE 802.1 with the least significant bit transferred first.

- TruthValue *(INTEGER):* Provides a means to indicate a Boolean value, with true being 1 and false being 2.

- *TestAndIncr (INTEGER (0..2147483647)):* Tests first whether a value provided using a management protocol matches the value of the object instance. If the value matches, then the value of the object instance is increased by 1. If the value of an object instance reaches the maximum value of 2147483647, then the object instance value wraps to 0. However, a mismatch between the value provided and the value of the object instance results in an *inconsistent value* error.

- *AutonomousType (OBJECT IDENTIFIER):* Can be used to extend objects with a distinct identifier. Here the key is "autonomous," and the extension must be easily distinguishable. The textual convention can be useful for defining additions to the hardware and protocols.

- *VariablePointer (OBJECT IDENTIFIER):* Is a pointer to a specific object instance.

- *RowPointer (OBJECT IDENTIFIER):* Is a pointer to a conceptual row.

- *RowStatus (INTEGER):* Used to manipulate the creation and deletion of managed objects in conceptual rows. RowStatus has the values of active, notInService, notReady, createAndGo, createAndWait, and destroy.

- *TimeStamp (TimeTicks):* The same as sysUpTime, which is the value in TimeTicks when an agent was last reinitialized.

- *TimeInterval (INTEGER (0..2147483647)):* Represents the interval in units of 0.01s between two time periods.

- *DateAndTime (OCTET STRING (SIZE 8 | 11)):* Used to indicate the date and time. The length of DateAndTime can be 8 or 11 octets. The different fields have significance, as shown in Table 8-5. We have already

TABLE 8-5

DateAndTime
Representation.

Field	Octets	Contents	Range
1	1—2	Year	0..65536
2	3	Month	1..12
3	4	Day	1..31
4	5	Hour	0..23
5	6	Minutes	0..59
6	7	Seconds (use 60 for leap second)	0..60
7	8	Deciseconds	0..9
8	9	Direction from UTC	"+"/"–"
9	10	Hours from UTC	0..11
10	11	Minutes from UTC	0..59

looked into what UTC means in Chapter 5. As can be observed from Table 8-5, we do not need octets 9, 10, and 11 for local time.

8.8.2 Conformance Statements

Conformance statements define the acceptable level of implementation. An implementation can compare the actual functions provided with the benchmark provided in conformance statements to check whether the implementation satisfies the requirements. There are two types of notations used in SNMPv2; these are defined in RFC 1904 (Reference 8.7). The conformance notations are:

■ *Compliance statements:* Refer to the minimum set of requirements imposed on one or more MIB modules. This compliance is checked with the ASN.1 MODULE-COMPLIANCE macro.

■ *Capability statements:* Refer to the actual functions provided by one or more MIB groups supported by an agent and the ASN.1 AGENT-CAPABILITIES macro. When an agent supports a MIB group, it has to support all the objects in a MIB group.

The objects used for conformance are combined to form a group, and the ASN.1 macro OBJECT-GROUP is used to provide the syntax and semantics for this group. For conformance purposes, RFC 1904 defines

NOTIFICATION-GROUP macro to represent a collection of notifications and AGENT-CAPABILITIES statements to refer to one or more MIB groups.

8.8.3 SNMPv2 Protocol Messages

SNMPv2 uses slightly different protocol messages (Figure 8-13) for communicating management information than does SNMPv1. SNMPv2 protocol messages are explained in RFC 1905 (Reference 8.8). The format of SNMPv2 PDUs such as GetRequest, GetNextRequest, SetRequest, SNMPv2-Trap, Response, InformRequest, and Report are similar to those of SNMPv1 PDUs; however, there are some minor differences, as follows:

- The GetBulkRequest PDU has been added as shown in Figure 8-13. InformRequest and Report PDU are also new PDUs. However, Report PDU is not defined in SNMPv2.

- A trap PDU of SNMPv1 is no longer there, and a PDU type of 4 used for the SNMPv1 trap is obsolete. The new value of the PDU type SNMPv2 is 7 for SNMPv2-Trap.

- The GetResponse of SNMPv1 is renamed the Response PDU in SNMPv2.

  A brief explanation of SNMPv2 PDUs is as follows:

- *GetRequest:* When an application requests an SNMPv2 entity, this PDU is generated by the entity and sent to an agent. This message is similar to the SNMPv1 GetRequest message. On the receiving end, this message is analyzed to check whether the request is a proper one. If it is proper, then the error status field is set to noError and the error index field is set to 0 in the response and the response is sent to the manager.

- *GetNetRequest:* This message is similar to the getNextRequest in SNMPv1 messages and is based on the tabular concept of the SNMP MIB. If there are no errors, then the response contains the next

Figure 8-13
SNMPv2 protocol operations.

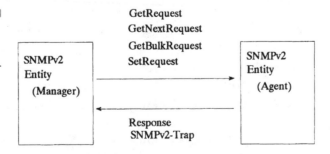

instance of a variable that has been sent in the request. If there are any errors, then the error status and error index fields correspond to the errors observed.

■ *SetRequest:* There are two steps involved. The first is a validation phase; if this succeeds, changes are made. During the validation step, a check is performed of whether change on a variable can be made. If this is not possible, then the error status and error index fields are set accordingly in the response PDU. However, if the validation step is successful, then the value of the variable is set to the value mentioned in the SetRequest PDU. If the variable is not there, it is created and its value is set. In this case, in the response PDU, the error status field shows noError, and the error index field is zero.

■ *GetBulkRequest:* This is primarily used for retrieving a large amount of table data from the MIB, unlike the GetRequest and GetNextRequest PDUs. Here also, if there are errors noticed in the receiving end, the error status and error index fields are set. If no errors are noticed, data is sent in the response PDU.

■ *InformRequest:* This is a protocol message for conveying MIB information from one SNMPv2 entity to another, both acting in the manager role. This PDU was originally meant for manager-to-manager communication. The receiving SNMPv2 checks to see if there are any errors. If errors are noticed during processing of this PDU, the response PDU has the corresponding error status and error index fields set. If there are no errors, the MIB information is passed on to the application using the receiving SNMPv2 entity and generates a response to the sending SNMPv2. Also note that RFC 1902 on SMI states that the NOTIFICATION-TYPE macro can be contained in an InformRequest PDU. In SNMPv3, InformRequest is used for carrying the notifications.

■ *Response:* This PDU is generated as a response for GetRequest, GetNextRequest, SetRequest, GetBulkRequest or InformRequest PDUs sent from a sender SNMPv2 entity. The sender SNMPv2 entity is the manager. The receiving SNMPv2 entity is the agent, and it prepares the response PDU and sends it back to the sending SNMPv2 entity. The sender SNMPv2 must be able to handle the errors generated and pass on the response PDU to the application using the sender SNMPv2 entity.

■ *SNMPv2-Trap:* When an exceptional situation occurs in an SNMPv2 entity acting in an agent role, then a trap is generated and sent to the SNMPv2 entity. The trap numbers in SNMPv2-Trap indicate the reasons why a trap has occurred. SNMPv2-Trap is unconfirmed in the sense that no response is generated from the manager on receiving an SNMPv2-Trap.

- *Report:* This PDU is not defined in RFC 1905. It is primarily used to account future SNMP administrative framework requirements such as to make use of faster error recovery. Currently, it is left to the implementers to define the usage and semantics. An example of the use of a Report PDU is to report time stamp information to a manager for time synchronization.

SNMPv2 and SNMPv3 use trap and InformRequest to report events. InformRequest is confirmed. An agent or a notification originator sends a notification to a manager or notification receiver and waits for confirmation from the manager or notification receiver. If the response is not received from the manager or notification receiver within a configured time, then agent transmits the notification again. These retransmissions will continue until the configured number of retries is reached or a response is received.

Event types are defined in NOTIFICATION-TYPE in RFC 1902 and the status of the event types is furnished by the STATUS clause. STATUS clause is not available in traps.

Reference 8.18 has a very good discussion on trap, event report, and notifications.

8.8.4 Transport Mapping for SNMPv2

RFC 1906 (Reference 8.9) describes the transport mappings. SNMPv2 management protocols must be associated with a transport service for transferring the management information. However, there are different types transport services that can be used for SNMPv2 (Figure 8-14). The term *snmpDomains* stands for the association of the SNMPv2 management protocols with a transport service. The following types of transport service for SNMPv2 have been defined:

- *snmpUDPDomain:* SNMPv2 over UDP is the preferred manner of transferring management information.

- *snmpCLNSDomain:* SNMPv2 over OSI's connectionless-mode transport service (CLTS) is an alternative. Connectionless transport service functions over the connectionless network service.

- *snmpCONSDomain:* Here, SNMPv2 is transferred using the connection-oriented network service (CONS). In this case, connectionless-mode transport service runs over the connection-oriented network service.

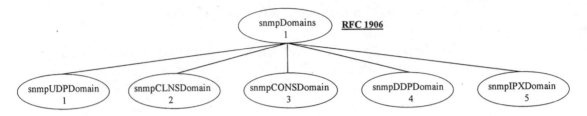

SNMPv2 - Transport Mappings

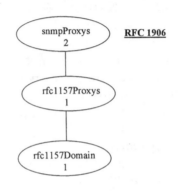

Figure 8-14
SNMPv2 transport mappings and snmpProxys.

- *snmpDDPDomain:* SNMPv2 uses the AppleTalk® DDP for the transport service.
- *snmpIPXDomain:* SNMPv2 uses the NetWare® IPX for the transport service.

8.8.5 SNMPv2 MIB

SNMPv2 MIB is explained in RFC 1907 (Reference 8.10). There are some changes between SNMPv2 and SNMPv1 MIBs. The IMPORT statement refers to MIBs used in SNMPv2, and they are to be used. Under the snmpModules subtree (Figure 8-15), there is the subtree of snmpMIB(1). snmpM2M(2), which was defined in RFC1451, Manager-to-Manager Management Information Base, and partyMIB(3), which was defined in RFC 1447, Party MIB for version 2 of the Simple Network Management Protocol (SNMPv2), have been removed from the SNMPv2 MIB in RFC 1907.

Figure 8-15
snmpModules.

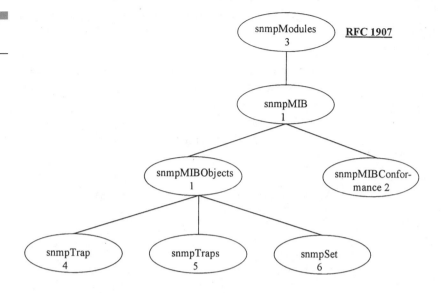

As can be seen from the Figure 8-15, snmpMIB has snmpMIBObjects and snmpMIBConformance subtrees. Again below the snmpMIBObjects, we have snmpTrap(4), snmpTraps(5), and snmpSet(6). All the other object groups under snmpMIBObjects are obsolete.

System group, which was part of MIB-II, has been included in SNMPv2 MIB, in RFC 1907. A new object, sysORUpTime, has been added to sysORTable. sysORUpTime refers to the time stamp when a resource with a particular sysORID value has been instantiated. sysORTable is a conceptual table for an SNMPv2 entity in an agent role.

8.8.5.1 snmpTrap Group. snmpTrap group objects are used by the SNMPv2 entities in the agent role to generate SNMPv2-Trap PDUs. Objects in this group are useful for fault management. In this group, there is one table, snmpTrapTable, which has one entry, snmpTrapNumbers.

8.8.5.2 snmpTraps Group. The snmpTraps group refers to the well-known SNMPv2 traps. We have seen these traps in the SNMPv1; they are useful for fault management. The definitions of linkUp and linkDown traps have been deleted from the snmpTraps Group, as they have become part of RFC 1573, Evolution of the Interfaces Group of MIB-II.

8.8.5.3 snmpSetGroup. The snmpSet group has one object and is used by the SNMPv2 entities acting in a manager role to coordinate the use of an SNMPv2 set operation. This object can be used for performance management.

8.8.5.4 snmpMIBConformance group.   The snmpMIBConformance group provides the compliance statements for SNMPv2 entities implementing SNMPv2 MIB. The compliance statements are provided by the snmpMIBCompliance. snmpMIBgroups refer to the compliance statements for the collection of objects for each of the SNMPv2MIB groups.

8.8.6 Coexistence between SNMPv1 and SNMPv2

For migration from SNMPv1, the proxy approach (see Figure 8-16) has been suggested. In this approach, an SNMPv2 entity may be acting as a manager; the SNMPv1 entity can be in an agent role. However, in this case, the SNMPv2 proxy agent will have to convert the GetBulkRequest PDU to GetNextRequest PDU and set nonrepeaters and maximum repetitions fields to 0. Traps will have to be modified in the proxy agent. In a bilingual approach, a manager functions as a proxy when dealing with an SNMPv2 agent. Here a manager maps SNMPv2 PDUs to SNMPv1 PDUs. Some of the strategies for migration are:

- Upgrading management stations to SNMPv2. If this is done, it is easy to support SNMPv2 agents as they become available.

Figure 8-16
SNMPv1 and SNMPv2 coexistence.

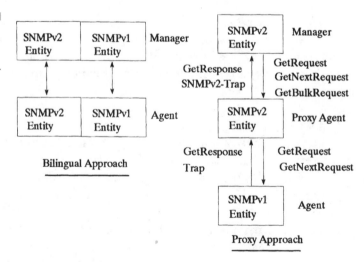

■ Upgrading and acquiring new SNMPv2 agents, if required. Once the management stations can handle SNMPv2, it is easy to add new SNMPv2 agents.

■ Handling the existing SNMPv1 agents; the proxy approach provides easy coexistence.

For more details on the migration and coexistence between SNMPv1 and SNMPv2 refer to RFC 1908 (Reference 8.11).

8.8.7 Device-Dependent Objects

In addition to the objects defined in MIB-II and other SNMPv1, SNMPv2, and SNMPv3 documents, objects are defined for different media types. These are useful, and they can be incorporated in agents.

8.9 SNMPv3

SNMPv3 is an extension of the SNMPv2 framework. It consists of a new SNMP message format, security for messages, and access control. The primary objectives of SNMPv3 were to work on security and administrative frameworks and to reuse, as much as possible, the ideas and work done in SNMPv2u and SNMPv2*. SNMPv3 standards include RFC 2271 through RFC 2275; the list of RFCs is furnished in Table 8-6. These RFCs are proposed standards.

TABLE 8-6

SNMPv3 Standard Documents (Proposed Standards).

RFC Number	Title of RFC
2271	An Architecture for Describing SNMP Management Frameworks
2272	Message Processing and Dispatching for the Simple Network Management Protocol (SNMP)
2273	SNMPv3 Applications
2274	User-based Security Model (USM) for Version 3 of the Simple Network Management Protocol (SNMPv3)
2275	View-based Access Control Model (VACM) for the Simple Network Management Protocol (SNMP)

Note that SNMPv3 RFCs need clarifications and corrections. As the SNMPv3 standards are in proposed standard status at the time of writing this book, these RFCs are expected to undergo some changes before advancing to other stages of Internet Standard track. Because of the experiences with SNMPv2, acceptance and implementations by the industry will be slow to come by. Therefore, caution is advised in implementing SNMPv3.

8.9.1 SNMPv3 Architecture

SNMPv3 architecture is explained in RFC 2271 (Reference 8.12). The concept of a management system (Figure 8-17) is slightly different from the earlier concepts of SNMPv1 and SNMPv2. A management system definition is based on SNMP entities. A manager in the traditional sense includes a command generator and a notification receiver. And an agent contains a command receiver and a notification generator. It is possible to have more than one agent in the SNMPv3 architecture.

The main concept of SNMPv3 architecture is centered on *SNMP entities*. An SNMP entity is an implementation feature. The components of an SNMP entity are shown in Figure 8-18. An SNMP entity has two main components. It consists of an SNMP engine and one or more applications. There is a one-to-one association between an SNMP engine and the SNMP entity.

An SNMP engine includes a dispatcher, a message processing subsystem, a security subsystem, and an access control subsystem. SNMPv3 applications are part of an SNMP entity. SNMPv3 applications make use of the services provided by an SNMP engine to accomplish specific tasks. Also, SNMPv3 applications may interact with information models and coordinate the processing of management operations. SNMPv3 applications currently include command generators, command responders, notification originators, notification receivers, and proxy forwarders as shown

Figure 8-17
SNMPv3 management system.

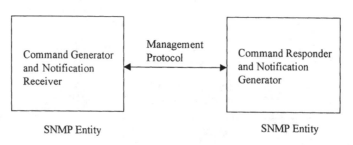

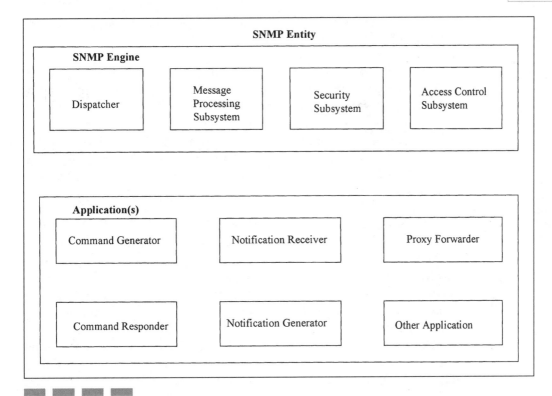

Figure 8-18
SNMPv3 architecture.

in Figure 8-18. The "Other Application" box in the figure is a placeholder for including other applications that may be developed in the future.

We now turn to some of the important concepts frequently used in SNMPv3.

8.9.1.1 contextEngineID.   An *SNMP context* is a collection of objects accessible by an SNMP entity. As discussed, a collection of objects represents management information. A context can be a physical device, a logical device, multiple devices, a subset of a single device, or a subset of multiple devices. This definition of a context permits a certain degree of flexibility in grouping devices.

A contextName identifies a context; this contextName has to be unique within an SNMP entity. An SNMP entity can have one or more contexts. Again within an administrative domain, contextEngineID is used to represent an instance of a context. An administrative domain may have one or more contexts. Therefore, contextEngineID and contextName uniquely identify a context within an administrative domain.

The PDUs, along with contextEngineID and contextName, are encapsulated in a scoped PDU.

8.9.1.2 Principal.   One of the important features of SNMPv3 security architecture is the concept of a *principal*. A principal uses the services provided by an SNMP engine. The SNMP engine does the processing for a principal. A principal can be one or more individuals, one or more applications, or a combination of individuals and applications. A principal is identified by a model-independent human readable string security-Name that can be a global name. A model-dependent securityName is represented by a securityID.

8.9.1.3 SNMP Manager.   The earlier concepts of an SNMP manager have been changed in SNMPv3. In the SNMPv3 architecture, an SNMP manager consists of one or more command generators, one notification receiver, and other components of an SNMP engine such as a dispatcher, message processing model, and transport mapper. Note that in SNMPv1 there is no concept of notification and a trap is used for sending unsolicited messages.

The interaction of a manager with the external components, along with the internal components of a manager, is shown in Figure 8-19. Though the RFC 2271 also shows a notification originator, we have excluded the notification originator, as a manager rarely issues a notification. However, it is possible that the notifications may be used in the future for some applications.

8.9.1.4 SNMP Agent.   Just as the concept of a manager has been changed, the SNMPv3 architecture has also modified the way an SNMP agent is viewed. An SNMP agent contains one or more command responders and notification originators. The interaction of an agent in SNMPv3 with the components inside and the external managers is shown in Figure 8-20. Notice in the figure that command responders and notification originators interact with the MIB instrumentation.

8.9.2 SNMP Engine

An SNMP engine provides services for sending commands and responses in the form of messages, authenticating messages, encrypting messages, and providing access control to managed objects. The components of an SNMP engine are shown in Figure 8-21. Message processing subsystem and dispatcher are described in detail in RFC 2272 (Reference 8.13). RFC

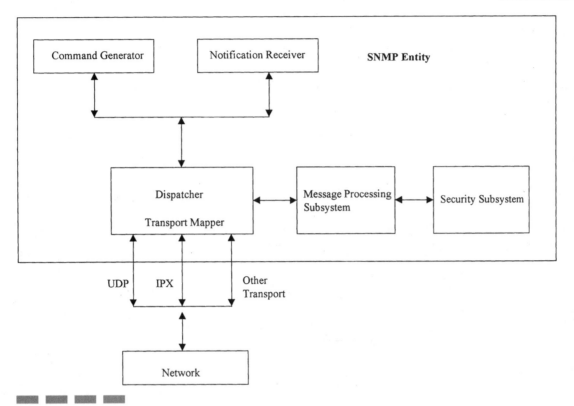

Figure 8-19
SNMPv3 manager.

2272 also defines the SNMPv3 message format and SNMPv3 message format furnished in Table 8-7.

We will briefly discuss each of the components of the SNMP engine.

8.9.2.1 Dispatcher.   There is only one dispatcher for an SNMP entity. The dispatcher is similar in functions to the dispatchers used in operating systems and other areas. The dispatcher is primarily responsible for sending and receiving messages to and from networks that transport these messages. As SNMP has different versions, the dispatcher interprets different versions of SNMP and interacts with the appropriate message processing systems. It also provides interfaces to SNMP applications to send PDUs to an application or to a remote SNMP entity.

8.9.2.2 Message Processing Subsystem.   The message processing subsystem is provided to account for different SNMP version messages. It aids

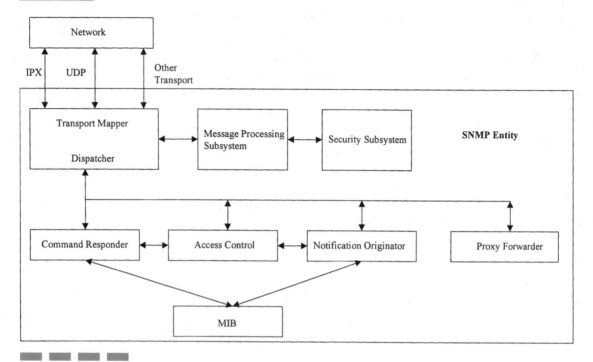

Figure 8-20
SNMPv3 agent.

in achieving interoperability with older SNMP versions and is responsible
for preparing messages for delivery and interpretation and extraction of
the data from received messages. These messages can be from or to
SNMPv3, SNMPv1, SNMPv2c, or other message processing models.

8.9.2.3 Security Subsystem.　The security subsystem includes one or
more security models. It is responsible for providing security services
such as authentication and privacy of messages, possibly by encryption.
The definition of a security model is quite generic and is broad so as to
include different security mechanisms to provide authentication and privacy. A security model includes threats against which security measures
are provided, a security protocol, and the goals of the security model. A
security protocol, in turn, includes mechanisms, procedures, and MIB
data to provide authentication and privacy. A message processing model
may control a security subsystem module.

8.9.2.4 Access Control Subsystem.　The access control subsystem
includes one or more access control models. Access control models include
logic to determine whether the appropriate access rights are available.

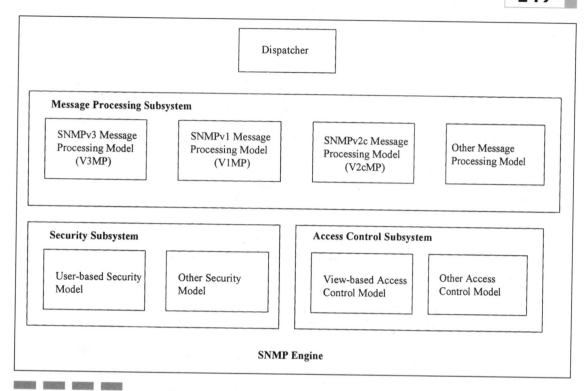

Figure 8-21
Components of an SNMP engine.

8.9.3 SNMPv3 Applications

RFC 2273 (Reference 8.14) explains SNMPv3 applications. It is essential to note that an SNMP engine does not have any restrictions on the type of applications that can be associated with it. As a result, an SNMP engine may be associated with a command generator, notification generator, or a proxy forwarder. We will now briefly look into each of the components of the applications.

8.9.3.1 Command Generator. A command generator performs the processing of requests and responses for the requests the command generator has initiated. The requests can be SNMP GetRequest, GetNextRequest, GetBulkRequest, or SetRequest.

8.9.3.2 Command Responder. A command responder receives requests such as SNMP GetRequest, GetNextRequest, GetBulkRequest, or SetRequest. It verifies whether the command is for the local system,

TABLE 8.7

SNMPv3 Message
Format.

SNMPv3 Message Field	Details
msgVersion	INTEGER. For SNMPv3, value is 3.
msgGlobalData	msgID—INTEGER (0..2147483647); msgMaxSize—INTEGER (484..2147483647); msgFlags—OCTECT STRING (SIZE (1)); msgSecurityModel—INTEGER (0..2147483647). This field contains header and other administrative data.
msgSecurityParameters	OCTET STRING. This field is used by security model and the format of this field is defined by security model.
msgData	conextEngineID—OCTET STRING; contextName— OCTET STRING; data (RFC 1905 PDUs); encryptedPDU— OCTET STRING. This field can be unique context and plain text or encrypted data. If the data is encrypted, then it should be decrypted at the receiving end.

checks for access rights if mentioned in the request, performs the operation specified by the request, and generates an appropriate response to be sent to the initiator of the request.

8.9.3.3 Notification Receiver. A notification receiver listens to a received InformRequest PDU and generates responses to the InformRequest. As mentioned earlier, the InformRequest PDU is used for carrying a notification.

8.9.3.4 Notification Originator. A notification originator is responsible for generating a trap or InformRequest for a trap or notification, respectively, when certain events occur. The notification generator needs to know where to send the trap or notification, the SNMP version, and security parameters to use when generating a trap or InformRequest.

8.9.3.5 Proxy Forwarder. The definition of *proxy forwarder* is quite restrictive in SNMPv3. A proxy forwarder simply forwards SNMP requests, notifications, or responses without regard to their contents. Here no translations are involved in forwarding the messages. This explanation is slightly different from the explanation of the proxy furnished in Section 8.6. The implementation of a proxy forwarder is optional.

8.9.4 Abstract Service Interfaces and Primitives

Abstract service interfaces are abstract interfaces between subsystems in an SNMP entity. An abstract service interface includes a primitive and the data elements to be passed when a service is invoked. Primitives define a set of services provided. The following primitives are defined for a dispatcher:

- *sendPDU:* An application uses this primitive to send an SNMP request or notification to a dispatcher.

- *processPDU:* A dispatcher sends this primitive to an application to process a PDU.

- *returnResponsePDU:* An application uses this primitive to send an SNMP response to a dispatcher.

- *processResponsePDU:* A dispatcher uses this primitive to send an incoming response PDU to an application.

An application requesting PDUs to be processed has to register with a dispatcher. For this registration, the primitive registerContentEngineID needs the parameters contextEngineID and pduType. pduType refers to one of the PDUs. When an application is ready to discontinue processing certain PDUs, it must deregister with the dispatcher. The primitive used for this is unregisterContextEngineID, and the parameters of unregister-ContextEngineID are contextEngineID and pduType.

The following primitives have been defined for a message processing subsystem:

- *prepareOutgoingMessage:* Used for preparing an outgoing SNMP request or notification message.

- *prepareResponseMessage:* Used for preparing an outgoing SNMP response message.

- *prepareDataElements:* Useful for preparing abstract data elements from an incoming SNMP message.

The access control subsystem uses the isAccessAllowed primitive to check whether access is allowed.

Security subsystem uses the following primitives:

- *generateRequestMsg:* Used to generate a request or a notification message.

- *processIncomingMsg:* Used for processing an incoming message.

- *generateResponseMsg:* Used for generating a response message.

A common primitive, stateRelease, is used to release memory held. Figure 8-22 provides a diagram showing how a command generator or a notification originator can use the primitives to process a message to be sent out and the response to the message sent out. Similarly, the diagram in Fig-

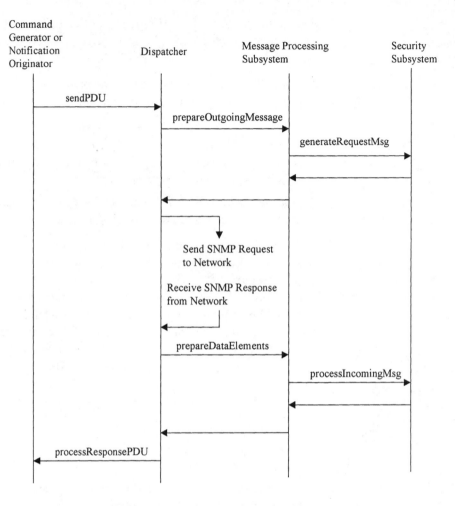

ure 8-23 shows how a command responder or a notification receiver processes an incoming message and sends the response to the incoming message.

8.9.5 SNMPv3 Textual Conventions

SNMPv3 Architecture (Reference 8.12) defines the following SNMPv3 textual conventions:

- *SnmpEngineID:* Is an SNMP engine's unique identifier within an administrative domain. As an SNMP entity has only one SNMP engine, SnmpEngineID also uniquely identifies an SNMP entity. The syntax of SnmpEngineID is OCTET STRING (SIZE(1..32)).

Figure 8-23

Command responder or notification receiver scenarios.

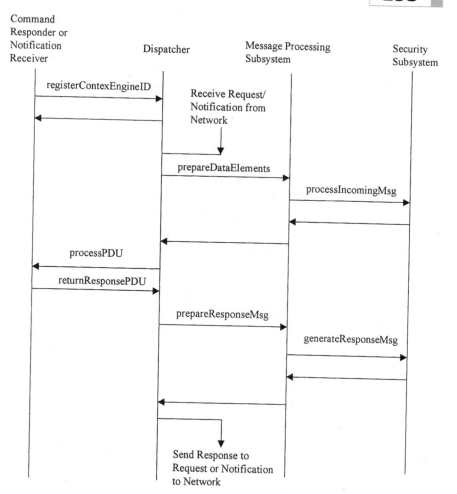

- *SnmpSecurityModel:* Is a unique identifier that identifies a security model within a security subsystem. The syntax is INTEGER (0..2147483647).

- *SnmpMessageProcessingModel:* Is an identifier to uniquely identify a message processing model within a message processing subsystem. Its syntax is INTEGER (0..2147483647).

- *SnmpSecurityLevel:* Indicates the security level for sending SNMP messages or processing messages. Three security levels have been defined: noAuthNoPriv (no authentication and no privacy), authNoPriv (authentication is used but there is no privacy), and auth-Priv (both authentication and privacy are used). The syntax of

SnmpSecurityLevel is INTEGER with values: noAuthNoPriv—1, authNoPriv—2, and authPriv—3.

■ *SnmpAdminString:* Contains administrative information. It is better to have this octet string in human readable form. The syntax of SnmpAdminString is OCTET STRING (SIZE (0..255)).

8.9.6 User-Based Security Model

The user-based security model (USM) is discussed in RFC 2274 (Reference 8.15), which describes different authentication and privacy mechanisms that can be used. While the procedure for timeliness is fixed, there are provisions for using different algorithms for authentication and privacy. The user of a security model is the principal, discussed earlier.

The user-based security model uses the following three modules:

■ *Authentication module:* Supports data integrity and data origin authentication.

■ *Timeliness module:* Protects against message delay and message replay. A timeliness check is performed if there is an authentication check.

■ *Privacy module:* Prevents unwarranted disclosure of a message. If privacy is selected, the architecture requires that authentication must also be performed.

We have already looked into some of the primitives provided by a security subsystem in Section 8.9.4. USM RFC introduces the following primitives:

■ *authenticateOutGoingMsg:* Used to call the authentication module which implements a user's authentication protocol to authenticate a message before it is sent.

■ *authenticateIncomingMsg:* Used to authenticate an incoming message.

■ *encryptData:* Used to invoke privacy module to encrypt a serialized scopedPDU.

■ *decryptData:* Used for unencrypting a received scopedPDU.

Each SNMP engine has the following three important objects:

■ *snmpEngineID:* Is the unique identifier within an administrative domain of an SNMP engine.

■ *snmpEngineBoots:* Refers to the number of times an SNMP engine has been rebooted or reinitialized since an snmpEngineID was last configured.

■ *snmpEngineTime:* Refers to the time elapsed since snmpEngineBoots was reconfigured.

Let us look into how timeliness is checked. snmpEngineBoots and snmpEngineTime indicate the notion of time with respect to an SNMP engine. These are part of authenticated messages sent or received. These values are checked against a time window, which indicates the time within which a message has to be received. Thus a timeliness check ensures that message delay is within permissible limits.

The elements of the procedure used for preparing outgoing messages using authentication has been simplified and is shown in Figure 8-24. For more details on USM, refer to the RFC 2274 [8.15].

8.9.7 View-Based Access Control Model

RFC 2275 (Reference 8.16) describes the view-based access control model (VACM). The primary objective of the VACM is to check whether users (principals) have proper access rights to access one or more objects in a MIB and perform operations on these objects.

One of the key ideas in VACM is the notion of *MIB view.* A subset of a management information is known as MIB view. Access to a context occurs via a MIB view. For a context, there is normally one MIB view. Each MIB view has associated access rights of read-view, write-view, or notify-view.

The read-view access right permits reading values of object instances. Reading is done when retrievals such as GetRequest, GetNextRequest, or GetBulkRequest are done. Write-view allows the values of managed object instances to be changed by operations such as a SetRequest. Notify-view indicates the object instances that are permitted to send a trap or a notification.

Figure 8-25 shows how the primitive isAccessAllowed is used to check whether an application has the proper access rights to a set of object instances. For more details on the VACM, readers can consult Reference 8.16.

8.9.8 SNMPv3 MIB Modules

SNMPv3 requires additional objects besides those already defined in SNMPv1 and SNMPv2 because of the additional features such as security. There is also a need for defining more objects in the future, if additional

Figure 8-24
Generating an outgo-
ing message.

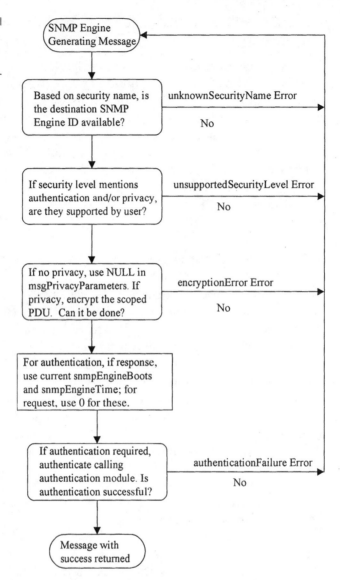

functionalities for SNMPv3 are to be provided. For this reason, the administrative objects are left without objects below them. In the following discussion, we have not included MIB modules used for compliance and conformance of objects. The key object hierarchy of SNMPv3 is shown in Figure 8-26. The brief explanations of MIB modules are:

■ *snmpFrameworkMIB:* Defines the MIB module for SNMPv3 architecture.

Figure 8-25
Processing of isAccess-Allowed service request.

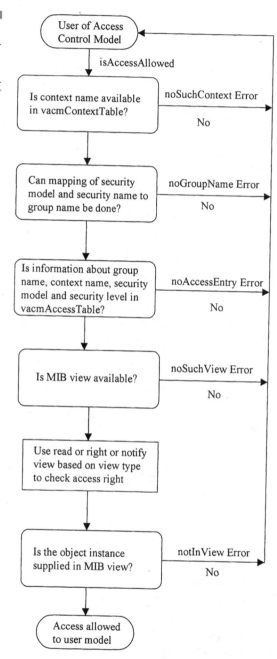

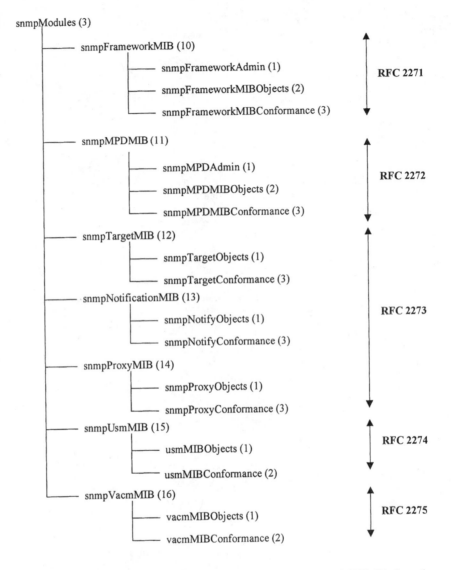

Figure 8-26
SNMPv3 MIB
modules.

- *snmpFrameworkAdmin:* Used for the registration of SNMPv3 authentication and privacy protocol objects.
- *snmpFrameworkMIBObjects:* Used to derive SNMP engine-related objects such as snmpEngineID, snmpEngineBoots, snmpEngineTime, and snmpEngineMaxMessageSize.
- *snmpMPDMIB:* The MIB module for message processing and dispatching.
- *snmpMPDAdmin:* Used for the registration of message processing and dispatcher objects.

- *snmpMPDMIBObjects:* Provides a collection of objects for statistics on the number of packets dropped due to referencing the wrong security model, invalid or inconsistent components of the SNMP message, or no proper registration of SNMP application.

- *snmpTargetMIB:* Objects in this module are used for defining the destinations, transport domains, and addresses of the targets.

- *snmpTargetObjects:* Includes two tables, one that contains information about the transport domains and addresses and one that includes information about the SNMP version and security information for sending messages to specific transport domains.

- *snmpNotificationMIB:* Has objects for remotely controlling parameters of SNMP entities that generate notifications.

- *snmpNotifyObjects:* Determines the set of management targets that should receive notifications and the type notifications that should be sent. The objects in this group permit association of a set of filters with a target and restriction of the type of notifications for targets.

- *snmpProxyMIB:* Module objects are used to remotely configure the parameters in a proxy forwarding application.

- *snmpProxyObjects:* Provides objects for use by proxy forwarder applications.

- *snmpUSMMIB:* Includes objects used in the user-based security model.

- *usmMIBObjects:* Objects in this module are used to perform authentication and privacy on the management operations of users.

- *snmpVacmMIB:* Objects in this module are used for the view-based access control model.

- *vacmMIBObjects:* Contains objects that have details of the access rights available.

RFC 2273 defines three types of MIBs, namely SNMP-TARGET-MIB for management target, SNMP-NOTIFICATION-MIB for notifications, and SNMP-PROXY-MIB for forwarding proxy operations. Prior to RFC 2273, there were no specific MIBs to specify the destination or target MIBs. SNMP-TARGET-MIB and SNMP-NOTIFICATION-MIB permit the target, whether it is a trap or an inform, and the time and retry values for each target to be specified.

For event reporting, SNMPv3 protocol uses Trap and InformRequest. In SNMPv2, InformRequest was used for manager to manager communication in SNMPv2; its usage is slightly different in SNMPv3. Also, in SNMPv2 the use of Report PDUs was not clearly defined. Report PDUs in

SNMPv3 are used for communications between SNMP engines and are processed by message processing models.

8.10 Advantages of SNMP

As mentioned earlier, SNMP is a simple protocol, and it is easy to add this protocol to agents. Many applications using SNMP protocols have been implemented. It is easy to get and modify the SNMP code. Besides, the Internet is quite popular and has a large base. This in itself is a big advantage for SNMP.

Also, it is easy to add objects required for specific implementations. This can be done by adding the objects to the MIB. Continuous improvements and extensions are being added to the protocol with implementation experiences.

8.11 Notes on SNMP

SNMP centralizes network management activities in NMSs with minimum functionality in agents. This approach leads to scalability problems. The centralized model is suitable for small networks, but when large networks and heterogeneous networks are involved, there can be performance problems.

However, remote network monitoring (RMON) takes a decentralized approach to network management. RMON probes collect data from the individual Ethernet segments or token ring networks, and perform processing and sorting locally and forward the data to the NMS using SNMP. Some of these issues, such as centralized management and decentralized management, are also treated well in Reference 8.19.

As we move into a client-server environment with a large number of networks, management domains and communications between them will assume a significant role. Management domains are also important for distributed network management. Incidentally, there is much work to be done in the Internet network management arena. Security is very critical in distributed environments, but currently this issue is not being addressed. This hole in SNMP security has to be addressed.

Common object request broker architecture (CORBA) is also becoming very popular in distributed network management. Therefore, the interoperability between CORBA and SNMP has to be worked out to utilize the power of CORBA. In the Internet, the distributed management (DIS-MAN) group is working on the distributed aspects of network management. This group should address some of the issues just mentioned.

When SNMP was designed, the idea was to keep the management protocol simple. This has its own drawbacks, however. The network management has a whole range of functions in addition to the SNMP protocols defined. An Internet network management framework for network management applications similar to systems management functional areas of the OSI needs to be delineated to standardize this area also.

It is also necessary to define objects for the different network management functions such as configuration management, fault management, security management, performance management, and accounting management. These may be borrowed from OSI. This is required as the convergence of network management of ITU-T and the Internet may not happen at all.

In configuration and fault management, relationships between different monitored objects are very important in tracing the origins of faults. Thus, relationships must be defined and standardized.

In configuration management, aggregation objects need to be defined. In some cases, the status of an object may affect the aggregation of objects below a subtree. In such cases, the status will have to be combined by either simple or weighted aggregation. Also, the configuration may be a combination of objects; for example, a network may be a combination of an IP network, telecommunications network, and a network using a proprietary protocol. To show the whole network, it is necessary to define aggregate objects.

The Internet group is focused on protocols used by the Internet community, and it expects a certain layer stack. It also assumes certain physical layer interfaces. As an example, SNMP protocols place emphasis on Ethernet LANs and the TCP/IP protocol suite. But there are protocols, such as token ring, which are also popular. The focus on Internet-related protocols may be regarded as a strength as well as a weakness. It is a strength in that problems facing the Internet community get immediate attention, but a weakness in that others may have to wait longer for standardization.

Therefore objects may have to be specifically defined and extensions added to the MIB for many resources. This may result in defining the same resources in different manners, which can create problems in the interoperability of network management functions.

The definition of managed object classes in ITU-T allows the use of inheritance and polymorphism. This makes possible the reuse of attributes; hence the implementations become simpler with this approach. We have already explained polymorphism in Chapter 4, Section 4.14. Polymorphism helps in the migration and coexistence of different versions of the same applications.

We have seen in the ITU-T that managed objects have attributes, operations, notifications, and behaviors. In SNMP, object definitions are less powerful and carry less information; this becomes a problem in some cases where performance is an important criterion.

In SNMP protocols, there are no clear-cut rules regarding how to partition MIB-II objects into different systems management functional areas. Unless there is standardization in this direction, the partitioning of MIB-II objects will not be uniform in implementations from different vendors. In addition to the MIB-II objects, there should be well-laid-out rules for partitioning the device- and protocol-specific objects into different systems management functional areas.

In TMN, ITU-T standards are widely used. In the computer industry, the standards are not so rigid, with leading computer vendors setting the trend on the "standards." Because of the simplicity of SNMP, SNMPv1 is popular and is attractive to device vendors doing instrumentation. To support or extend new device features, MIBs have to be extended. This can be done easily. As a result of these strong points of SNMP, there are also implementations based on SNMP in the TMN arena.

However, one of the major problems with SNMP and the Internet RFCs is that they are frequently changed or updated. Sometimes this can create problems for implementers. SNMPv2 has not made much headway in the industry because of the complexity and controversies. We have alluded earlier to the fact that SNMPv3 RFCs have many outstanding issues to resolve. To address these issues, it is expected that updated RFCs will replace the existing SNMPv3 RFCs.

Besides, SNMP is just a management protocol. Network management involves more than the management protocols. The success of network management will depend primarily upon the ease of use and the variety and usefulness of management applications. As far as SNMP is concerned, a lot of work needs to be done to standardize management applications as in OSI systems management, TMN, distributed network management, interoperability with CORBA, and so on.

Without much standardization in these areas, it is difficult for the vendors to develop management applications. Development of management applications is very important if SNMP is to get much of a foothold in TMN. Besides, some management applications have a long life, and few people are willing to replace or change these management applications. So, caution is advised before adopting SNMP in TMN.

8.12 Coexistence Between SNMP and CMIP

Initially, while Internet network management protocols were being developed, the intention of SNMP was to merge eventually with ITU-T and OSI management protocols. SNMPv1 got a boost and some following in the industry because of the simplicity of implementation and its value in small applications. However, due to the existence of a large base of SNMP managed devices, there is no effort to merge SNMP and CMIP.

The telecommunications management models are more appropriate for transmission systems and cross-connections than for packet networks such as those used in the Internet. In the Internet, packets may be routed differently at different times.

CMIP is generally regarded as complex and is good for large systems. SNMP is simple and good for small systems. In CMIP, managed objects can contain other managed objects or point to other managed objects using attributes. In SNMP, the objects can point to other objects and collection of data is limited to data on attributes and behavior descriptions. As a result, in reality, there is a need for coexistence of the CMIP and SNMP management protocols. TeleManagement Forum has addressed the issue of interoperability between CMIP and SNMP.

8.13 Interoperability with ITU-T/OSI

For interoperability between ITU-T/OSI and TCP/IP protocols, RFC 1006 is recommended. RFC 1006 mimics the transport layer on top of TCP as shown in Figure 8-27. In this way, layers such as the session, presentation, and application layers can run on top of TCP/IP protocols. This enables applications such as TMN and mail services to operate on TCP/IP. Some of the salient features of RFC 1006 are:

■ *ISO transport Class 0 is supported.* Class 0 provides the most simple basic connection-oriented support during connection establishment and connection release phases. It does not provide a mechanism to detect protocol errors. Quality of service, which classifies transport services in terms of Class 0, Class 1, Class 2, Class 3, and Class 4, is not supported.

Figure 8-27
Interoperability with
OSI.

Application Layer
Presentation Layer
Session Layer
RFC 1006 (ISO TP0)
TCP/IP

- *Some departures from Class 0 are made.* Initial data may be exchanged during the connection establishment phase; expedited data service is supported; and much larger transport protocol data unit (TPDU) size is supported. For performance reasons, a default TPDU size of 65531 is taken. However, smaller TPDU sizes are allowed, but they must be negotiated.

- *Network service is provided by the TCP.*

- *TPDU is encapsulated within each packet designed specifically for this RFC.* This packet consists of a packet header and the TPDU. The packet header has 8 bits for version, 8 bits of reserved field, and 16 bits of length field.

8.14 Implementation Notes

TCP/IP protocol suite RFCs, including those of network management, change quite frequently to meet new requirements. Before any RFC is implemented, it must be ascertained that it is the latest and is not superseded by a more recent RFC. To do so, the first document to consult is the *RFCINDEX,* which is an up-to-date index of the RFCs that have been released. The next document to consult during design and implementation is the RFC on *IAB Official Protocol Standards,* which furnishes the maturity levels of RFCs. These documents are regularly updated.

Also, for implementation purposes, informational, experimental, and historical states are not of much use. By and large, it is better to go for full-scale implementation after an RFC has reached at least the draft stage.

8.15 Internet Standardization Process

In the Internet community, topics of interest are written as requests for comments (RFCs). There are standard formats for writing RFCs. There are two separate tracks for RFCs: standard and nonstandard. Nonstandard RFCs include experimental, informational, and historic RFCs. A document that is not ready for standard track is delegated to the experimental stage. An RFC that is replaced by some other document or whose contents are obsolete enters the historical state.

The interests, activities, and development of standards for the Internet are controlled by the Internet Activities Board (IAB). The IAB is subdivided into different functional subgroups. One of the subgroups, the Internet Engineering Task Force (IETF), is involved in protocol development and standardization activities. The main objective of the IETF is to resolve any issues that may crop up and come up with solutions, standards, and architectures for short- and mid-term protocols. Another subgroup, the Internet Engineering Steering Group (IESG), studies RFCs and recommends movements of standards to different maturity levels.

The RFCs in the standard track enter different maturity levels in stages and time frames. When a specification is developed with the intent of moving it in the standard track, it can be termed a *prototype*. An RFC starts as a prototype and moves to the proposed state, advances to a draft standard state, and then becomes a full standard. When an RFC advances to the next maturity levels, rigorous review is done. Also, implementation and interoperability are required for moving from the proposed to the draft standard stage. At any stage, an RFC can be moved to different states in the nonstandard track. The Internet standard process is explained in RFC 2026 (Reference 8.17).

8.16 Summary

In this chapter, we have examined the basic philosophy of Internet network management and introduced the SNMP management protocols framework. We started the chapter with a detailed discussion of SNMPv1. As SNMPv1 is very popular in the computer industry, and, to a lesser degree, in the telecommunications industry, it is essential to look into the basic concepts of SNMPv1 protocols. We next discussed the SNMPv2 and the RFCs associated with SNMPv2, which are draft standards. SNMPv3, which is an extension SNMPv2, is discussed briefly. We have also looked into the topics of interoperability with OSI/ITU-T, as well as the advantages and limitations of SNMP protocols. We end this chapter with an overview of the Internet standardization process for a better understanding of the different versions of SNMP protocols and their standing with respect to the Internet standard track.

8.17 References

8.1. McCloghrie, K. and M. T. Rose, Structure and Identification of Management Information for TCP/IP-based Internets, RFC 1155, 1990.

8.2. Case, J. D., M. Fedor, M. L. Schoffstall, and C. Davin, Simple Network Management Protocol, RFC 1157, 1990.

8.3. Rose, M. T. and K. McCloghrie, Concise MIB Definitions, RFC 1212, 1991.

8.4. McCloghrie, K. and M. T. Rose, Management Information Base for Network Management of TCP/IP-based Internets: MIB-II. RFC 1213, 1991.

8.5. Case, J., K. McCloghrie, M. Rose, and S. Waldbusser, Structure of Management Information for Version 2 of the Simple Network Management Protocol (SNMPv2), RFC 1902, 1996.

8.6. Case, J., K. McCloghrie, M. Rose, and S. Waldbusser, Textual Conventions for Version 2 of the Simple Network Management Protocol (SNMPv2), RFC 1903, 1996.

8.7. Case, J., K. McCloghrie, M. Rose, and S. Waldbusser, Conformance Statements for Version 2 of the Simple Network Management Protocol (SNMPv2), RFC 1904, 1996.

8.8. Case, J., K. McCloghrie, M. Rose, and S. Waldbusser, Protocol Operations for Version 2 of the Simple Network Management Protocol (SNMPv2), RFC 1905, 1996.

8.9. Case, J., K. McCloghrie, M. Rose, and S. Waldbusser, Transport Mappings for Version 2 of the Simple Network Management Protocol (SNMPv2), RFC 1906, 1996.

8.10. Case, J., K. McCloghrie, M. Rose, and S. Waldbusser, Management Information Base for Version 2 of the Simple Network Management Protocol (SNMPv2), RFC 1907, 1996.

8.11. Case, J., K. McCloghrie, M. Rose, and S. Waldbusser, Coexistence between Version 1 and Version 2 of the Internet-standard Network Management Framework, RFC 1908, 1996.

8.12. Harrington, D., R. Presuhn, and B. Wijnen, An Architecture for Describing SNMP Management Frameworks, RFC 2271, 1998.

8.13. Case, J., D. Harrington, R. Presuhn, and B. Wijnen, Message Processing and Dispatching for the Simple Network Management Protocol (SNMP), RFC 2272, 1998.

8.14. Levi, D., P. Meyer, and B. Stewart, SNMPv3 Applications, RFC 2273, 1998.

8.15. Blumenthal, U. and B. Wijnen, User-based Security Model (USM) for Version 3 of the Simple Network Management Protocol (SNMPv3), RFC 2274, 1998.

8.16. Wijnen, B., R. Presuhn, and K. McCloghrie, View-based Access Control Model (VACM) for the Simple Network Management Protocol (SNMP), RFC 2275, 1998.

8.17. Bradner, S., The Internet Standards Process—Revision 3, RFC 2026, 1998.

8.18. Perkins, D. T., "Questions Answered," *The Simple Times*, vol. 6, no. 1, pp. 17—21, 1998.

8.19. Meyer, K., M. Erlinger, J. Betser, C. Sunshine, G. Goldszmidt, and Y. Yemini, *Decentralizing Control and Intelligence in Network Management.* Integrated Network Management IV, Proceedings of the Fourth International Symposium on Integrated Network Management, 1995, Sethi, A. S., Raynaud, Y., and Faure-Vincent, F. (eds.), London: Chapman & Hall, pp. 4—15, 1995.

8.20. McGloghrie, K., "SNMP Framework," *The Simple Times*, vol. 4, no. 2, pp. 23—24, 1996.

8.21. SNMP Research, Inc., Is SNMPv2 Really Dead? 1995. Also visit the SNMP Research SNMPv2* Web Site.

8.22. McGloghrie, K., "SNMP Framework," *The Simple Times*, vol. 4, no. 3, pp. 21—22, 1996.

■ ■ ■ **8.18 Further Reading**

8.1. Rose, M. T., *The Simple Book: An Introduction to Internet Management* (2d ed.), Englewood Cliffs, NJ: Prentice Hall, 1996 (1st ed. published 1991).

8.2. Stallings, W., *SNMP, SNMPv2, and RMON: The Practical Network Management Standards,* (2d ed.), Reading, MA: Addison-Wesley, 1996. At press time, this book was being revised to include SNMPv3 and RMON2.

8.3. Postel, J., Transmission Control Protocol, RFC 793, 1981.

8.4. Leinwald, A., and K. Fang, *Network Management: A Practical Perspective,* (2d Edition) Reading, MA: Addison-Wesley, 1995.

TMN
Applications

CHAPTER 9

Network Management for Mobile Communications

9.1 Introduction

Because the subject of this book is TMN, we will only discuss abstractly the different forms of communications technologies. Those who are interested in the specifics of these technologies should refer to one of the many good books available on the subject.

Communication between any devices can be classified as wired or wireless (Figure 9-1). In wired communication, conductors such as copper twisted pair, fiber optics, or coaxial cable carry information between two or more devices, whereas in wireless communication, space is the communication media.

Another classification of communication is based on the type of connection between an end user and network services. In fixed communication, there is a permanent association between an end user device and a single network access point. In mobile communication, however, an end user device can connect to multiple access points and use network services for communication between end-user devices. Mobile communication consists of portable and frequently moving devices. A mobile communication network includes personal communications services (PCS) networks, wireless LAN networks, and satellite networks.

PCS is a wireless technology based on digital communications. Cordless phones and cellular phones are early versions of the PCS. For PCS, two digital technologies—time division multiple access (TDMA) and code division multiple access (CDMA) are popular protocols. For TDMA, there are again two standards: North American standards based on TIA/EIA/IS-136, and Digital Cellular System 1800 (DCS 1800) standards developed by the European Telecommunications Standards Institute (ETSI).

Wireless communication is increasing in market penetration. For TMN of PCS, ANSI standards are available. In European nations, ETSI global system for mobile communication (GSM) standards are quite popular. Bellcore has also developed its own TMN documents for wireless communications.

Figure 9-1
Differences between communication terminologies.

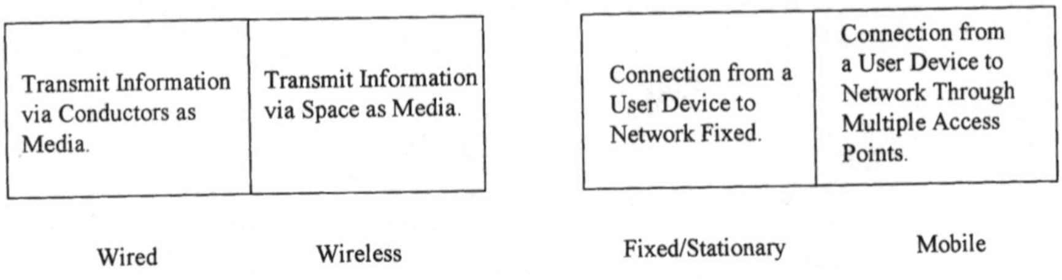

Transmit Information via Conductors as Media.	Transmit Information via Space as Media.	Connection from a User Device to Network Fixed.	Connection from a User Device to Network Through Multiple Access Points.
Wired	Wireless	Fixed/Stationary	Mobile

9.2 Overview of Network Management for Mobile Communications

Network management for mobile networks is more complex than network management for fixed or stationary networks. Some of the important issues involved in the network management of mobile networks are:

■ The design of MIBs has to satisfy the requirements of dynamic topology changes; operations under stress; and interactions with different physical environments including rugged physical factors such as varying weather conditions, electromagnetic interference, and multipath effects.

■ Mobile networks operate under operational stress due to the limited bandwidth available. Mobile networks are operated near capacity limits, unlike stationary networks, which are normally operated below capacity limits. This causes problems in distinguishing stress conditions from failure conditions. Operational stress also creates problems when alarm correlation is used to capture the root cause of a problem. One solution is to partition a network into smaller domains. These smaller domains constrain alarm correlation and problem diagnosis to a manageable level. Reference 9.15 treats this issue thoroughly.

■ Network topology in mobile networks can frequently change because of roaming and handoff, so element managers must be able to handle dynamic topology changes. In fixed networks, topology changes are normally minimal.

■ Mobility effects billing and routing. As an example, there must be coordination between the visiting domain and the home domain during roaming. To support roaming, routing functions must track the locations of mobile stations (MSs). A cellular phone is an example of an MS. Similarly, the billing function must be able to correctly collect and share the billing information among the visiting and home domains.

■ At the service level, managing QOS parameters is more complicated. In mobile networks, there are QOS parameters such as connection setup time and call losses.

■ Provisioning is more complex in mobile networks than in stationary networks. End-to-end communication involves mapping of names to addresses and addresses to routes. These are maintained in different configuration databases. Access authorization, accounting, and service parameters depend upon the data maintained in the configuration databases. In the case of mobile networks, as the changes are dynamic, the data in these configuration databases dynamically change. This entails keeping track of rapid changes in databases as well as maintaining consistency.

CMIP and SNMP are popular management protocols for mobile communications. We have already covered these management protocols in Chapters 7 and 8.

One of the challenges faced in network management of mobile communications is the variety of vendor services and ownerships available. As an example, in a PCS network, one vendor may own both the radio and switching resources. In another model, one vendor may own radio services and another may own the switching services. This leads to the challenge of managing hybrid modes of operation. Even though there are multiple service providers, these service providers must be able to share data related to billing, security, and subscriber profiles.

9.3 ANSI Network Management for PCS

A brief introduction to management mobility application protocol (MMAP) is furnished to make readers aware of the management capabilities available for some components of PCS. ANSI T1.651-1996 (Reference 9.13) defines the MMAP for exchange of information and invocation of operations to support terminal mobility in a wireless environment. MMAP is useful for providing functions such as call waiting, call control, call setup, call manipulation, call clearing, registration, location updating, authentication, roaming, and handover. Extensions and revisions to ANSI T1.651-1996 are furnished in ANSI T1.651a-1996 (Reference 9.14). MMAP protocol is an application layer protocol to be used between radio systems and network elements such as mobility management platforms, switching systems, and other radio systems. For more details on MMAP, consult References 9.13 and 9.14.

ANSI T1.244-1995 (Reference 9.11) contains details of information model and OAM&P requirements. This standard is an extension to ANSI T1.210 and ITU-T Recommendation M.3010, Principles for a Telecommunication Management Network.

A Q3 interface is used between an OS and network elements representing different functional elements used in PCS. Functional elements of a PCS network are:

- *Radio Access System Controller (RASC):* Is used to manage terminal mobility.

- *Radio Port Controller (RPC):* Provides access to wireless components.

- *Terminal Mobility Controller (TMC):* Provides terminal mobility within a PCS network.

- *Terminal Mobility Datastore (TMD):* Provides storage for the data needed for terminal mobility.

- *Personal Mobility Controller (PMC):* Is used for controlling personal mobility.

- *Personal Mobility Datastore (PMD):* Contains data on personal profiles.

- *PCS Switching Center (PSC):* Connects and routes user traffic from a wireless network to a wireline or other wireless networks.

These functional elements are described in Reference 9.12. There are no well-defined rules for mapping these functional units to network elements. A network element may represent one or more functional units. ANSI T1.244 defines the information model for RASC and RPC only. Many object classes are drawn and derived from ITU-T Recommendation M.3100, Generic Network Information Model, and ITU-T Recommendation X.721, Structure of Management Information: Definition of Management Information.

Network management for PCS uses the following principles laid out in TMN architecture:

- A logical layered architecture is used that contains five layers, namely business management, service management, network management, element management, and network elements.

- The physical architecture defines operations systems, communication, networks, and network elements.

- The functional architecture is similar to that defined in TMN M3010. Refer to Chapter 2, Section 2.3.1 of this book for details.

- SMFAs such as configuration management, fault management, performance management, accounting management, and security management are used.

ANSI T1.244 covers fault management and configuration management function areas in detail, as well as requirements for PCS management function areas such as configuration management, fault management, performance management, accounting management, and security management. Some of the ITU-T recommendations that are useful for network management of PCS are as follows:

- *Configuration Management:* Uses the services and functions defined in X.730, Systems Management: Object Management Function.

- *Alarm Surveillance:* Uses the services and functions defined in Q821, Stage 2, and Stage 3 Description for the Q3 Interface, Alarm Surveillance.

- *Failure Localization:* Needs the services and functions defined in X.745, Systems Management: Test Management Function, and X.737, Systems Management: Confidence and Diagnostic Test Categories.

- *Testing:* Employs the services and functions defined in X.745, Systems Management: Test Management Function, and X.737, Systems Management: Confidence and Diagnostic Test Categories.

- *Performance Monitoring:* Uses services and functions defined in Q822, Stage 1, Stage 2, and Stage 3 Description for the Q3 Interface, Performance Management.

9.4 ETSI Network Management for DCS

GSM standards developed by ETSI are standards accepted in many countries for digital cellular systems. GSM standards have been developed in three phases. Phase 1 standards are devoted to the introduction of GSM services. Phase 2 covers enhancements for Phase 1. The next phase, known as Phase 2+, includes enhancements such as voice coding and improved data transmission services.

9.4.1 GSM Architecture

The GSM system architecture is shown in Figure 9-2. We will discuss the GSM architecture (Reference 9.10) as it is relevant to network management.

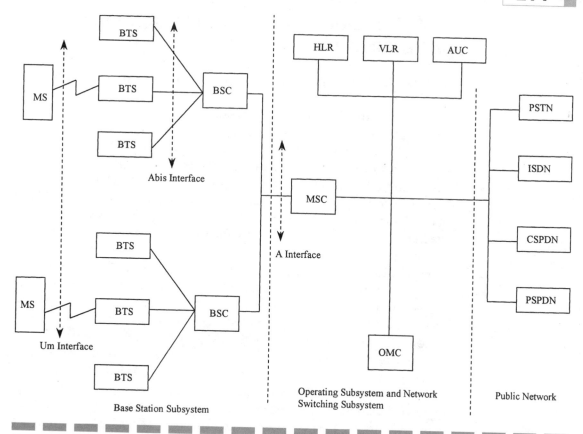

Figure 9-2

GSM architecture (© 1997 IEEE).

There are basically three interfaces: the air interface (Um), Abis, and A, as shown in Figure 9-2. A base station subsystem (BSS) includes a base transceiver station (BTS) and a base station controller (BSC). The BTS handles radio interfaces with mobile stations (MSs), and the BSC manages the handovers and radio resources. As can be seen from the figure, a BSC can manage one or more BTSs.

A mobile switching center (MSC) is responsible for communication with other networks such as public switched telephone networks (PSTNs), ISDNs, circuit-switched public data networks (CSPDNs), and packet-switched public data networks. There are three databases, namely home location register (HLR), visitor location register (VLR), and authentication center (AUC).

9.4.2 Overview of Network Management of PLMN

ETSI has developed GSM 01 thru 11 series standards for implementing a public land mobile network (PLMN). Note that European Telecommunications Standard (ETS) and GSM standards are identical. As an example, GSM 12.00 (Reference 9.1) is also named ETS 300 612-1.

ETSI GSM 12 series standards cover management of PLMN components; interconnectivity of management components; and operations, administration, and maintenance (OAM). Basically, GSM 12 series standards extend the ITU-T TMN standards and ISO standards to the PLMN network management standards. We have included some ISO standards in the discussion, as some of the ISO standards do not have equivalent ITU-T standards.

As stated in Reference 9.1, "a PLMN is a telecommunications system consisting of several functional units necessary to perform mobile telecommunications services." A PLMN consists of different mobile equipment such as location registers, mobile services switching centers (MSCs), base station systems (BSSs), mobile stations (MSs), authentication center (AUCs), transcoders, transmission equipment, echo suppression equipment, and so on. As the focus of the chapter is on network management for mobile communications, we will not look into each component of PLMN. For more information on these, refer to 0 through 11 series GSM standards. The management of a PLMN includes the existing terrestrial telecommunications and the extensions to cover mobile telephony.

The scope of network management of PLMN covers integrated operation of PLMN components, inter-PLMN operation of the mobile systems, and delivery of the promised QOS. The management PLMN should also support service and business areas. Service and business areas are not included in the 12 series standards. However, they are important as they are related to management of PLMN. Services and business areas perform the following functions:

- *Administration of Subscribers:* Is concerned with connecting and disconnecting services of a subscriber, testing the services offered, and upgrading the services available to include providing additional services and new services when they become available.

- *Collection of Charges from Subscribers:* Involves efficient and accurate recording of billing amounts from subscribers and resolution of billing discrepancies.

- *Collection of Revenue from Other Operators:* Deals with issues involved in intercompany billing. It is necessary to have a precise division of revenue between companies to avoid conflicts.

- *Maximization of Revenue from Network Resources:* Has to do with optimum utilization of resources, for example, maximizing operational revenues.

- *Customer Services:* Includes services such as repair, directory assistance, billing details, assistance in using service, and others. These services can generate additional revenues and are important to keep subscribers satisfied.

9.4.3 Operation, Administration, and Maintenance (OAM)

Operation, administration, and maintenance (OAM) is different from OSI SMFAs, which we have considered in Chapter 1, Section 1.6. OAM is also not as exhaustive and complete as the TMN management services defined in M.3200. OAM components are:

- *Administration and Commercial:* Includes functions for collecting data that can be used for billing, such as management of subscribers and collection of subscriber data, mobile equipment data, and call data. These functions are initiated by an administration center (ADC). ADC control is within the TMN. These functions are further explained in GSM 12.02 (Reference 9.4) and GSM 12.05 (Reference 9.7).

- *Security:* Is based upon the responsibilities to be enforced. Subscriber access and usage of services must be permitted only to authorized persons. Similarly, security of TMN data, especially billing-related data, must be maintained. There is also a provision for security audit trails to enable any security violations to be studied in detail. The security function area is explained in GSM 12.03 (Reference 9.5).

- *Operations and Performance:* Objectives are to enable an operator to monitor performance and, if required, to permit the operator to alter the configuration to improve performance and QOS provided to subscribers. To do this, it is necessary to collect the right data at the right time for analysis and display of performance-related data. For this it may be necessary to execute traffic management commands and functions. Operations and performance-related functions are treated in GSM 12.04 (Reference 9.6) and 12.06 (Reference 9.8).

- *Change:* Related to functions that minimize the impact of changes on the integrity and stability of PLMNs. Changes include logging of data and changes in data. This function is described in GSM 12.06 (Reference 9.8).

- *Maintenance:* An important activity in delivery of the agreed-upon QOS. There are proactive and reactive maintenance activities: Proactive maintenance includes routine maintenance to detect the problems ahead; reactive maintenance is done after the fact or after the occurrence of a problem. A problem is noticed when a failure message in the form of an alarm, customer complaint, or an alert caused by thresholds is received. Maintenance is covered in GSM 12.11 (Reference 9.9).

Some of the maintenance functions are:

- *Monitor:* Includes monitoring the network for alarms or changes in operational trends. Some of the operational trends can be detected by alerts generated by crossing of thresholds.

- *Detect:* The detection of a problem includes an effective reporting mechanism. Sometimes detection of a problem can be linked to trouble ticket administration.

- *Localize:* Once a problem is reported, the cause of the failure is isolated to enable corrective action.

- *Rectify:* Deals with solving a previously reported problem.

- *Restore:* Involves making the service or services a customer was using available again after a problem is corrected.

- *Record:* Aids in recording a failure, its causes, and how the failure was rectified. This record keeping helps in solving similar problems and in analyzing problems at a later date.

9.4.4 PLMN Information Model

Modeling is an important activity in the formation of information models. Modeling provides abstract representation of the resources and the management actions that can be performed on these resources. In GSM, as in TMN, object-oriented techniques are widely used for the definition of managed object classes. GDMO and ASN.1 definitions use object-oriented principles. The inheritance hierarchy of managed object classes defined for GSM is shown in Figure 9-3. The containment hierarchy of the managed object classes defined in GSM series documents is shown in

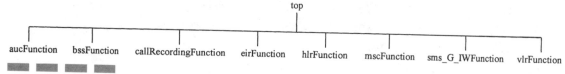

Figure 9-3

Inheritance hierarchy of GSM object classes.

Figure 9-4. In this figure, a network is imported from M.3100 and represents the identifier of the telecommunications network. plmnNetwork represents the characteristics of the PLMN. managedElement represents an NE and is the starting point for modeling GSM-specific managed object classes. In addition to the MOCs defined in the GSM series, some of the MOCs defined in M.3100 are reused during formation of the information model for GSM.

GSM 12 series standards have defined PLMN-specific managed object classes. Their short descriptions are as given below:

■ *aucFunction:* Includes all functions required to implement AUC.

■ *bssFunction:* Includes all functions required to implement network element BSS.

■ *callRecordingFunction:* Is used to model the mechanism and controls required to generate and collect data for a network usage.

■ *eirFunction:* Is used to model the equipment identity register (EIR).

■ *hlrFunction:* Represents the resource HLR.

■ *mscFunction:* Includes all functions required to implement MSC.

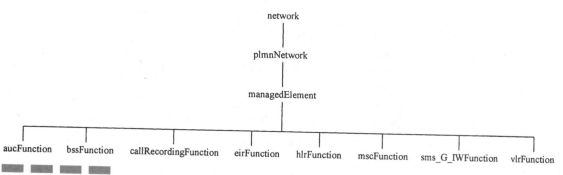

Figure 9-4

Containment hierarchy of GSM object classes.

- *sms_G_IWFunction:* Is used to model the ability of a PLMN to receive and send short messages to a short message service center.

- *vlrFunction:* Is used to model VLR.

9.4.5 Common Management Functions

Some of the management functions are generic in nature and are required by management services. These are known as common management functions. The common management functions treated in Reference 9.1 are forwarding of event reports, logging, and bulk data transfer between an OS and NE.

Managed object classes can emit notifications that are sent in the form of event reports to an OS from NEs. These notifications can be sent to the OS in a controlled manner by using the managed object class event-ForwardingDiscriminator (EFD). EFD is defined in X.734 (ISO 10164-5), Event Report Systems Management Function.

Notifications emitted by managed object classes are required to be stored locally in NEs so that they can be accessed later by the OS. The OS retrieves these logged data either in bulk or selectively. The details of logging are defined in X.735 (ISO/IEC 10164-6), Log Control Systems Management Function.

9.4.5.1 FTAM for Bulk Data Transfer.

There are cases where a large amount of data has to be transferred between an OS and an NE. When large volumes of data have to be transferred, CMIS M-GET may be one of the methods. Another method of transferring a large amount of data as a file is to use FTAM services. We discuss the use of FTAM for transfer of management information between an OS and an NE in detail, as it is an interesting alternative to CMIP for the transfer of a large amount of data in cases such as performance management and software downloading. Besides, the author has noticed, while implementing network management solutions for wireless communications, that FTAM is very useful in many cases.

As an example, performance on selected attributes can be stored every 15 minutes in files in an NE. There can be a policy to transfer four performance files every hour from NEs to the OS for analysis and reporting. Depending upon the data collected, the sizes of these files can vary from small to very large. FTAM is a suitable means to transfer these files from NEs to the OS. Similarly, when there are cases in which data is not visible at management interfaces, FTAM is a good alternative for data transfer.

GSM 12.00 (Reference 9.1) identifies the following cases of data transfer using FTAM:

■ *Data from NE to OS (requested by OS):* This scenario can be used to perform bulk transfer from NEs to the OS of log files, data files, or object instance data. This case is shown in Figure 9-5.

■ *Data from NE to OS (requested by NE):* This case can be useful in performing transfer from NEs to the OS of threshold-related bulk data or bulk data. This case is shown in Figure 9-6.

■ *Data from OS to NE (requested by OS):* This is useful when software upgrades or new software must be downloaded to an NE, or multiple managed object commands must be transferred. This case is shown in Figure 9-7.

9.4.6 Different Protocol Layers and Standards

As observed in Chapter 7, CMISE does not include services for the establishment and release of application associations. CMISE services rely on ACSE for the control and release of application associations. In the application layer, normal operation mode is used. For management protocols, we use CMISE.

File transfer capability can be used for software downloading or transfer of data files. File transfer access and management (FTAM) ASE and

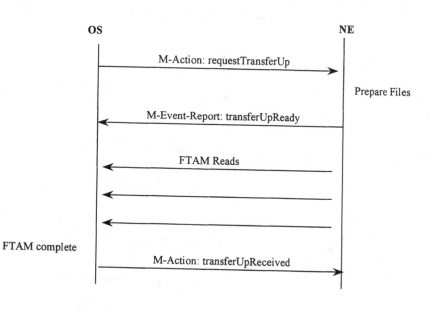

Figure 9-5
Data from NE to OS
requested by OS.

Figure 9-6
Data from NE to OS
requested by NE.

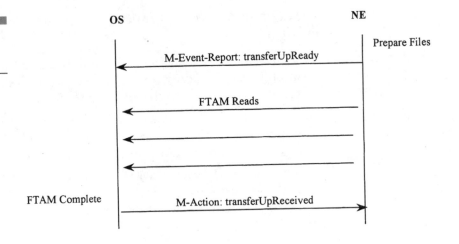

ACSE provide this capability. FTAM implementation uses ISO 8571-4, File Transfer, Access and Management—Part 4: File Protocol Specification. FTAM requires kernel, read, and grouping functional units for file transfer between manager and NE.

Each OSI layer has QOS parameters that refer to the characteristics provided by each layer between the endpoints of a connection.

For presentation services, we use presentation protocols defined in X.226 (ISO 8823), Presentation Protocol Specification for Open System Interconnection (OSI) for CCITT Applications. Here the functional units supported are based upon the session layer requirements. However, the kernel presentation functional unit implementation is a basic require-

Figure 9-7
Data from OS to NE
requested by OS.

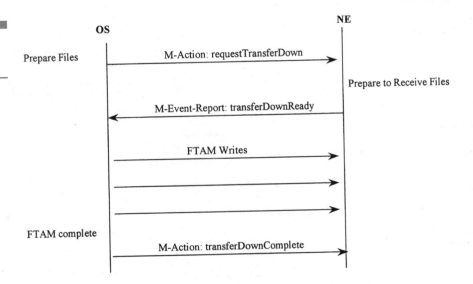

ment. ASN.1 (X.208) and BER (X.209) are used for the specification of application protocols and for transfer syntax.

For the next lower layer, the session layer, we use X.225 (ISO 8327), Session Protocol Specification for Open System Interconnection for CCITT Applications. Kernel and duplex are the required functional units. For providing recovery at this layer, the minor synchronize and resynchronize functional units are required. For simultaneous establishment of session, presentation, and application connections, version 2 of session protocol is required.

For the transport layer we use X.224 (ISO 8073), Transport Protocol Specification for Open System Interconnection for CCITT Applications. The class and options used depend upon the user requirements including QOS parameters and the network service provided. The default transport layer settings are:

■ Class 2 for SCCP for end-to-end flow control.

■ Class 2 for X.25 PSPDNs or ISDNs for multiplexing enabling and flow control (need not be used if the network provides end-to-end flow control).

■ Class 0 for X.25 PSPDNs or permanent connection or ISDNs (when multiplexing is not required).

■ Class 4 for OSI-LAN.

For the lower layers (1—3), GSM 12.01 (Reference 9.2) uses the examples of SS#7, X.25, ISDN, and OSI-LAN. This scenario is shown in Figure 9-8.

Figure 9-8
Different protocol layers for GSM network management.

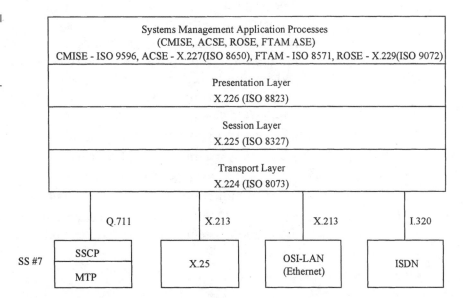

9.5 Summary

In this chapter, we have discussed network management for mobile communications, and have presented a brief overview of issues involved in the network management for mobile communications. For mobile communications, ANSI and ETSI GSM standards are widely accepted; for this reason, we have introduced the ANSI network management for PCS with related issues. As a prelude to the discussion of network management for DCS, we have briefly explained GSM architecture, in order to introduce different components of DCS systems. The chapter ends with a discussion of DCS network management details and issues.

9.6 References

9.1. ETSI, GSM 12.00 (ETS 300 612-1), European Digital Cellular Telecommunication System (Phase 2), Network Management (NM): Part 1: Objectives and Structure of Network Management, 1996.

9.2. ETSI, GSM 12.01 (ETS 300 612-2), European Digital Cellular Telecommunication System (Phase 2), Network Management (NM): Part 2: Common Aspects of GSM/DCS 1800 Network Management, 1996.

9.3. ETSI, GSM 12.07 (ETS 300 612-3), European Digital Cellular Telecommunication System (Phase 2), Network Management (NM): Part 3: Operations and Performance Management. This is a draft document at the time of publication.

9.4. ETSI, GSM 12.02 (ETS 300 613), European Digital Cellular Telecommunication System (Phase 2), Subscriber, Mobile Equipment (ME) and Services Data Administration, 1996.

9.5. ETSI, GSM 12.03 (ETS 300 614), European Digital Cellular Telecommunication System (Phase 2), Security Management, 1996.

9.6. ETSI, GSM 12.04 (ETS 300 615), European Digital Cellular Telecommunication System (Phase 2), Performance Data Measurements, 1996.

9.7. ETSI, GSM 12.05 (ETS 300 616) (2nd ed.), European Digital Cellular Telecommunication System (Phase 2), Event and Call Data, 1998.

9.8. ETSI, GSM 12.06 (ETS 300 617), European Digital Cellular Telecommunication System (Phase 2), GSM Network Configuration Management, 1996.

9.9. ETSI, GSM 12.1 V4.2.0 (ETS 301 251), European Digital Cellular Telecommunication System (Phase 2), Fault Management of the Base Station System (BSS). Draft, 1998.

9.10. Cai, J. and D. J. Goodman, "General Packet Radio Service in GSM," *IEEE Communications Magazine*, vol. 35, no. 10, pp. 122–131, 1997.

9.11. ANSI T1-244-1995, American National Standard for Telecommunications—Operations, Administration, and Provisioning (OAM&P) Interface Standards for Personal Communication Services, 1995.

9.12. T1-TR34 *Technical Report: Network Capabilities, Architectures and Interfaces for Personal Communications.*

9.13. ANSI T1-651-1996, American National Standard for Telecommunications—Mobility Management Application Protocol (MMAP), 1996.

9.14. ANSI T1-651a-1996, American National Standard for Telecommunications—Mobility Management Application Protocol (MMAP)—Extensions, 1996.

9.1.5. Yemini, Y. and G. Moss, "Managing Mobile Networks: From Cellular Systems to Satellite Networks," *The Telecommunications Network Management, Technologies and Implementations*, Aidarous, S. and Plevyak, T. (eds.), New York: The Institute of Electrical and Electronics Engineers, pp. 176–196, 1998.

9.7 Further Reading

Garg, V. K., "Management of Personal Communications Services (PCS) Networks," *The Telecommunications Network Management, Technologies and Implementations*, Aidarous, S. and Plevyak, T. (eds.), New York: The Institute of Electrical and Electronics Engineers, pp. 150–175, 1998.

Rauhala, K., *Baseline Text for Wireless ATM Specifications*, Wireless ATM Working Group, 1997.

ITU-T Recommendation M.3020, TMN Interface Methodology, 1995.

CHAPTER 10

Broadband Network Management

10.1 Introduction

In this chapter, we briefly introduce the basic concepts involved in broad-band communications as a starting point to discuss broadband network management. We primarily discuss network management for SDH and asynchronous transfer mode (ATM). Network management topics include the ITU-T recommendations and the ATM Forum. As Internet MIBs are popular, we also explain IETF SONET/SDH MIB and ATM MIB. As SONET and SDH are very similar, we do not include much discussion on SONET network management.

The topic of broadband network management covers a vast area and includes plenty of published material. Consult the references at the end of the chapter for detailed information.

There are different interpretations of the term *broadband*. Broadband uses the broadband-integrated services digital network (B-ISDN) architecture and integrates SONET/SDH and ATM into the B-ISDN architecture. Broadband networks use fiber coaxial cable and intelligent network elements. In comparison to broadband communications, narrowband communications uses copper wires and carries voice communications. POTS is an example of narrowband communications.

10.2 B-ISDN Protocol Reference Model

As B-ISDN forms the basis for broadband communications, it is necessary to briefly introduce the basic concepts. ITU-T Recommendation I-321 (Reference 10.1) explains the B-ISDN protocol reference model (PRM). B-ISDN architecture (Figure 10-1) forms the basis for technologies used in broadband communications, such as ATM, SDH, and SONET. Different components of B-ISDN protocol reference model are the following:

- *Physical layer:* This layer is dependent upon the physical medium used. An important function of this layer is to synchronize the transmission and reception of continuous information flow in the form of bits.

- *ATM layer:* This layer is independent of the physical layer and is responsible for sending and receiving fixed-size cells between a user node and a network node. As there can be one or more logical connections between two interfaces, this layer handles multiplexing of cells from virtual connections at the originating end point and demulti-

Figure 10-1
B-ISDN protocol
reference model.

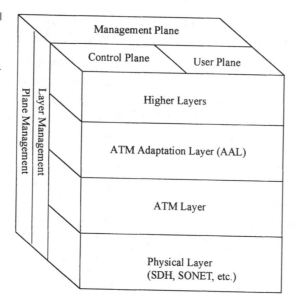

plexing of cells at the terminating end point. Virtual path identifier
(VPI) and virtual channel identifier (VCI) are used to identify a virtual
connection. VPI and VCI processing is done in this layer. Flow control
information for cell headers is also generated in this layer.

- *ATM adaptation layer (AAL):* This layer primarily transforms higher-
  layer information to fixed-size ATM cells that are suitable for the
  ATM layer when sending information. When receiving information,
  this layer transforms the fixed-size ATM cells to the format of the
  higher layers.

- *Higher layers:* These layers contain the switched virtual circuit (SVC)
  signaling protocol, CMIP, SNMP, FTAM protocols, and so on.

- *Control plane:* This plane's functions manage call control, network
  connection setup, and network connection release. The control plane
  is required for SVCs and is not required for permanent virtual circuits (PVCs).

- *User plane:* This plane controls user information transfer, including
  flow control and error recovery.

- *Management plane:* This plane consists of layer management and
  plane management.

- *Layer management:* This concerns the management of resources and
  parameters in entities and the operation and maintenance (OAM)
  operations of each of the ATM protocol reference model layers.

- *Plane management:*   This covers the overall management of a system and coordinates management between different planes.

The B-ISDN physical layer may include SONET or SDH. SONET provides protocols for the optical transmission interface. The SONET interface was originally developed by Bellcore and subsequently was standardized by ANSI. SONET hierarchy specifies digital data rates of multiples of 51.84 mbps, with that being the lowest rate. SONET is widely used in North America.

ITU-T has developed synchronous digital hierarchy (SDH) standards that are compatible with SONET for the high-speed transmission of data over optical fiber. The lowest data rate for SDH is 155.52 mbps. SDH is popular in Europe. ITU-T recommends the use of ATM with SDH in the physical layer. SONET can also be used in the physical layer instead of SDH.

We have provided a brief overview of B-ISDN and SDH. There are many good reference books for those who are interested in B-ISDN and SDH (References 10.19, 10.20, and 10.21).

10.3 SDH Network Management

It is very important to know the terms used in SDH before we jump into the discussion of SDH management. This will make it easier for readers to understand and appreciate SDH network management. We therefore briefly introduce the ITU-T Recommendations, which explain the important terminology used in SDH.

ITU-T Recommendation G.805 (Reference 10.5) broadly splits a telecommunications network into a transport functional group and a control functional group. The *transport functional group* transfers telecommunications information from one point to another. The *control functional group* is responsible for performing ancillary services, operations, and maintenance functions.

ITU-T Recommendation G.805 provides the generic functional architecture for transport networks. The functional architecture divides telecommunications networks into functional layers and reference points between layers. The adjacent layers are described in terms of client/server relationships. ITU-T Recommendation G.803 (Reference 10.4) has the specific functional architecture for transport networks based on SDH. Refer to these recommendations for details on the SDH terms used in the following discussion.

ITU-T Recommendation G.831 (Reference 10.6) describes the requirements and processes involved in the management of SDH networks. SDH management permits the management of transmission networks and the fabric supporting them. A *fabric* is responsible for establishing and releasing cross-connections and is represented as a fabric MOC in M.3100. Some of the important SDH management requirements are the following:

- Set up, maintain at assured performance levels, and continuously monitor paths between all client access points, across all domains, and across network operator boundaries.

- Identify and restore failed branches. Should also be able to inform external network operators or domain management systems about problems.

- Perform simple remote maintenance actions on equipment supported by NEs.

- Identify significant network points, such as access points.

- Set up, validate, and monitor trails. Once a path or section has been set up, it should be validated to determine whether the access points are correct. The path or section should be continuously monitored to ensure that the transmission integrity does not cross a predetermined threshold. If the transmission integrity falls below the threshold, it is treated as a defect. If there is a defect, the path or section has to be restored to the original transmission integrity.

SDH management is described in detail in ITU-T Recommendation G.784 (Reference 10.7). SDH management architecture uses distributed network management principles. Each network management tier provides some network management capabilities. The lowest tier includes SDH NEs, which provide transport services. An NE has an MAF and an MCF. As we have seen in Chapter 2, the MCF is the vehicle for exchanging management information between peers. The MAF can have agent roles only, manager roles only, or both manager and agent roles. Managers in the MAF manage other NEs and communicate with SDH OS/MD. The SDH management hierarchy also includes SDH MD and SDH OS.

For easy management, SDH management is functionally partitioned into the SDH management network (SMN) and the SDH management subnetwork (SMS), as shown in Figure 10-2. SMN includes a subset of TMN functions and is responsible for managing SDH NEs. As can be seen in Figure 10-2, an SMN includes more than one SMS.

For communications between SDH NEs (Figure 10-3), an embedded control channel (ECC) provides a logical operations channel between SDH NEs. The ECC utilizes a data communications channel (DCC) as the physical layer. There are two DCC channels, with speeds of 192 and 576 kbps. SDH NEs can access the lower-speed channel. The high-speed channel

Figure 10-2
Relationship between
TMN, SMN, and SMS.

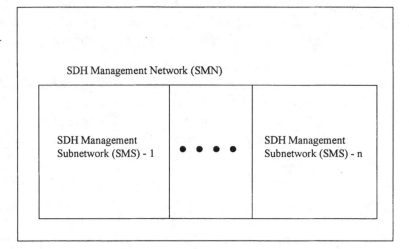

Telecommunication Management Network (TMN)

SDH Management Network (SMN)

SDH Management
Subnetwork (SMS) - 1

• • • •

SDH Management
Subnetwork (SMS) - n

(576 kbps) can be used to support communication between the OS and NEs and between the OS and other OSs.

Each SMS must have at least one gateway network element (GNE) (Figure 10-3) connected to an OS/MD. The GNE acts as an intermediate system, providing network layer routing for ECC messages to end systems in the SMS. Some of the salient points of a SMS are the following:

- A single site may have multiple NEs.
- All NEs must act as end systems.
- Some NEs may be required to perform functions of intermediate systems. This means that ECC messages have to be routed according to the routing control information in the NEs.
- NEs may be required to support Q and F interfaces.
- SDH NEs can communicate using an ECC or via a local communications network (LCN). The LCN is suggested as an alternative to the use of an ECC. The LCN can also be used for communication between SDH NEs and non-SDH NEs (NNEs).

An SDH NE is connected to other components of TMN as shown in Figure 10-3. The different possibilities of NE connections to other components are as follows:

- Workstation using an F interface
- Mediation device using a Q interface,

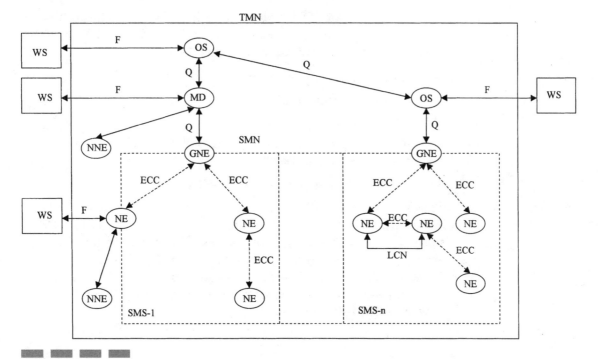

Figure 10-3
SMN, SMS, NE and interfaces.

- Operations system with a Q interface
- Non-SDH NE (NNE) or site-related information

    SDH NEs need to manage the ECC. Some of the ECC management functions are as follows:

- Retrieval of network parameters such as packet size, time outs, quality of service, window size, and so on
- Management of network addresses
- Retrieval of operational status of the DCC at a node
- Enabling and disabling of access to a DCC
- Message routing between DCC nodes

10.3.1 Fault Management

Some of the fault management functions, such as testing and external events, have not been defined. However, alarm surveillance and alarm history management for SDH have been defined. We have already looked into the alarm surveillance function in detail in Chapter 3. The alarm-related functions supported are the following:

■ Autonomous reporting of alarms

■ Request for reporting of all alarms

■ Reporting of all alarms

■ Control of alarm reporting, which permits suppression of some alarms and reporting of selected alarms

■ Reporting on the status of alarm reporting

ITU-T Recommendation G.784 (Reference 10.7) furnishes details of SDH-specific parameters for which alarm conditions are reported. Alarm history management describes how alarms are stored for future reference. Alarms are recorded in registers with relevant parameters. The OS retrieves these alarms periodically or on demand. The OS controls how the alarms can be stored in registers. A register can either wrap around or stop when the register is full.

10.3.2 Performance Management

Performance management includes performance data collection. Recommendation G.784 includes SDH-specific performance parameters on which data are collected. The strategy of data collection and storage is quite important. Performance data must be available for analysis at a later stage to pinpoint and locate sources of faults.

The performance data is stored in registers in NEs. Each performance event is stored in a register. Note that the registers can be files. The performance data can be collected at 24-h or 15-min intervals. Data collection is done in the current registers. At the end of each data collection period, the data are time stamped and transferred to recent registers. After the transfer of data from the current registers to the recent registers, the current registers are reset to zero.

The 15-minute time interval can be selected when you want to monitor the performance events very closely. Here, at least 16 registers are selected. The current data is transferred to the recent register at the end of each 15-min interval. When the stack of registers is full, the oldest information is discarded. OSs retrieve the performance data at regular time intervals or on demand, based on the need to analyze the performance data.

The OS also controls the threshold settings on SDH parameters. When thresholds are crossed, notifications are sent from the NEs to the OS.

10.3.2.1 Configuration Management. The configuration management for SDH is not fully defined. A very important part of configuration management—namely provisioning—has not been defined. The installation function is also not defined. However, the status and control functions have been defined. The following operations are defined for status and control:

- Operate and release manual protection switching.
- Operate and release force protection switching.
- Operate and release lockout.
- Request and set automatic protection switching (APS) parameters. APS features enable the alternate optical lines to take over when the normal optical lines or interfaces fail.

ITU-T Recommendation I.751 (Reference 10.3) describes the ATM NE management. This recommendation also includes the SDH management functions. The following SDH management functions have been identified:

- *Transport management:* This includes the management of transmission media layers and lower- and higher-path layers. Fault management and configuration management of transport-related layers also have to be done.
- *Connection management:* This covers the configuration and fault management of higher- and lower-order connections and subnetwork connection protections.
- *Synchronization:* This covers the configuration and fault management of timing reference points.
- *Performance management:* This covers monitoring performance parameters such as gauges and counters associated with SDH layer networks and protection switch events.
- *Overhead management:* This includes the fault and configuration management of SDH overhead fields.

10.3.3 SDH Managed Object Classes

ITU-T Recommendation G.774 (Reference 10.8) describes the information model for the SDH NEs. SDH-specific managed object classes are subclassed from the MOCs at the termination point fragment defined in M.3100. If the trail termination and adaptation functions are combined in one class, then this combination is represented as a trail termination point class. If the functions are separate, then adaptation functions are represented by a connection termination point class and the trail termination functions are denoted by a trail termination point class (Reference 10.17). For managing connections, the connection point is represented as a cross-connection class. Classes required for testing, filtering, scoping, and logging are used from the MOCs defined in the X.700 series documents.

Refer to Recommendation G.774 for more information on SDH-specific MOCs.

10.3.4 SDH Management Protocol Stack

SDH management information related to OAM&P messages is transmitted using the protocol stack specific to SDH. In the physical layer, SDH DCC is used. For the data link layer, link access protocol on D channel (LAPD) is used. The data link layer should support both the unacknowledged and acknowledged information transfer services. Acknowledged information transfer service is the default mode of operation. The network layer protocol conforms to the network services specification in Q811 for the lower-layer profiles of the Q3 interface. The transport, sessions, and applications layers support the specifications laid out in Q812 for the upper-layer profiles of the Q3 interface. Application layer options such as CMISE, ROSE, and ACSE are also used.

10.4 SONET Network Management

We begin the discussion of SONET network management with a brief overview of SONET. In this section we cover the IETF SONET/SDH MIB. As SONET network management is similar to SDH network management, we cover it only briefly.

10.4.1 Overview of SONET Architecture

SONET architecture has four layers, as shown in Figure 10-4. ATM layers—the virtual path and virtual channel layers—operate on the top of the SONET layers. The SONET layers are the following:

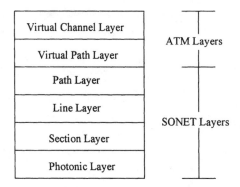

Figure 10-4

Relationship between
SONET and ATM
layers.

- *Photonic layer:* This is the physical layer. It includes specifications for the optical fiber to be used, details such as the dispersion characteristics of the transmitter, and the sensitivity of the receivers to be used to receive transmitted lasers.

- *Section layer:* This layer creates SONET frames and converts electronic signals to photonic signals.

- *Line layer:* This layer performs functions such as synchronization, multiplexing of data to SONET frames, switching, and so on.

- *Path layer:* This layer performs end-to-end transport of data.

Work on implementing interoperable SONET products and services based on open industry and international standards is currently being done by the SONET Interoperability Forum (SIF). The SIF is a nonprofit consortium of equipment vendors, service providers, and end users. Refer to the SIF Web pages for more details on the SIF documents.

Note that the SONET TMN architecture (Reference 10.16) is only a draft document. File transfer is included in the SONET TMN architecture. FTAM-based file transfer facilitates software downloads and remote backup management. The file transfer function is further broken down to the file transfer initiator function (FTIF) and file transfer responder function (FTRF) blocks. The roles of the FTIF and FTRF are similar to those of the directory server agent (DSA) and directory user agent (DUA). Here, the FTIF and FTRF are part of the OSF and the FTIF is within the NEF. Also, additional reference points have been added to include the FTIF and FTRF function blocks.

10.4.1.1 SONET/SDH MIB. SONET/SDH managed objects are defined in RFC 1595 (Reference 10.11). As can be seen in Figure 10-5, sonetMIB is derived from the transmission object. The primary SONET/SDH objects

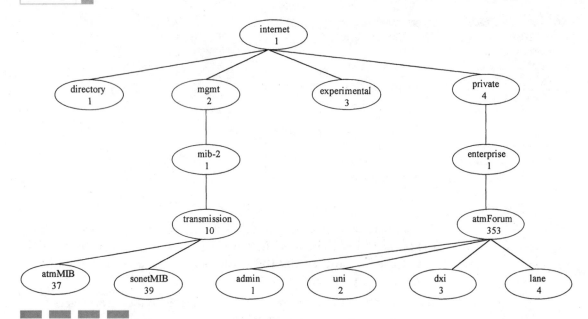

Figure 10-5
SONET/SDH and ATM MIB registration hierarchy.

are sonetObjects, sonetObjectsPath, sonetObjectVT, and sonetConformance (Figure 10-6). The main object groups in the SONET/SDH MIB are the following:

■ *sonetMedium:*   These objects are used to collect data on the electrical and optical configuration parameters. Data collection is done on sonetMediumLineCoding, sonetMediumLineType, and sonetMedium-CircuitIdentifier. Also, counters are maintained on the elapsed seconds and partial seconds since the start of error measurement and on the number of previous intervals for which data is stored. The minimum number of intervals is 4 and the maximum number of intervals is 96. The default value is 32. The time interval is 15 min. Data is collected on the following parameters:

   • *sonetMediumLineCoding:*   This includes measurement on the line coding for the SONET/SDH interface. The interface type—whether it is a SONET or SDH interface—is given by sonetMediumType. SONET interface has a value of one and SDH interface has a value of two.

   • *sonetMediumLineType:*   This refers to the line type of this interface. The line types are single mode or multimode fiber, or coaxial and UTP for electrical interfaces. Those line types that do not belong to any of these interfaces are included in the sonetOther value.

Figure 10-6
SONET/SDH MIB
(RFC 1595).

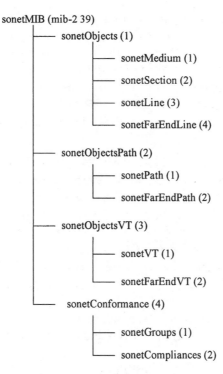

- *sonetMediumCircuitIdentifier:*   This indicates the transmission vendor's circuit identifier.

■ *sonetSection:*   These objects contain data on the SONET/SDH section layer. sonetSection includes the SONET/SDH current table and interval tables. The measurements given here for the sonet current entry table refer to the current 15-min interval. Their explanations are as follows:

  - *sonetSectionCurrentStatus:*   This indicates the status of the SONET/SDH interface. Current status represents the cumulative value of defects. sonetSectionDefect has a value of 1, sonetSection-LOS has a value of 2, and sonetSectionLOF has a value of 4. LOS means loss of signal defect and LOF means loss of frame defect.

  - *sonetSectionCurrentESs:*   This is a counter that refers to the number of errored seconds.

  - *sonetSectionSESs:*   This indicates the number of severely errored seconds.

  - *sonetSectionCurrentSEFs:*   This refers to the number of severely errored framing seconds.

  sonetSectionIntervalTable includes measurements taken during previous 15-min intervals. The table can have previous data from 4 to a maximum of 96 completed intervals. The default number of intervals is 32. The parameters of this table are as follows:

- *sonetSectionIntervalNumber:* This is an integer from 1 to 96.
- *sonetSectionIntervalESs:* This indicates the number of errored seconds.
- *sonetSectionIntervalSESs:* This indicates the number of severely errored seconds.
- *sonetSectionIntervalSEFs:* This indicates the severely errored framing seconds.
- *sonetSectionIntervalCVs:* This counts the coding violations.

■ *sonetLine:* This is similar to the sonetSection. The data for the SONET line layer are collected here. It also contains a current table and an interval table. The measurements are done in 15-min intervals. The parameters included in the sonetLineCurrentTable are as follows:

- *sonetLineCurrentStatus:* This is a sum of all the defects in the line.
- *sonetLineCurrentESs:* This indicates the number of errored seconds.
- *sonetLineCurrentSESs:* This indicates the number of severely errored seconds.
- *sonetLineCurrentCVs:* This indicates the number of coding violations.
- *sonetLineCurrentUASs:* This refers to the number of unavailable seconds.

sonetLineIntervalTable includes the previous 15-min intervals for which measurements are available. The parameters of the sonet-LineIntervalEntry are sonetLineIntervalNumber, sonetIntervalESs, sonetLineIntervalSESs, sonetLineIntervalCVs, and sonetLineInterval-UASs. As the explanations of these terms are similar to those in the sonetLineCurrentEntry, we will not repeat them here.

■ *sonetFarEndLine:* This is valid only for far-end block error at the SONET/SDH line layer. sonetFarEndLine includes current and interval tables. The parameters used in the current and interval tables are similar to those used in sonetLineCurrentEntry and sonetLineIntervalTable.

■ *sonetPath:* This also has current and interval tables. These tables contain measurements on the SONET/SDH path layers. The values are for 15-min intervals. The parameters included in the current entry table are as follows:

- *sonetPathCurrentWidth:* This indicates the type of SONET/SDH path. For SONET the values of N are 1, 3, 12, 24, and 48. For SDH the values are 1, 4, and 16.
- *sonetPathCurrentStatus:* This is the sum of the defects in the interface.
- *sonetPathCurrentESs:* This indicates the number of errored seconds.
- *sonetPathCurrentSESs:* This includes measurements on the severely errored seconds.

- *sonetPathCurrentCVs:* This contains measurements on coding violations.
- *sonetPathCurrentUASs:* This indicates the number of unavailable seconds.

Sonet interval table parameters are similar to the current table parameters, and they include the values taken in the previous 15-min intervals.

■ *sonetFarEndPath:* This is similar to sonetFarEndLine. It is valid for far-end block error code. sonetFarEndPath has also current and interval tables.

■ *sonetVT:* This includes statistics on virtual tributaries for SONET and virtual channels for SDH. There are also current and interval tables. Statistics on errored seconds, severely errored seconds, code violations, and unavailable seconds are included.

■ *sonetFarEndVT:* This includes statistics collected for the far-end block error code. There are also current and interval tables for statistics.

■ *sonetConformance:* This includes sonetGroups and sonetCompliances groups. These groups are collections of objects that include information on SONET/SDH virtual tributaries, section, line, and path interfaces, and far-end information where applicable. This information is used as a benchmark for checking whether the SONET/SDH interfaces meet the requirements.

The managed objects defined in RFC 1595 can be used by SNMP protocols.

10.5 Operation and Maintenance (OAM)

Before we look into the OAM aspects of the ATM layer and the physical layer, it is essential to introduce the commonly used concepts of *virtual channel connection* (VCC) and *virtual path connection* (VPC). A VCC is a connection that forms a path between two end points. The VCC is the result of the concatenation of virtual channel links (VCLs) and this concatenation occurs at an ATM switch, as shown in Figure 10-7. The VCC is used for information transfer between user to user, user to network, and network to network. A virtual channel identifier (VCI) is unique across a VC link and identifies a VC link. Just like VCCs, VPCs are formed over virtual path links (VPLs). A virtual path identifier (VPI) identifies a VP link.

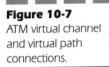

Figure 10-7
ATM virtual channel
and virtual path
connections.

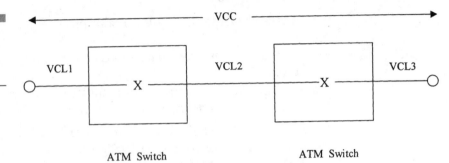

Virtual Channel Links and Virtual Channel Connection

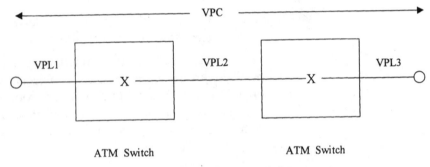

Virtual Path Links and Virtual Path Connection

ITU-T Recommendation I.610 (Reference 10.2) describes the operation and maintenance (OAM) functions at the physical and ATM layers. OAM functions are performed at five hierarchical levels, namely F1, F2, F3, F4, and F5 (Figure 10-8), and they result in corresponding bidirectional information flows. Levels F1, F2, and F3 are associated with the physical layer, and levels F4 and F5 are for ATM layer. OAM flows at the ATM and physical layers are shown in Figure 10-9. Explanations of the five information flows are as follows:

■ *F5:* Information flow extends between the NEs responsible for virtual channel connection functions. There are two types of F5 flows: *end-to-end* F5 flow is used for end-to-end VCC operations; *segment* F5 flow communicates OAM information within one VCC link or interconnected VCC links. A VCC may have one or more OAM segments. F5 is used for continuity checks on the active VCCs per interface at

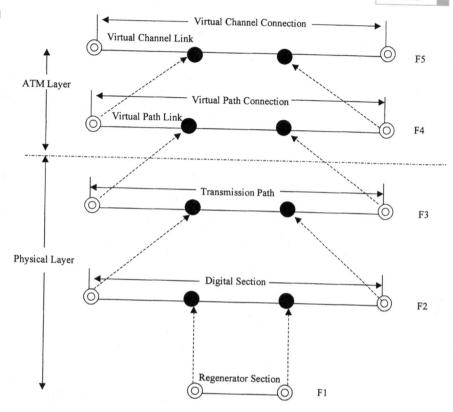

Figure 10-8

Relationship between OAM levels and ATM layers.

the end-to-end or segment level. F5 flows are also used for fault and performance management of VCCs.

- *F4:* This refers to the bidirectional information flow containing OAM cells at the virtual path level. Here also, the F4 information flow can be end-to-end or be restricted to one segment. F4 information flow can be used for fault and performance management of VPCs. F4 information flows are useful for detecting degradation of VP performance, loss or misinsertion of cells, and late-arriving cells.

- *F3:* Information flows are between the NEs that perform payload assembling and disassembling, cell delineation, and header error control (HEC) functions.

- *F2:* Information flows are between section end points.

- *F1:* Information flows are between regenerator sections. A regenerator section is a portion of a digital section.

The OAM flows depend upon the type of transmission used. As we have seen, ATM can use either SDH or SONET at the physical layer. F1, F2,

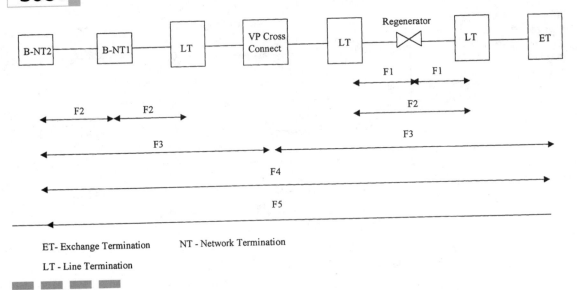

Figure 10-9
OAM flows at the physical and ATM layers.

and F3 flows help detect and report unavailability states, carry defect information on the affected end points, and help monitor and report equipment failures. These flows also aid in error monitoring and reporting at the regenerator section, multiplex section, and transmission path levels for SDH and SONET. Some of the errors reported can be loss of signal, loss of frames, degraded performance, loss of pointer or path, loss of cells, defective insertion, or suppression of cells.

Refer to Section 10.2 for more details on OAM for the physical and ATM layers.

10.6 ATM Network Management

ATM network management follows the standards developed by the ATM Forum and ITU-T. ITU-T Recommendation I.751 (Reference 10.3) describes management of the ATM NE view. In this recommendation, MOCs are grouped into ensembles for convenience and these ensembles perform certain specific management functions. ATM transport-specific ensembles are the following:

- *ATM Layer Management:* This includes configuration and fault management for transport path and virtual path adaptation, for the virtual path layer, and for the virtual channel layer. Configuration of an ATM interface, allocation of bandwidth and VPI/VCI ranges associated with ATM interfaces, and detection and reporting of alarms within the ATM layer are also part of the layer management.

■ *ATM VP/VC Connection Management:*   This covers such functions as establishing and releasing VP and VC channel connections, allocating the virtual path identifier (VPI) and virtual channel identifier (VCI) for these connections, and managing the VP and VC channel connections.

■ *ATM Performance Management:*   This covers the monitoring of performance parameters such as gauges and counters for the VP and VC layers and transport paths.

10.6.1 ATM Forum Network Management

The ATM Forum network management model is specific to ATM networks. Primarily, ATM Forum defines a set of protocol-independent requirements for management services and MIBs for managing the ATM networks. The management protocols can be either CMIP or SNMP. The ATM Forum network management reference model (Figure 10-10) is similar to the TMN physical architecture. The reference model defines network management interfaces for managing ATM devices, private networks, and public networks. The ATM forum management interfaces are as follows:

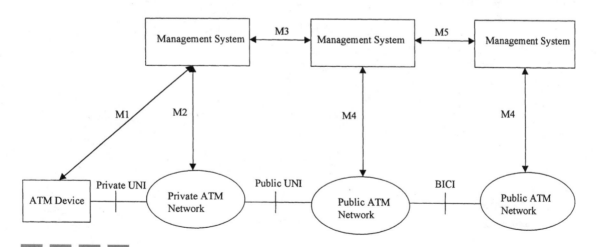

Figure 10-10
ATM Forum network management interfaces.

- *M1:* This is the interface for managing ATM terminal devices.
- *M2:* This is the interface for managing an ATM private network.
- *M3:* This is the customer network management interface. It provides management functions for the customer portion of an ATM network.
- *M4:* The OS or the managers manage individual network elements using the M4 interface. Network elements refer to ATM switches, ATM cross-connects, ATM concentrators, remote ATM switches, and distributed ATM switching systems. The M4 interface also supports element management and service management functions.
- *M5:* This is the network management interface between two network providers.

10.6.1.1 M3 Interface. The M3 interface (Figure 10-11) includes two classes of functions that users can access (Reference 10-13). Class 1 functions include monitoring configuration, fault, and performance management on the customer's portion of an ATM public network. Customer network management (CNM) must be able to retrieve the following:

- Details on the CNM agent and the protocols used for customers' user network interfaces (UNIs).
- Performance information on the ATM layers and physical layers of customers' UNIs.

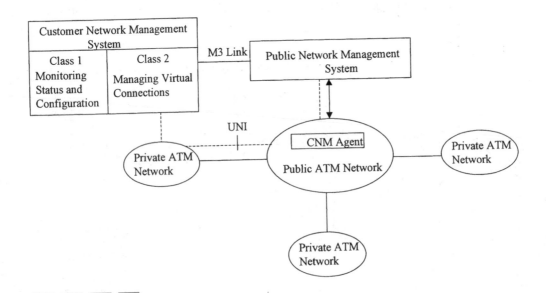

Figure 10-11
Customer network management for private and public networks.

- Information on how the ATM UNIs are configured and the status of UNIs at the cell level. This is useful for dynamically updating the configuration information.

- Configuration information at the UNI physical layer and the alarm status of the physical line.

- Configuration and status information on ATM VPLs and VCLs of customers' UNIs.

- Configuration and status information on VPCs and VCCs associated with customers' UNIs.

- Alarms and alarm-related information associated with the status of customers' UNIs.

- Descriptors associated with customers' UNIs on preconfigured traffic.

Class II functions basically perform addition, deletion, or modification of virtual connections and subscription information on an ATM public network. CNM customers must have the ability to add, delete, or modify the following:

- ATM layer configuration information
- VPL and VCL configuration and status information
- VPC and VCC configuration and status information
- ATM traffic descriptors and information objects for virtual path and virtual channel connections

Each segment of an ATM PVC network is modeled as an ATM public network. In each ATM public network, a CNM agent supports the MIB required to manage M3 interfaces. If there are many ATM PVC networks, element managers use multiple CNM agents to collect the information required for end-to-end management.

Figure 10-11 shows CNM functions as a subset of the management functions provided by the public network management system of a public network provider. The M3 link can be a dedicated link (private line), as shown in the figure. The CNM can access the public network management system using ATM UNI, as shown by dotted lines in the figure. The M3 link uses the SNMP protocol for managing class 1 and class II functions. If UNI is used, then AAL5 is used. Instead of defining new managed objects, managed objects defined in other MIBs are reused for the M3 interface. The M3 interface is fully explained in Reference 10.13.

10.6.1.2 M4 Interface. Network elements use the protocol-independent MIB for the M4 interface. Protocol-specific MIBs are developed from the protocol-independent MIBs. These protocol-specific MIBs can be used with CMIP or SNMP. The M4 interfaces specified are for PVCs. The M4 interface is fully described in Reference 10.14.

Protocol-independent MIBs are described by managed entities. Managed entities are defined by the purpose of the entity, the attributes of the entity, the managed operations performed on the entity, the notifications emitted by the entity, and the relationship with other entities. Note that there can be one or more managed entities within an ATM NE.

ATM Forum network management uses five logical layers (management) of M.3010. These layers represent functional components and are not physical systems. These functional components can be implemented in different ways. For example, functions of NML and EML can be combined into a single physical implementation.

The basic functions of SMFAs, such as configuration management, fault management, performance management, and security management, are similar in ATM. However, there are some ATM-specific requirements that need to be implemented in ATM.

We have already looked into configuration management, fault management, performance management, and security management in Chapter 3. In this section, we discuss the ATM-specific issues related to these functional areas.

10.6.1.3 Configuration Management. ATM NE configuration identification and change reporting are important for the effective management of the ATM network by the manager or OS. Information on initialization, installation, changes in the externally manageable physical and logical components of ATM NE, and the relationships between these components must be available for effective systems management. Some of the physical and logical components are circuit packs, equipment, physical path termination points, and so on. The views of these physical and logical components presented by the NEs have to be current.

To present the current configuration view, it is essential that configuration changes are automatically reported to the managing systems. Notifications of configuration changes to the operational states of managed entities are sent to the ATM NEs. The managed entities that support the configuration identification and change reporting function (defined in Reference 10.14) are ATM NE cross-connection control, ATM NE, attribute value change record, equipment, equipment holder, event forwarding discriminator, latest occurrence log, log, managed entity creation log record, managed entity deletion log record, physical path termination point, plug-in unit, software, state change record, TC adaptor, TC adaptor PM current data, and threshold data.

A managing system must be able, if required, to configure and reconfigure physical path terminations on an ATM NE as either a user network interface (UNI), a broadband interswitching system interface (BISSI), or a broadband intercarrier interface (BICI). The managing system must also be able to retrieve configuration data associated with UNI, BISSI, or BICI.

In addition to configuring ATM parameters, a managing system must be able to establish VPL-to-VPL cross-connections and VCL-to-VCL cross-connections in an ATM NE. Once VPL and VCL cross-connections are made, the managing system should be able to bring down the existing VPL and VCL cross-connections in an ATM NE and release the associated resources. The managing system must be able to retrieve the configuration data associated with the previously configured VPL and VCL termination points for analysis purposes. The configuration of VPL/VCL termination points and cross-connections must include the capability to establish and tear down multipoint VPL and VCL cross-connections in the ATM NE, and add or remove VPL and VCL termination points to and from existing multipoint cross-connections.

Managing systems must be able to configure and reconfigure active VPL and VCL termination points as either segment (Figure 10-12) or non-segment end points. However, VPC and VCC segments across UNI and

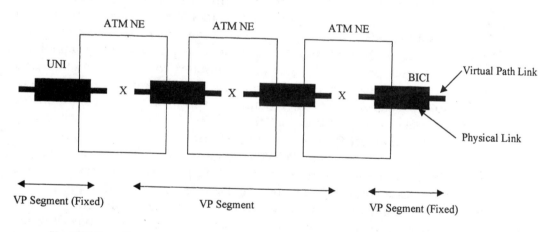

X - ATM Cross-Connect

Figure 10-12
Example of a VP segment.

BICI are automatically configured as segment end points when VPLs and VCLs are configured.

Event flow control includes the event-forwarding discriminator function in ATM NEs. NEs should be able to forward alarms, configuration updates, and threshold crossing alerts to managing systems. It should also be possible to suppress the forwarding of selected notifications. The suppression of notifications must be based on notification type, on specific details of notification type, on the type of managed entity reporting the notification, or on some specific aspects of a managed entity.

10.6.1.4 Fault Management. ATM NEs must be able to send notifications of detected failures to an OS via the M4 interface. A managing system must be able to retrieve the alarm notifications log from an ATM NE. A managing system must also be able to perform loopback testing on VPC/VCC operations, administration, and maintenance cells. The results of the loopback tests are returned as pass or fail.

10.6.1.5 Performance Management. ATM-specific performance management consists of monitoring performance, managing traffic, monitoring user parameter control (UPC) or network parameter control (NPC) disagreement, and collecting performance management control and network data.

ATM performance monitoring consists of monitoring physical layer performance and cell level protocol. Physical layer performance monitoring must support ITU-T Recommendation G.774.01 (Reference 10.9) and ANSI T1.231 (Reference 10.10) for monitoring SDH transport performance.

Cell level protocol monitoring must be supported by the M4 interface. Cell level performance monitoring involves collecting threshold data counts to detect protocol abnormalities at the transmission convergence sublayer and the ATM layer. Managing systems must be able to retrieve the detailed log information stored in ATM NEs to detect, statistically analyze, and rectify cell-processing defects.

Two scenarios affect VPC/VCC performance. In one case, cells may be discarded due to transmission errors and problems in the network. In the other case, incoming cells may be discarded because incoming cells do not conform to the prenegotiated cell specifications. Managing systems must be able to distinguish between these two scenarios while collecting data on cell abnormalities.

10.6.1.6 Security Management. Security management includes verifying a session requester's unique user identifiers. There must be a record of the user identifiers requested by session requesters that can be used to detect any security violations. Authentication involves verifying whether a session requester's user identifiers are authorized.

Security management also involves ensuring that only authorized users access resources in ATM NEs. To maintain data and system integrity, data and resources in ATM NEs must be created, modified, and deleted by authorized users. There must be a security audit record of all the security-related activities performed that can be used to detect and recover from intrusions and disruptions. Security administration develops and maintains these security-related aspects in the ATM NEs.

10.6.1.7 Integrated Local Management Interface.

Integrated local management interface (ILMI) was supposed to be an interim solution when it was published. However, it has continued as a permanent one. ILMI (Reference 10.15) furnishes a link-specific view of the configuration of an ATM interface and status and control information about its physical and ATM layer parameters. Here, an ATM device such as a switch or an end system supports one or more ATM interfaces. Each ATM interface includes a set of managed objects and ATM interface ILMI attributes for achieving ILMI functions.

An interface management entity (IME) is associated with each ATM interface in an ATM device, as shown in Figure 10-13. The ATM end system has one interface, so there is one IME. The private ATM switch has two IMEs as there are two ATM interfaces. Either SNMP or AAL5 protocol is used between IMEs. An IME can access ATM interface MIB information associated with an adjacent IME. Each IME contains an SNMP agent and a management application. Adjacent IMEs must include the same MIB. SNMP for ILMI does not use UDP and IP addressing. For ILMI, SNMP uses a well-known VPI/VCI value.

ILMI MIB has the following characteristics:

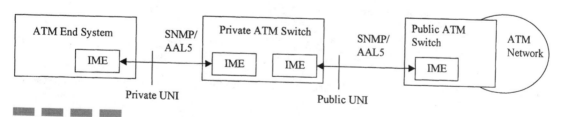

Figure 10-13
Integrated local management interface.

- *Textual conventions MIB:* This includes common textual conventions and object identifiers. These definitions are included in a single module such that other MIB modules can import the definitions. Some of the definitions are borrowed from other RFCs, and some object identifiers have been defined exclusively for the ATM interface.

- *Link management MIB:* This includes descriptions of the objects, procedures on how these objects can be used, and the actual definitions of the objects required for link management of ATM interfaces.

- *Address registration MIB:* This is used for address registration at the UNI. Address registration procedures include capabilities such as dynamic addition/deletion of additional network prefixes and user parts, and deregistration of addresses with the loss of ILMI connectivity.

- *Service registry MIB:* includes a service registry. This registry is useful for locating ATM network services.

ATM interface MIB groups for ILMI are shown in Figure 10-14. The details of MIB object groups are as follows:

- *Physical layer group:* This provides details of the physical interface over a physical link or the virtual interface over a virtual link.

- *ATM layer:* This includes objects for the ATM layer.

- *Virtual path connection:* This contains objects that provide details on the VPC, such as VPI value, VPC status, and QOS parameters at the VPC local end point.

- *Virtual channel connection:* This includes objects that provide details on the VCC, such as VCI and VPI values, VCC status, and QOS parameters at the VCC local end point, just like VPC. When ILMI communication takes place over a physical link, the VPI and VCI values identify a VCC. However, when ILMI communication is done using a virtual link, the VPI value is set to zero.

- *Network prefix:* This permits switches to automatically configure network prefixes in end systems.

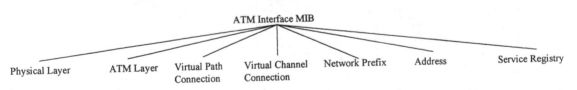

Figure 10-14
ATM ILMI MIB groups.

- *Address:* This mechanism permits end systems to automatically configure the ATM address for ATM interfaces on switches.

- *Service registry:* This is provided to locate network services.

Customers can use ILMI to retrieve UNI-related information. For this, ILMI must be part of UNI and customer access must be done through ILMI.

Figure 10-14 explains how network management functions such as discovery for configuration, fault isolation, and troubleshooting can be done. A network management system can request data from RFC 1695 MIB, as shown in the firm lines for MIB data on ATM device B. If management data is required from ATM device A, the proxy relays the SNMP commands via the IME in ATM device B, and traps to and from the IME in ATM device A.

10.6.1.8 ATM MIB. ATM uses different types of MIBs at different interfaces. Internet ATM MIB, defined in RFC 1695 (Reference 10.12), is used between switches. ILMI MIB is used at the UNI interface. ATM MIB is primarily used to manage permanent virtual circuits (PVCs). Additional objects are required to manage SVCs. ATM MIB can be used with the SNMP protocol.

In addition to the managed objects defined in RFC 1695, managed objects such as those defined in RFC 1213 (MIB-II), RFC 1407 [managed objects for digital signal 3 (DS3)/E3 interface], RFC 1595 (SONET MIB),

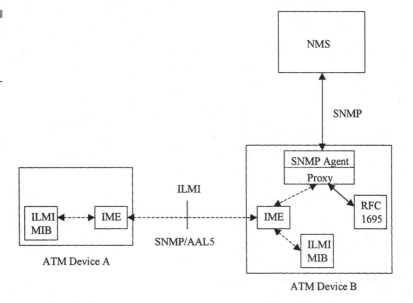

Figure 10-15
ATM network
management, SNMP,
and ILMI.

and RFC 1694 (SMDS) may also be required. The Main object groups of ATM MIB are shown in Figure 10-16. Explanations of the main ATM MIB object groups are as follows:

■ *Configuration group:* This consists of objects for ATM cell layer configuration and local ATM interfaces, which are not supported by the ifTable. Managed objects supported in this group provide the following details:

- Maximum number of VPCs and VCCs supported at the ATM interface
- Number of VPCs and VCCs configured at this interface
- Maximum number of active VPI and VCI bits
- VPI and VCI values supporting the ILMI at the ATM interface
- The type of ATM address at the ATM interface, such as native, private, E.164 or other
- IP address and textual name of the neighbor to which a NMS can send SNMP messages

■ *DS3 physical layer convergence protocol (PLCP) group:* This provides for the configuration and state parameters of the DS3 PLCP sublayer. DS3 PLCP is used to carry ATM cells over DS3 transmission paths. Some of the details available from this group are the following:

- Number of severely errored framing seconds.
- Indication of whether there is an alarm for DS3 PLCP. The conditions for alarm are an incoming yellow signal and an incoming loss of frame.

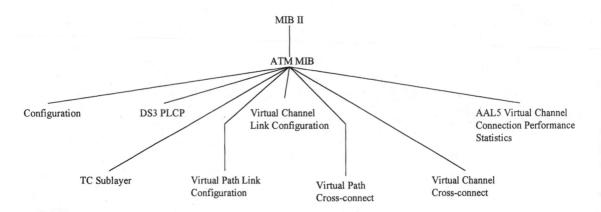

Figure 10-16
ATM MIB object groups (RFC 1695).

■ *Transmission convergence (TC) sublayer group:* This provides objects for configuration and state parameters for the TC sublayer. The TC sublayer is used to carry ATM cells over SONET or DS3. Some of the details that can be gathered from the objects in the group are the following:
  • The number of times that out-of-cell delineation events occur.
  • Indication of whether an alarm condition is present for the TC sublayer. The alarm condition is available for loss of cell delineation; otherwise, there is no alarm condition.

■ *VPL configuration group:* This contains information on the configuration and state information of a VPL. The objects in this group can also be used to create, delete, or modify a VPL that terminates in an ATM host or switch or that is cross-connected to another VPL. ATM VPL is implemented in an ATM host, ATM switch, and ATM network. VPL traffic parameters are manipulated by setting the ATM receive and transmit traffic descriptor indices in VPL tables. The receive and transmit traffic descriptor indices are associated with receive and transmit VPLs (Figure 10-17). There are many objects defined in this group that can be used to control the functioning of a VPL.

■ *VCL configuration group:* This contains information on the configuration and state of a VCL at an ATM interface. Managed objects defined for this group can also be used to create, delete, or modify a VCL that terminates in an ATM host and ATM switch or that is cross-connected to another VCL.

■ *VP cross-connect group:* This contains information on the configuration and state of VP cross-connects. The cross-connects can be point-to-point, point-to-multipoint, or multipoint-to-multipoint. A cross-connect index identifies the VPLs that are cross-connected to each other. The managed objects in this group can also be used to create, retire, and reconfigure VP cross-connects.

■ *VC cross-connect group:* This contains information on the configuration and state of point-to-point, point-to-multipoint, or multipoint-to-multipoint VC cross-connects. VC cross-connect managed objects are functionally similar to VP cross-connect group managed objects.

Figure 10-17
VPL Bidirectional
traffic flows.

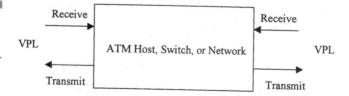

■ *AAL5 VCC performance group:*   There are two parts associated with the performance management of AAL5. In one part, if Table is used to collect performance statistics on an AAL5 entity in a switch or a host (Figure 10-18). In the other part, managed objects defined in the AAL5 VCC performance group are used to gather AAL5 performance statistics per VCC. The VCC interface with an AAL5 entity in an ATM switch is done via a proprietary virtual interface, as shown in Figure 10-18. The managed objects in the AAL5 VCC performance group contain the VPI and VCI values of the AAL5 VCC identified by the ifIndex interface. The objects defined in this group can also be used to make available a number of Cyclic Redundancy Check (CRC)-32 errors, partially reassembled AAL5 PDUs, and AAL5 PDUs discarded due to large size.

Figure 10-18
Managing AAL5 in a
switch and a host.

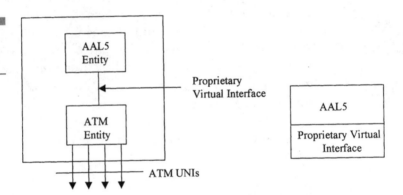

AAL5 Entity in a Switch

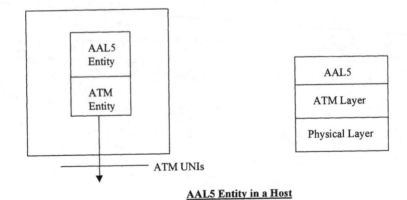

AAL5 Entity in a Host

10.7 Important Issues in Broadband Network Management

Broadband network management is currently limited to the management of PVCs, and there is a broad consensus on managing PVCs. However, the same cannot be said for the management of SVCs. Additional modeling effort is required to manage SVCs to extract signaling information from ATM VCs, the analysis and routing of calls, and the administration of customers' numbers and services. These issues are treated in detail in Reference 10.17.

We have specifically discussed network management approaches that are covered by ITU-T and the ATM Forum, and we have also included the IETF MIBs for SONET/SDH and ATM. In addition, organizations such as ETSI, TINA-C, ANSI, and SIF are also actively involved in different aspects of broadband network management, and OMG is involved in different aspects of distributed network management. ITU-T has also defined an open distributed management architecture for distributed network management. TMN models are mostly static, covering limited regions and centralized network management; these static models must be integrated in a distributed manner to cover the different management protocols and transport technologies of global telecommunications network management. We will examine distributed network management in detail in Chapter 11.

Integrating broadband and distributed network management is one of the most important challenges in implementing broadband network management solutions. The issues involved are highlighted in Reference 10.18. For a good, sound design, designers should be well aware of the issues involved with different broadband network management architectures and the impact of distributed network management on the implementation of broadband network management.

10.8 Summary

The chapter begins with a brief overview of the B-ISDN reference model. We also introduce some of the important concepts and terms associated with ATM, SONET, and SDH, and we examine the network management of SONET and SDH. As the ATM Forum has made significant contributions to ATM implementation and network management, we describe ATM Forum network management in detail. We also discuss the Internet MIBs defined for SONET and ATM, and briefly highlight some of the important issues involved in broadband network management.

10.9 References

10.1. ITU-T Recommendation I.321, B-ISDN Protocol Reference Model and Its Application, 1991.

10.2. ITU-T Recommendation I.610, B-ISDN Operation and Maintenance Principles and Functions, 1995.

10.3. ITU-T Recommendation I.751, Asynchronous Transfer Mode Management of the Network Element View, 1996.

10.4. ITU-T Recommendation G.803, Architectures of Transport Networks Based on the Synchronous Digital Hierarchy (SDH), 1993.

10.5. ITU-T Recommendation G.805, Generic Functional Architecture of Transport Networks, 1995.

10.6. ITU-T Recommendation G.831, Management Capabilities of Transport Networks Based on the Synchronous Digital Hierarchy (SDH), 1996.

10.7. ITU-T Recommendation G.784, Synchronous Digital Hierarchy (SDH) Management, 1994.

10.8. ITU-T Recommendation G.774, Synchronous Digital Hierarchy (SDH) Management Information Model for the Network Element View, 1992.

10.9. ITU-T Recommendation G.774.01, Synchronous Digital Hierarchy (SDH) Performance Monitoring for the Network Element View, 1994.

10.10. ANSI T1.231, *Layer 1 In-Service Digital Transmission Performance Monitoring*, New York: American National Standards Institute, 1993.

10.11. Brown, T., and Tesink, K., Definitions of Managed Objects for the SONET/SDH Interface Types, RFC 1595, 1994.

10.12. Ahmed, M., and Tesink, K., Definitions of Managed Objects for ATM Management Version 8.0 using SMIv2, RFC 1695, 1994.

10.13. ATM Forum, Customer Network Management (CNM) for ATM Public Network Service (M3 Specification), 1994.

10.14. ATM Forum, M4 Interface Requirements and Logical MIB, 1994.

10.15. ATM Forum, Integrated Local Management Interface (ILMI) Specification Version 4.0, 1996.

10.16. SIF Architecture Group, SIF SONET TMN Architecture E-OS and NE, 1994.

10.17. Gillespie, A., Broadband Management after Permanent Connections, *IEEE Communications*, vol. 35, no. 10, pp. 54—59, 1997.

10.18. Manley, A., and C. Thomas, Evolution of TMN Network Object Models for Broadband Management, *IEEE Communications*, vol. 35, no. 10, pp. 60—65, 1997.

10.19. Black, U., *ATM Foundation for Broadband Networks*, Englewood Cliffs, N.J.: Prentice Hall, 1995.

10.20. Stallings, W., *ISDN and Broadband ISDN with Frame Relay and ATM* (3d ed.), Englewood Cliffs, N.J.: Prentice Hall, 1995.

10.21. Kumar, B., *Broadband Communications* (signature ed.), New York: McGraw-Hill, 1998.

11

Recent Trends: Distributed Network Management, CORBA, Java, Web, and TMN

11.1 Introduction

Telecommunications and computer networks are expanding in size and complexity because of the liberalization and globalization of the telecommunications industry. At the same time, new services are being offered by the telecommunications industry. These add to the complexity of the telecommunications networks. To reliably manage these complex networks, the TMN workload and functionality required have also increased manyfold. One of the means of coping with the increased workload is partitioning the TMN workload and functions into smaller, manageable subsets. Here distributed network management comes into the picture.

For distributing the TMN functions, ITU-T and ISO are working on open distributed management architecture (ODMA). At the same time, common object request broker architecture (CORBA) is getting increased acceptance as a means to distribute the TMN workload.

In addition to the impact of CORBA on TMN, Java (Sun Microsystems) has contributed significantly in the TMN arena as a platform-independent simple programming language. Java has impacted the ways in which TMN services are provided on different platforms.

Similarly, recent advances in Web technology have made their impact on TMN. Web technology is yet another technology that is available for managing TMN functions. Also, some of the Web technologies help the users of TMN by facilitating easy customer interfaces and service provisioning.

When we have many useful technologies impacting TMN, it is also important that these new technologies be integrated in a meaningful and useful manner to provide the maximum advantages. From this perspective, we will study different technologies in this chapter. As it is not our intent to dwell on each one, only a brief overview of each technology is presented. The focus is primarily on how these technologies can be used in TMN. Therefore, those who are interested in learning more about these technologies should refer to the references at the end of the chapter.

11.2 Distributed Processing

Distributed processing forms the basis for distributed network management. Therefore we will introduce the topic of distributed processing and subsequently examine distributed network management architecture and issues. Some of the important distributed processing architectures are:

- *RM-ODP:*   The details of the reference model for open distributed processing (RM-ODP) are furnished in ITU-T Recommendations X.901 through X-904. RM-ODP includes the concepts and characteristics of distributed systems such as different levels of abstraction, modeling approach, and distributed-processing-related transparencies. Implementation details are not included in these documents.

- *CORBA:*   This is an architecture for distributed computing published by OMG. OMG is devoted to promoting the object-oriented theory and practice for software development. OMG publishes industry guidelines and object management specifications for application development.

- *COM/DCOM:*   Component Object Model (COM) and Distributed Component Object Model (DCOM) are the components of Microsoft's distributed computing architecture. While COM is used for interprocess communication within a system, DCOM is used for communication between clients and servers in different processes across an intranet or Internet.

- *SOM/DSOM:*   System Object Model (SOM) and Distributed System Object Model (DSOM) are the components of IBM's distributed computing architecture. SOM and DSOM functions are similar to those of COM/DCOM.

11.3 Open Distributed Processing

Of the above prominent architectures, we will limit ourselves to the RM-ODP and CORBA. ITU-T and ISO are working on standardization for open distributed processing (ODP). The ODP standards consist of the following ITU-T recommendations:

- *X.901 (Reference 11.6):*   Explains the overview of ODP and contains details on key concepts, the outline of ODP architecture, and how ODP is to be interpreted and applied.

- *X.902 (Reference 11.7):*   Defines the concepts and framework for distributed processing systems.

- *X.903 (Reference 11.8):*   Referred to as the architecture document; contains specifications for open distributed processing.

- *X.904 (Reference 11.9):*   Contains interpretations of concepts using formal description techniques.

Distributed processing systems are required to solve the problems of scalability of single architecture systems, heterogeneous computing environments, and legacy systems. Though there are many requirements of distributed processing systems, we will look into only some of them. The important requirements of distributed systems are:

■ *Distribution transparency:* The details and problems and differences due to the distribution of functionality and workload in different components of a distributed system must not be visible to the users. Also, the implementation details of combining heterogeneous components must be hidden.

■ *Security:* As the systems are remote and data are distributed in many systems, these systems must be protected against unauthorized access and users.

■ *Fault tolerance:* When the distributed systems are large and complex, the possibility exists of some component failing. Failure of one or more components should not affect the operation of the other components of the distributed system.

■ *Federation:* It should be possible to coordinate the activities of various components in the distributed systems belonging to different administrative and technical domains.

■ *Modularity:* The different components of the distributed systems have to be autonomous and, at the same time, must be able to be coordinated to work in a cooperative manner.

Standardization of distributed processing has four stages: system specification in terms of object modeling, interrelation of system specifications to viewpoint specifications, system infrastructure definition using relevant distribution transparency categories, and establishment of a framework for distributed system conformance.

Object modeling has to cover all the resources in the distributed systems and must apply to all viewpoints, provide tools for the requirements and design of specification languages, and address structuring issues in the distributed systems.

To simplify and categorize the specifications of a whole system, different abstraction levels have been identified; these abstractions are known as viewpoints. The viewpoints considered are:

■ *Enterprise:* Focuses on the purpose, scope, and policies of a system within an organization and its environment.

■ *Information:* Relates to the semantics of information handled by a distributed system, the constraints on the information, and the interpretation of the information.

- *Computation:* Covers the functional decomposition of a distributed system resource into a set of objects that interact with interfaces.

- *Engineering:* Deals with the infrastructure required to support interaction between objects of distributed systems.

- *Technology:* Covers implementation details such as design methodology, programming languages and details, details on databases, and so forth.

As we have seen, distribution transparency (hiding the implementation of distributed systems from the users of the systems) is an important requirement. Note that it is not necessary to implement all the distribution transparency categories given below. The following distribution transparencies have been defined in ITU-T Recommendation X.901:

- *Access transparency:* Enables distributed components to work together irrespective of differences in architectures, data representation, and programming languages.

- *Failure transparency:* Is required to hide failure and recovery of other objects and itself. Necessary for providing a fault-tolerant distributed system.

- *Location transparency:* Specifies that location of an object in a distributed system is not important during interaction with other objects.

- *Migration transparency:* States that even if an object has moved, the distributed system will not be affected.

- *Persistence transparency:* Ensures that activation and deactivation of an object do not impede the sharing of resources.

- *Relocation transparency:* Provides availability of the interfaces associated with an object despite changing location.

- *Replication transparency:* Allows an object to be replicated while still maintaining a single interface.

- *Transaction transparency:* Is required to coordinate transactions involved in scheduling, monitoring, and recovery of multiple objects to maintain data consistency.

When a distributed system is built with different components, with the possibility of some of the components being procured from vendors, it is necessary to establish well-set rules governing the behaviors of each of the components of a distributed system. These rules have to be elaborately laid out with reference to the different viewpoints. The rules also must be covered in conformance specifications and must later be validated by conformance testing.

To construct distributed systems, a set of ODP functions has been defined. These ODP functions are divided into the following groups:

- *Management function:* Consists of node, object, cluster, and capsule management functions. A *node management function* controls the processing, storage, and communication functions within a node. An *object management function* provides for the checkpointing and deletion of an object. A *cluster* is a combination of engineering objects for the purposes of deactivation, checkpointing, reactivation, recovery, and migration. A *cluster manager* manages basic engineering objects in a cluster. A *capsule* is a combination of objects for the purpose of encapsulation of processing and storage; a *capsule manager* manages the engineering objects in a capsule. Capsule managers and cluster managers provide the cluster management functions.

- *Coordination function:* Consists of event notification, checkpoint and recovery, deactivation and recovery, group, replication, migration, transaction, and engineering interface reference tracking functions. Here the group function coordinates interactions of objects in a multiparty binding.

- *Repository function:* Includes storage, information organization, relocation, type repository, and storage functions. A *trading function* supports importation of service offers by service users or clients and exportation of service offers by service providers or servers.

- *Security function:* Consists of access control, security audit, authentication, integrity, confidentiality, nonrepudiation, and key management functions.

We have only included basic concepts of ODP here; for more details, consult References 11.6, 11.7, 11.8, and 11.9.

11.4 Distributed Network Management

Earlier, centralized network management systems were the norm. Network management systems on mainframes were used to control the network management functions. These systems present a scalability problem when the NEs or agents to be managed grow in numbers. This increase in workload leads to performance bottlenecks. In addition to the increased workload, the network management functions performed were relatively simple, such as detection of warning conditions, and many problem modifications were done manually. However, these scenarios are changing with the ever increasing demands from the network management systems, increasing intelligence in NEs, and, sometimes, a need to solve the problems in a nearly real-time environment.

To alleviate some of these problems, distributed network management is gaining popularity. The trend is also toward Windows NT—based server solutions on Intel processors. This reduces the cost and permits the growth of network management systems by adding more and more computing systems. Distributed network management permits the incremental growth of network management systems, enabling legacy systems to coexist with new network management systems. There are also other advantages to distributed network management, such as load balancing and better reliability through redundancy.

Distributed network management solutions come with a price and are rather complex because of the various technological issues involved. Some of the important issues to be addressed are: how to handle security of EMs and NEs in different domains, time synchronization, distribution transparency, data integrity, appropriate distribution of workload between EMs and NEs, coordination between EMs, management of failures and failure policies, and so on. The adoption of distributed systems architecture to network management has been studied in detail by the Telecommunications Information Networking Architecture Consortium (TINA-C), OMG, ITU, and ETSI.

11.5 Open Distributed Management Architecture (ODMA)

ODMA is outlined in X.703 (Reference 11.5). ODMA provides the architecture for distributed network management as well as management of open distributed applications and distributed resources. It uses the principles of RM-ODP and extends them to the OSI systems management. The ODMA document describes the enterprise, information, computational, and engineering viewpoints.

Open distributed management includes support for management of resources, coordination of distributed management activities, management of systems of different sizes and complexities, distribution transparencies, portability of management applications, modularity of different components used, seamless integration with legacy systems, and access transparency to support different communication protocols.

No specific notational technique is suggested for explaining enterprise viewpoint specifications. An enterprise specification should describe the relationship between objects with respect to the managing and managed roles.

The information viewpoint contains invariant, static, and dynamic schema. An *invariant schema* contains relationships between information objects; these relationships are always valid. A *static schema* refers to the assertions that are true at a given point in time. A *dynamic schema* includes the assertions that are applicable when a system operates. Object Modeling Technique (OMT), developed by Rumbaugh, is used for describing the information viewpoint.

The computational viewpoint is described using GDMO and GRM. A computational management template specification consists of computational interfaces, a behavior specification, and an environment contract specification. There are three types of computational management interfaces: management-operation, notification, and linked replies interfaces. Interface signatures definitions may be done either using interface definition language (IDL) or TMN CMIS services.

The engineering viewpoint includes functionality of objects that support distribution transparencies. While the computational viewpoint focuses on when and why objects interact, the engineering viewpoint is concerned with how the objects interact. The engineering viewpoint also includes how communications protocols are used between objects.

Some specific functions have been defined for distributed management. They are:

- *Operation dispatching function:*   Controls the binding of management operation client interface and management operation server interfaces. It also aids in adjusting to the dynamic changes in management operation server interfaces.

- *Notification dispatching function:*   Facilitates binding between notification server interfaces and notification clients.

- *Policy enforcing function:*   Ensures that management policies are enforced and that any violations of management policies are reported to the appropriate components.

We have introduced the basic concepts involved in ODMA. For more details on ODMA, refer to Reference 11.5.

11.6 CORBA

It is important to note that CORBA is a distributed computing architecture. CORBA is being slowly accepted as a solution for distributing the TMN workload among different element managers. It can also be used to distribute TMN workload in the network element management layer, service management layer, and business management layers as well. CORBA can be used in the following scenarios:

■ *Functional distribution:* CORBA can be used when one network element wishes to distribute the workload to one or more element managers. As an example, alarm monitoring can be done in one element manager and performance management can be done in another element manager. In this case, the agent receives management-related commands and transmits responses and M-EVENT-REPORTs related to alarm monitoring to one element manager. The same agent, however, receives management-related commands and transmits responses and M-EVENT-REPORTs related to performance management to another element manager.

■ *Geographical distribution:* When the number of network elements reporting to an element manager increases, the performance of the EM application is affected. One solution is to partition the workload of an EM by adding another EM. This can be based on the geographical distribution. As an example, all the network elements in the United States can report to one EM in the US, and all the network elements in Japan can report to another EM in Japan. This concept of TMN workload based on geographical distribution is similar to that of domains and subdomains.

11.6.1 Overview of CORBA Architecture

The latest CORBA document is The Common Object Request Broker: Architecture and Revision 2.2, dated February 1998 (Reference 11.10). Figure 11-1 illustrates the basic CORBA architecture. As per CORBA architecture, there are four primary components that interact with each other using a communication bus. These primary CORBA components are:

■ *Application objects:* Are not standardized by OMG; these are products developed by vendor groups and do not use standard interfaces. Application objects use the other CORBA services.

Figure 11-1
Basic CORBA
architecture.

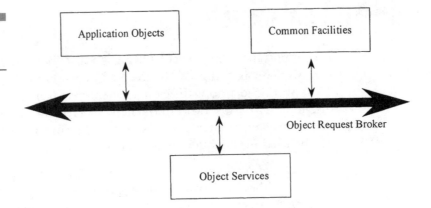

- *Common facilities:* Contain high-level application services and do not provide basic services such as object services. Some of the examples of the common facilities are: telecommunications, finance, healthcare, network/systems management, graphical user interfaces, and business-related objects.
- *Object services:* Provide the important services required for CORBA and are used by common facilities and application objects. Object services are responsible for providing basic services that can be independently used by applications, for example naming service, trading service, concurrency, persistency, security, event service, transaction services, and others.
- *Object request broker (ORB):* Is the communication bus used by CORBA applications in a distributed environment. It also enables communication and interoperability between applications in different environments.

For communication between CORBA applications, general interface ORB protocol (GIOP) is used. GIOP is a connection-oriented transport protocol that defines seven message formats that cover all the ORB request and reply semantics. Internet inter-ORB protocol (IIOP) specifies how GIOP messages are exchanged over TCP/IP connections. IIOP is positioned in TCP/IP stack as shown in Figure 11-2. IIOP has become a standard protocol for linking objects across a TCP/IP network.

11.6.2 CORBA Services

CORBA architecture provides many additional services that enhance the functionality of CORBA.

■■ ■■ ■■ ■

Figure 11-2
IIOP relationship to
TCP/IP.

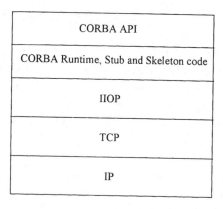

| CORBA API |
| CORBA Runtime, Stub and Skeleton code |
| IIOP |
| TCP |
| IP |

The CORBA implementations require a naming service. The CORBA objects are registered in the naming service. The naming service takes the name of an object and returns the object reference in the server. CORBA implementations have naming service implementations. However, if the number of objects is large, this creates a large load on the naming service. Partitioning the naming service or using a multitiered lookup strategy are some of the solutions to this problem (Reference 11.3).

CORBA has a flexible event service. An event service primarily consists of one or more consumers, suppliers, and an *event channel* (the transmission medium between consumers and suppliers). The supplier places the message to be transmitted to a consumer on the event channel. Depending upon whether the channel operates under a push or a pull model, the message is pushed to the consumer or the consumer retrieves the message from the event channel. The event service is very useful for forwarding notifications and alarms to element managers.

The life cycle service provides services to create, delete, move, and copy objects. It controls the life cycle of an object.

The CORBA trader service accepts and stores service offers from servers. A client requests information from the trader service and receives the information requested from trader service if it is available.

The CORBA level 1 security service provides authentication, authorization, encryption, delegation, auditing, and logging. CORBA level 1 security over DCE/Kerberos is also provided by some vendors. Similarly, security over the socket layer and IIOP are also being worked out. With these security implementations, security, which can be a major issue in a distributed environment, is no longer an issue in CORBA.

For more details on CORBA services, consult Reference 11.11.

11.6.3 How CORBA Applications Work

Many vendors have CORBA implementations. Some of these are: Orbix (IONA Technologies), PowerBroker (ExperSoft), VisiBroker (VisiGenic), and others. CORBA object classes are defined using interface definition language (IDL). An IDL interface definition defines a CORBA object class. A CORBA interface definition specifies the services provided by the CORBA object class, the exceptions that can be generated by that class, and the attributes of that class.

The services provided by and the exceptions generated by a CORBA object class are furnished by the *operation declarations*. An operation declaration contains input parameters, output parameters, the operation type, and the exceptions that can be raised. While mapping IDL to C++, each operation is mapped to a C++ member function. An IDL attribute has information on the state of an object, and the attribute declaration states whether the attribute value can be set to one or more values, whether the attribute value or values can be retrieved, or whether both operations can be performed. Here also, while mapping IDL to C++, each attribute is mapped to a set of C++ member functions. IDL compilers do this IDL to C++ mapping.

As the focus of the chapter is on CORBA and TMN, we will not look further into IDL. For more information on IDL, refer to one of the many books on the subject.

The applications written using IDL must be compiled using an IDL compiler. The IDL compiler produces the mappings to C++, Java, Smalltalk, or C. The results of IDL compilation are client and server stubs. The client and server codes, along with the client and server stubs, are normally implemented as libraries (Figure 11-3).

CORBA needs an activation component to start the server. The activation component forms the initial connection between a client and server. Usually, a client requests a connection with the server. The server contains the executable code, which an ORB can activate to create a server process. The server code has to populate initial objects and transfer control to ORB to receive incoming calls from one or more clients.

CORBA uses an implementation repository and an interface repository. The implementation repository contains information on where the server executables reside. The activation component queries the implementation repository to look for the server and gets back the address of the server. The interface repository is involved in run time type checking.

One IDL interface is required for client-managed applications, and another for server applications.

Figure 11-3
Building a CORBA
application.

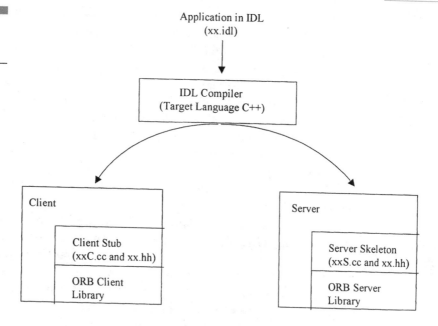

11.6.4 CORBA-based TMN

TMN is well established in the telecommunications arena. It includes four standard components: distributed management functions, layered TMN architecture, communication protocol (CMIP), and information models using GDMO/ASN.1. The primary focus of CORBA is in distributed computing environments. CORBA is appealing for TMN implementations as a solution to some of the scalability problems in TMN. Also, pure TMN solutions require a large investment of money and development effort. CORBA, however, requires less development effort and expense. As a result, there is an ongoing effort in the telecommunications industry to implement TMN architecture using CORBA.

Both TMN and CORBA attempt interoperability at syntactical and semantic levels, but the approaches are slightly different. TMN provides communication interoperability. CORBA targets interoperability at the application process level and heterogeneous programming environments, providing the flexibility to decompose system components with standard interfaces. The ability to decompose systems facilitates easy integration in heterogeneous programming environments and legacy systems.

To implement the TMN architecture with CORBA, the basic CORBA services would need to provide standard management functions used in TMN. IIOP can be used instead of CMIP. However, the generic nature of

CORBA services does not allow for powerful domain-specific systems management function support as specified by TMN standards. There is a good discussion on OSI and CORBA in Reference 11.13.

CORBA standards for TMN are being looked into by industry consortiums such as TeleManagement Forum and OMG. In an attempt to preserve the great value of the TMN information model, Joint Inter-Domain Management (JIDM) of TeleManagement Forum is developing formal translation from GDMO/ASN.1 models into IDL and vice versa. However, as with other standard body activities, there is a good deal of politics involved in preparing these standards. The practical and political considerations are going to decide some of the issues of how CORBA will penetrate TMN arena.

There are some fundamental differences between CORBA and TMN (Reference 11.12). In TMN, message transfer between an EM and NEs is asynchronous. In the case of CORBA, the member operation between a client and a server is synchronous. A member operation has one result. However, in the case of CMIS M-GET, there can be multiple replies. Also, in the case of CORBA event service, there is no confirmation of a delivery from a supplier to a consumer. However, the notifications in TMN carried in an M-EVENT-REPORT can be confirmed or nonconfirmed.

There are also some differences between CORBA and TMN in the information model. In TMN an object is identified by object identifiers. In TMN, containment hierarchy provides the relationship between object classes and can be used for uniquely naming an object. Also, scoping and filtering can be used to perform operations on object instances on a selective basis. In the OMG model, an object cannot be identified by object reference, as there can be one or more references to the same object. As a result, the notion of object identity is weak in the OMG model. In TMN, object classes can have conditional packages. This facilitates object instances of a class to have different properties. This feature is not available in interface definitions in IDL.

ASN.1 has more complex data types than CORBA, such as tag values, subrange types, and compound types. But IDL allows only primitive type constants such as boolean, integer, floating point, character, and string. As a result, in mapping GDMO/ASN.1 to IDL, some information can be lost.

Many TMN applications using CORBA are available. CORBA is useful for service management layer applications. Some of the service management applications that can use CORBA are service order entry, provisioning, and billing. There are some CORBA-based applications in the areas of fault and performance management as well. Some of the motivations for using CORBA in TMN are:

- In TMN, resources, including networks and equipment of different types, are defined using GDMO/ASN.1. The information models used in TMN use the object-oriented design and implementation concepts. CORBA IDL supports the concepts of managed object classes and managed objects. In CORBA, IDL can accommodate information models in TMN by mapping of GDMO/ASN.1 data types to CORBA data types.

- It is necessary to distribute the TMN workload among different element managers. These element managers may be in different workstations. As an example, alarm summary and alarm history may be displayed on one workstation, while the traffic management—related data may be on another manager on another workstation. Figure 11-4 shows this type of architecture.

Figure 11-4

Example of CORBA and TMN integration.

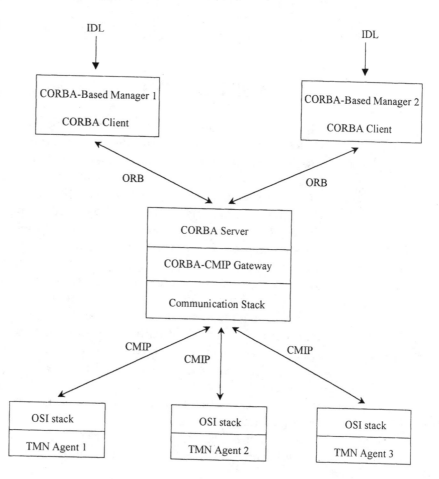

- CMIP requires the BER encoding and decoding to transfer CMIP commands and replies. This key paradigm is available in IDL without the encoding and decoding requirements of GDMO.

- Simple mappings from IDL to C++ and other languages are available. This also makes IDL attractive as a means to define the resources and integrate them with existing management applications without rewriting.

- CORBA services such as naming, event service, transactions, security, trading, and so on, are being continuously added to the already existing CORBA implementations. These additional services make it easy for developers and implementers to concentrate on building new applications and to extend the existing CORBA-based applications.

- The ability to dynamically discover objects at run time using a dynamic invocation interface (DII) provides for the separation of management applications and the underlying technology.

11.6.5 TMN and CORBA Integration

There are different approaches to organizing managers and agents in CORBA clients and servers. In one approach, the manager code libraries reside in clients' workstations or desktops. These agent workstations or desktops need to have OSI seven-layer stacks. In the workstation, which has a CORBA server, we have the server code, the CORBA-CMIP gateway, and the communication stack. The CORBA-CMIP gateway primarily converts the CORBA member operations to CMIP commands downstream and converts responses from the CMIP commands back to CORBA member operations. The communication stack consists of the OSI seven-layer protocol stack with ACSE to provide the association establishment and release between the server and the agent. This scenario is shown in Figure 11-4.

With this approach, it is possible for one or more managers to exchange management information with one or more agents. As an example, TMN agent 1, TMN agent 2, and TMN agent 3 may send fault management data to CORBA-based manager 1. On the other hand, TMN agent 1, TMN agent 2, and TMN agent 3 may send performance management data to CORBA-based manager 2. This is an example of functional distribution of management information.

Instead of the preceding scenario, TMN agent 1 and TMN agent 2 may be responsible for collecting management information in a particular geographical region. These data may be consolidated in CORBA-based manager 1. Similarly, TMN agent 3 may refer to another geographical region. The management information of this region may be sent to CORBA-based manager 2. This distribution of management information is an example of the geographical distribution of management information.

Let us go into more detail on how the CMIP and CORBA flows work. In Figure 11-4, CORBA-based manager 1 sends the CMIP commands such as M-GET, M-SET, M-CANCEL-GET, M-CREATE, and M-DELETE using IDL member operations to the server. The server, which has a CORBA-CMIP gateway, converts the member operations to the CMIP commands. These CMIP commands will be sent to the TMN agent 1 using the communication stack in the CORBA server workstation. The responses to these CMIP commands will be sent from the TMN agent 1 to the CORBA server workstation using the communication stack in the agent. In the CORBA server workstation, CORBA-CMIP gateway converts the CMIP responses from TMN agent 1 to IDL member operations and the responses are sent to CORBA-based manager 1 as a function call.

However, notifications in the M-EVENT-REPORT come in the opposite direction of the CMIP commands such as M-CREATE, M-DELETE and others. These are sent from the TMN agents to the server, and the CORBA-CMIP gateway converts the M-EVENT-REPORT to IDL invocations, which are sent to the managers. These managers must be able to interpret the IDL methods.

Alternatively, we can use another approach to exchange management information between managers and agents (Figure 11-5). In this case, the manager is TMN based and the agents reside in CORBA clients. The communication between agents in the CORBA clients and CORBA server is done using ORB. In the CORBA server, the CORBA-CMIP gateway converts the IDL member operations and attributes to CMIP commands and transmits the management information to the TMN managers. Here also, the server needs to have an OSI communication stack and ACSE component.

The responses to the CMIP commands from the TMN-based managers or to M-EVENT-REPORTS from the CORBA-based agents are in the form of IDL member operations and are received by the CORBA server. In the CORBA server, the CORBA-CMIP gateway converts IDL member operations to CMIP-based responses or M-EVENT-REPORTS and dispatches the CMIP responses or M-EVENT-REPORTS to the TMN managers over the OSI communication stack. Reference 11.2 has an example of how OSI and CORBA framework can be integrated.

Figure 11-5
Example of CORBA
and TMN integration.

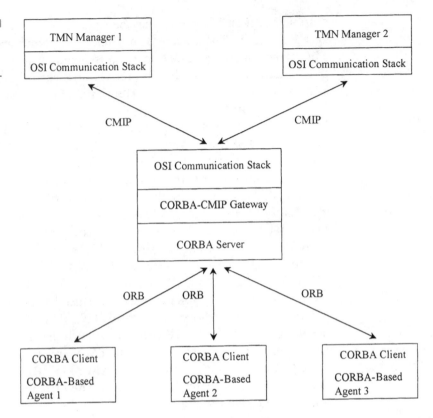

11.6.6 Joint Interdomain Management (JIDM)

Many TMN applications use CMIP as management protocol and GDMO and ASN.1 as information models. Similarly, there are a large number of NMSs and NEs that use SNMPv1 or SNMPv2 for management protocols and structure of management information (SMI)-based MIBs as information models. For distributed network management, the CORBA-based managers and CORBA-based clients use GIOP or IIOP for transport and CORBA IDLs for object class definitions.

In the telecommunications and computer industries, the trend is initially for these different protocols to coexist and interoperate because of the cost and development effort involved. After the initial coexistence stage, the general practice is to migrate network management toward stable management protocols and information models. Therefore there is a demand for CMIP, SNMP, and CORBA to be able to work together. Figure 11-6 shows how CORBA managers, OSI managers, and SNMP managers can coexist.

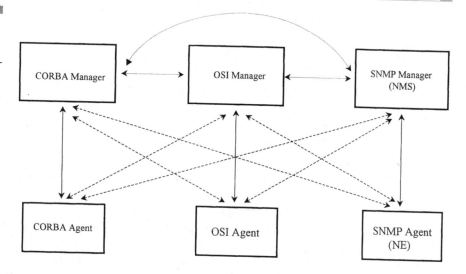

Figure 11-6
Different management domains.

Some of the issues involved in interoperation between GDMO/ASN.1 and CORBA, and between CMIP and SNMP and CORBA, are:

- The application interfaces to CORBA managers and clients are done using IDL declarations. However, in TMN, resources are defined using GDMO and ASN.1. So if management protocols using IDL are to be interpreted, then object definitions in IDL have to be translated to GDMO and ASN.1. Similarly, the applications interfacing with managers need to understand the responses and notifications from the network elements in IDL form.

- Similarly, for TCP/IP-based Internet network management, information models for the network elements are in the form of SMI-based MIBs. Thus the transfer of management information from NEs and NMSs involves the conversion of the information model from IDL to SMI-based MIBs and vice versa.

- In addition to the differences in the information models, there are differences in management protocols. In TMN, CMIP protocols are used, and in Internet network management, SNMP protocols are used. In CORBA there are no management protocols; only the transport protocols are defined. As a first step for CORBA to be used as a management protocol, CORBA needs to have management protocols.

- As can be observed from Figure 11-6, for coexistence of managers based on different management protocols, there is also a need to have CORBA management protocols for communication of management information between the CORBA managers and TMN managers or SNMP managers. Work is not being done on this issue.

Issues such as information and management protocol translations, which are required for CMIP, SNMP, and CORBA to be able to work together, have been worked out by the Joint Inter Domain Management Group (JIDM). JIDM is a joint task force of X/Open and TeleManagement Forum.

The static translation of GDMO/ASN.1 to IDL, IDL to GDMO, and SNMP SMI-based MIBs to IDL is addressed by specification translation. The algorithms for specification translation are furnished in detail in Reference 11.1. Some commercial translators are currently available to perform the specification translation.

The other major issue of interoperability is that of differences in management protocols. As an example, CORBA uses GIOP and IIOP protocols for communication between clients and servers. Note that GIOP and IIOP are generic transport protocols. In TMN, communication of management information between OSI managers and OSI agents is done using CMIP protocols. Similarly, in the case of Internet network management, network management stations and network elements use SNMP protocols for communicating management information.

Another major issue is the communication of management information between managers in CORBA, CMIP, or SNMP domains. This management information communication requires protocol translations between domains. This protocol translation is handled by the interaction translation. Some of the challenges involved in mapping between CORBA and CMIP for conveying management information are nicely highlighted in Reference 11.1.

The interaction translation can be done by a gateway. This gateway has to map between CORBA IDL and CMIP PDU and vice versa. While CMIP PDU and IDL are mapped, the GDMO identifiers have to be mapped to IDL method invocations. GDMO is case sensitive, and this aspect has to be taken into consideration too. Besides, the CMIP scoping and filtering have to be mapped to a sequence of IDL invocations and vice versa.

For coexistence between CORBA and TMN, the gateway will require the use of many CORBA services. The OSI managers and agents require AE titles or distinguished names to form associations. This will require the use of CORBA naming service. Life cycle services to create new object instances and event services for forwarding notifications are also required.

11.6.7 CORBA Implementation Notes

In software development, object-oriented design and analysis are becoming popular in TMN. OMT object modeling is one of the popular tools for developing the designs. Commercial tools are available to translate OMT object models to IDL interface definitions. After the objects are declared in IDL, IDL compilers can be used to map the IDL interfaces to C++ application stubs and skeletons.

There are many vendors with CORBA implementations. These vendors are adding new CORBA services to cater to the increasing requirements of TMN and the computer industry. So, instead of building CORBA services from scratch, it is better to use the services provided by CORBA implementations available from vendors. IONA is one of the popular CORBA vendors, and many telecommunications equipment and service providers are using IONA's Orbix.

Note that for sending notifications, event services are required. Multithreading is required for better performances, especially in cases where lengthy responses are involved. Linked replies from M-GET constitute one such example.

For many TMN applications, Windows 95/98 and Windows NT operating systems on Intel-based platforms are being selected because of the relative less cost when compared to the Unix systems. Alternatively, CORBA clients can be on Windows 95/98 and the CORBA servers on Windows NT or different Unix platforms. Similarly, many TMN applications on Windows NT are also becoming popular for managers. So the availability of CORBA applications on Windows 95/98 and Windows NT must be carefully examined when selecting CORBA vendors.

Many TMN applications use traditional relational databases and, in some cases, object-oriented databases for providing data persistence. It is very important to check whether, along with the CORBA implementations, the operating systems provide interface to the right type of databases. Also, some C++ applications use standard template libraries (STL) extensively. Along with the language used for implementations, issues such as whether C++ STL support is available also have to be considered.

The naming service is quite an important component. When a large number of objects are being used, performance has to be considered. This aspect has to be looked into when selecting CORBA vendors.

These days, many TMN applications such as fault, performance, and service management using CORBA are also available. So, depending upon the functionality required, it is better to go for applications already available in the market instead of reinventing the applications all over.

11.7 Web-based TMN

Web browsers such as Netscape Navigator and Microsoft Internet Explorer are available in most of the computer platforms. These Web browsers can be used as TMN application end user interfaces. Web applications use hypertext markup language (HTML) to display a Web page in a browser. HTML is a formatting language for creating Web pages.

Hypertext transfer protocol (HTTP) is a connection-oriented application-level protocol for transferring files to Web pages. There are many versions of HTTP. The first, referred to as HTTP/0.9, was a simple protocol for raw data transfer across the Internet. HTTP/1.0 was an improvement over HTTP/0.9 and is defined in RFC 1945. The improved version permitted Multipurpose Internet Mail Extensions (MIME)-like messages (References 11.14, 11.15, and 11.16). These MIME-like messages, in addition to the data, contain information about the data transferred and modifiers on the requests and responses. HTTP/1.1, which is a proposed standard, is yet another improvement on HTTP/1.0. HTTP/1.1 contains more stringent implementation requirements and permits hierarchical proxies, caching, persistent connections, and virtual hosts.

Most of the Internet documents go through frequent revisions, so HTTP/1.1 is not the end of the story. There will be more revisions, clarifications, and improvements. As already mentioned in Chapter 8, readers must use the latest documents before implementing any RFCs.

HTTP is basically a request/response protocol. A client or a user agent sends a request to a server over a TCP/IP connection. A client that initiates a request to a server is known as a *user agent.* The request contains the server location, protocol version, MIME-like message containing the type of request, client information, and, if required, the body content. The response from the server contains the protocol version, status of the request, and MIME-like message, which itself contains the server response, entity-related information, and entity body. The status of the request indicates whether or not the request was successful. If the request was not successful, then the status will contain an error code.

In HTTP, persistent connection is the default behavior in HTTP/1.1. The connection between a client and server is always maintained and is closed only after the closing of the TCP connection is signaled by either the client or the server. This is an improvement where a separate TCP connection is established to retrieve URL from a server. A persistent connection allows a client to make multiple requests to a server without waiting for responses.

HTTP permits access authentication whereby a server can challenge a client request and a client may be asked to provide authentication information. Digest authentication for HTTP as per RFC 2069 is also allowed (Reference 11.17).

A connection to a server from a client or user agent can be of three types, as shown in Figure 11-7. In a *proxy*, the request is rewritten and is forwarded to a server, whereas in the case of a *gateway*, the request is translated to the server's protocol and sent to the server. A proxy can be either a server or client for requests from other clients; a gateway is an intermediary server for some other servers. In the last type of connection, the *tunnel* is simply a relay mechanism that forwards the messages to the other connection.

Figure 11-7
Different HTTP
connections.

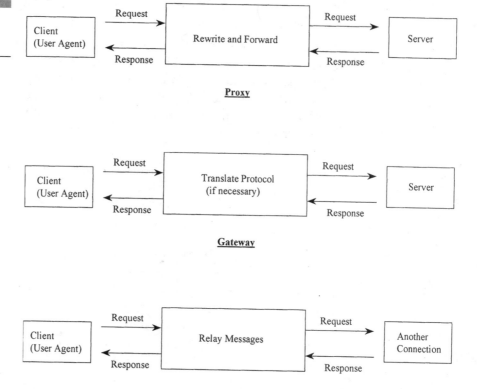

A Web browser (Figure 11-8), which is a client or a user agent, can use HTTP to request information from a Web server, which runs an HTTP daemon. A common gateway interface (CGI) reads the HTTP data, parses the data, and processes the data in the HTTP server. The CGI can be written in C, C++, Fortran, PERL, TCL, any Unix shell, or any language that can be executed on a system. Data can be transferred to a CGI process using a method. There are many methods available to a CGI. In response to a request from a Web browser, a Web server can retrieve HTML documents or any type of file. Files can be viewed in the Web browser.

One of the advantages of using Web browsers is that TMN applications can be viewed from anywhere. Also, it is easy to make changes, as it is only necessary to perform modifications or updates in the Web server once. These changes will be available to all the Web browsers connected to the Web servers.

Due to security considerations, it is not prudent to access all management information from a Web. For Web security, firewalls can be used to restrict the information to viewers. Some of the TMN applications that are suitable for viewing and performing changes from Web browsers are as follows:

- A customer must be able to access different telephone or Internet service providers using Web browsers. The customer must be able to compare the rates and types of services offered by different service providers. These services may be used while requesting a new telephone service or changing telephone service from one telephone service provider to another.

Figure 11-8
Document retrieval by Web browser.

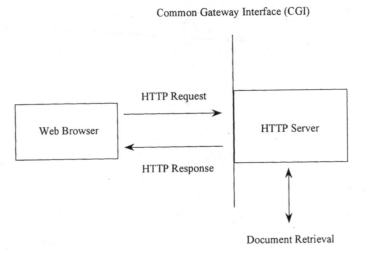

Common Gateway Interface (CGI)

- Once a customer shortlists the service providers, the customer must be able to negotiate the rates and types of services to be received.

- Once a telephone service provider is selected, the customer must be able to order telephone services or Internet services using a Web browser. The service provider checks these requirements and validates customer credit history. Here, the service provider provides the necessary security to protect vital customer data. The service provider also checks whether the required services can be provided on the due date and time and internally informs concerned departments and the customer about the customer order.

- Small individual customers must be able to view performance data from the Web browsers whenever required.

- In another scenario, the topology, fault, and performance data must be available to customers via Web browsers. These are useful for customers who have their own networks and use service providers to access other networks.

- A telephone customer must be able to change the types of services, such as number of telephone connections, line speeds, and so on, using the Web browsers.

As HTTP is a static protocol, it is not possible to dynamically refresh the Web pages in cases such as an alarm being received. This is where Java is useful. Java applets can be executed in different platforms and provide the dynamic capability required to update the network management applications dynamically.

There are many CORBA implementations that have integrated Java and the Web. IONA's OrbixWeb is one such implementation. Though there are many considerations to keep in mind when selecting vendor applications, the integration of CORBA and Java can be an important factor.

11.8 Web-based Enterprise Management

Some of the computer industry leaders, such as BMC Software, Cisco Systems, Compaq, Intel, and Microsoft, have joined hands to propose a Web-based architecture to manage varied types of systems, networks, and applications. This architecture was proposed in 1996. The result of this work is Web-Based Enterprise Management (WBEM). WBEM is a collection of technologies to manage enterprises and is touted as independent of vendor, protocol, or management standards.

A note of caution is required here. Especially in the computer industry, there is a tendency to form different groupings of vendors to produce "standards" for different technologies. Over the years, many groupings and bodies were formed, many meetings were held, and then the groups and bodies dissolved and the people in the computer industry forgot about them.

In a similar manner, leaders in the computer industry support WBEM. However, in the TMN arena, where mostly ITU-T, ANSI, and others guide the standards, computer industry—based technologies such as WBEM have limited impact and appeal. They cannot have a major impact in the telecommunications industry without the endorsement of industry service providers such as AT&T, BT, NTT, MCI, and others, and equipment manufacturers such as Lucent, NEC, Nortel, Siemens, Erricson, and others. In addition, the investments and development efforts required to implement the technologies in the telecommunications industry are quite large. Therefore, at best the solution for the TMN industry can be the coexistence of TMN and WBEM with some features of WBEM being utilized. Keeping in mind this note of caution, we will briefly look into the important aspects of WBEM.

The primary objectives of WBEM are:

■ To manage devices and applications using Web browsers

■ To support all devices and applications using existing standards and protocols

■ To unify management schemas

■ To provide for accessing of management information

Figure 11-9 shows the architecture for WBEM. The Internet browser is used to browse different management information. Between the Internet browser and the HyperMedia Object Manager (HMOM), HyperMedia Management Protocol (HMMP) is used. The HyperMedia Management Schema (HMMS) provides the management information. HyperMedia Object Manager and the devices or applications, communicate management information using management protocols such as SNMP, Desktop Management Interface (DMI), CMIP, HMMP, and others.

Let us look in some more detail into the different pieces of the puzzle. HMMP is the management protocol to access management information. HMMP is a request/response protocol. A process acting as a client sends management requests to a process acting in the role of a server. The server performs the requested task and sends a response to the client. HMMP

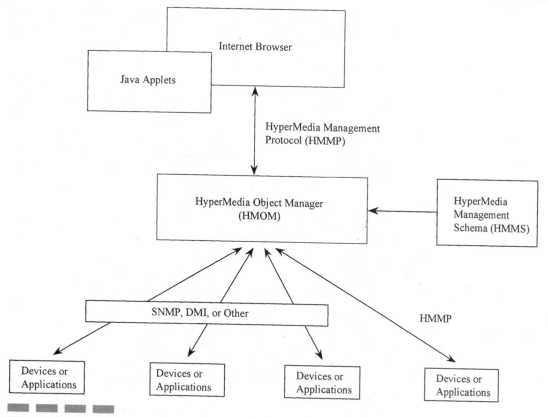

Figure 11-9
Web-based enterprise management architecture.

supports dynamic properties and associations. Work on HMMP is still being done, and there are working documents.

A server that implements most of the operations of the HMMP is known as an HMOM. A client makes a request to an HMOM (here, the HMOM is the server). If the HMOM cannot satisfy the client's request, then the HMOM switches the role to a client and forwards the client's request to another server to satisfy the client's request. Here, the HMOM acts as a proxy. The HMOM reference implementation in C++ is expected to be placed in the public domain.

Common Information Model (CIM) is the data model used along with HMMP. CIM is used to represent real-world objects on the lines of an object-oriented paradigm. The logical view of CIM is similar to the object-oriented database views. CIM is divided into metamodel and standard schema. The metamodel defines what constitutes a schema in terms of classes, instances, and qualifiers and how these can be used to represent real-world objects. Here *qualifier* refers to a modifier, which can be applied to a class definition.

The standard schema refers to the well-published standard classes that represent well-known devices and other manageable objects. In the case of new devices, either the class definitions have to be inherited from the standard class hierarchy or an entirely new class hierarchy has to be created. All servers are expected to implement the standard schema. This requirement brings some standardization to the classes supported in servers. The components of a schema, such as object classes, object instances, and qualifiers, can be described in the textual format using Managed Object Format (MOF).

CIM supports references that are just a sort of pointer to other classes or instances within the schema. References are in the form of a string of object paths. A pair of references is known as an *association*. Instances of association classes are used to establish binding relationships between object instances or object classes.

Object instances are identified by keys, just as in relational databases. Classes and instances are grouped into namespaces. Namespaces can be nested in a hierarchical manner and can be manipulated by using a standard class _Namespace. HMMP protocol operation specifies in which namespace a given protocol operation is being performed. This is also known as *namespace binding.*

HMMP does not provide transport level functionality. For transport protocol, HMMP proposes to use HyperMedia Transport Protocol (HMTP). HMTP is basically a transaction-oriented transport protocol. A unique transaction identifier identifies the request-response transactions. This transaction identifier can be used to identify the responses with the requests. HMTP permits explicit and implicit acknowledgments. In the implicit acknowledgments, the response to a request is the acknowledgment of the request itself. The explicit acknowledgment is useful for lengthy operations. In addition to the HMTP for HMMP transport, mapping of other transport protocols such as TCP is also being considered. Use of different prevalent transport protocols is very essential if the HMMP is to cover a wide range of transport protocols in use.

In HMMP, a notification or event is referred to as an *indication*. The source of an indication is known as a producer and the receiver of the indication is known as the *consumer*. Registration to receive notifications is required to receive indications. An indication can be acknowledged or unacknowledged.

There are different levels of security. Level 1 security requires the authentication of the client. This is enough to protect a server from unauthorized access from average users with no mala fide intentions. Security level 2 is not yet defined. It is proposed to have this level use an RSA public key at first for authentication and RC4 symmetric cryptography for subsequent transfer of PDUs between client and server.

HMMS describes the management information data and is owned by Desktop Management Task Force (DMTF). DMTF is yet another computer industry consortium devoted to development, support, and maintenance of management standards for desktop computers and products. DMTF was started in 1992 by PC industry leaders. The prominent members of this consortium are Microsoft, Intel, IBM, Compaq, Dell, NEC, SunSoft, and others.

Desktop Management Interface (DMI) is the management standard for describing and accessing information about all types of PCs and PC components. DMI specification DMI 2.0 was completed in 1996. The latest document, DMI 2.0s, includes DMI 2-0 and security extensions. DMI further enables remote troubleshooting using DMI access to information about any system in the network. DMTF is also working on the common information model to model the management information data in a standard object-oriented manner. For more information on DMTF, DMI, and CIM, interested readers may visit the DMTF web site (http://www.dmtf.org).

11.8.1 WBEM and TMN

Our interest in WBEM is on how WBEM and TMN can be integrated. A large amount of the material discussed here is taken from a Vertal white paper on WBEM and TMN. Here we will only briefly discuss the WBEM and TMN integration.

In Figure 11-10, the HMMP client and HMOM are the WBEM components; we have already briefly looked into these. Managers and agents are the TMN components. Two new components are introduced in the architecture for protocol mapping and informational model mapping. The HMMP TMN gateway is an important component that acts as a link between WBEM and TMN environments. It performs mapping of HMMP operations to CMIP operations and vice versa.

Another important component required for the informational model mapping is the metadata compiler. TMN uses the GDMO/ASN.1 for defining MIBs. In the case of WBEM, CIM is the informational model.

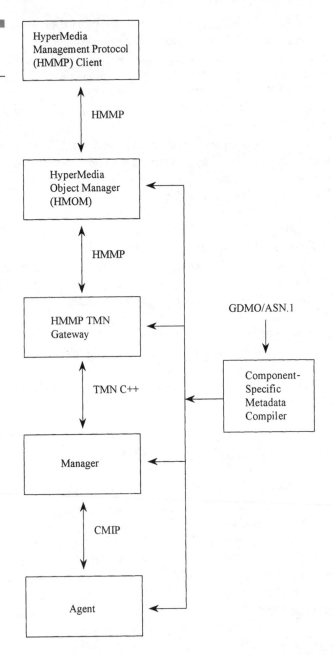

Figure 11-10
WBEM and TMN
integration.

The metadata compiler produces C++ header files and code based on the TMN MIBs used, and makes them available to the manager, agents, and manager applications. However, for a WBEM environment, the metadata compiler must be able to generate the MOF from the MIB. This MOF is imported to the HMOM and the CMIP-TMN gateway.

Namespace and naming in CIM are slightly different than the RDN and DN. So mapping of names is one of the issues when WBEM is to be integrated into TMN.

11.9 Java and TMN

Java is useful in TMN applications for providing platform independence. Java applets, which are just TMN applications, can provide the fault, performance, service management, or similar applications.

Some of the salient points of Java are:

- Java is an interpreter language. Therefore execution of the code is slower than in those cases in which the run time codes of languages such as C++ are used.

- Java uses no pointers.

- Java has no union types.

- Java clients are platform independent.

- Java code executes where it resides.

- Java clients and CORBA objects can combine well to create dynamic content in Web pages.

- Java has a built-in native ORB called remote method invocation (RMI). RMI facilitates method invocation on remote objects. RMI provides similar functionality to ORB, but is limited to Java environment.

- Alerts and notifications between CORBA objects and Java clients can be easily implemented. This property is very useful for depicting details of alarms in Web browsers.

Java Abstract Window Toolkit (AWT) is available for developing application GUIs. Java AWT supports standard widgets such as scrollbar, checkboxes, and different layout options. Java also supports access to different databases. Java furnishes a set of classes for Internet connectivity, parsing of URLs, HTTP messages, and HTML.

Java is very popular in the programming community. From a TMN perspective, for providing dynamic capabilities to Web browsers and for taking advantage of distributed environment provided by CORBA, there is a need for Java to IDL mappings and vice versa. Because of the differences in the syntax and semantics of Java and IDL, some of the IDL features are mapped indirectly to Java as given in the following list:

- Unsigned IDL integers are mapped to Java signed counterparts.

- IDL structs are mapped to Java classes.

- IDL unions are mapped to Java classes.
- IDL sequences map to Java array.
- IDL exceptions are mapped to Java classes.
- As Java has no pointers and reference arguments, IDL out and inout are handled by Holder Objects.
- IDL permits aliasing by using typedef. However Java lacks the concept of aliasing. So while mapping IDL alias, the Java type is mapped to the underlying IDL type.

Java features have been extended by Sun Microsystems to provide network, systems, and service management solutions. This collection of extensible objects and methods is known as JavaManagement API (JMAPI).

11.10 Java Management API

JMAPI can be used on different operating systems, network protocols, and various computer architectures. JMAPI consists of the following features:

- *Admin view module (AVM):*   An extension of Java Abstract Window Toolkit (AWT). AVM can be used to develop user interfaces for distributed management applications. The AVM base set consists of image button, multi-column lists, scrolling windows and panels, state button, toolbar, image canvas, convenience dialogs, and busy tool. In addition, applications are available to build help systems, tables, charts, and graphs.
- *Base object interface:*   Supports construction of objects for distributed services and resources. These allow defining distributed attributes and methods and persistent attributes.
- *Managed container interface:*   Permits users to perform management operations on a group of object instances of a managed object.
- *Managed notification interface:*   Allows asynchronous event notifications between managed objects or management applications. This feature is useful for building event management services.
- *Managed data interface:*   Useful for mapping managed object classes and instances to a relational database. These interfaces are available on different relational databases.
- *Managed protocol interface:*   Classes provided in this feature can be used to build an infrastructure to perform distributed operations in

a secure manner. The security is provided by validating that only trusted Java code runs on a client. The remote invocation method authenticates all requests for Java classes and platform-specific native libraries in a server.

■ *SNMP interface:*   Can be used to extract information from SNMP agents. This feature has only limited application and can be used only where SNMP protocol is used.

■ *Applet integration interface:*   Permits integration of Java applets with JMAPI.

JMAPI is a useful toolkit for developing network management applications. It integrates well with Java as both have been developed by Sun Microsystems. For more information on the JMAPI, visit the Web page http://java.sun.com/products/JavaManagement/overview.html.

However, note that URLs of Web pages and contents of Web pages frequently change and that the latest information should be used when designing and developing TMN applications.

11.11 Summary

In this chapter we have looked at the recent trends in TMN. We have introduced the concepts of distributed processing and distributed network management. CORBA implementations are becoming popular in the TMN arena for providing distributed network management. Web-based TMN is also an increasingly popular trend. Many TMN applications, especially in the service management area, are being accessed via Web browsers. WBEM is another promising network management architecture in the desktop arena; therefore we have briefly looked into WBEM and also one of the ways WBEM and TMN can coexist. Finally, Java has generated a keen interest because of the platform independence and simplicity of the language. It is becoming popular as a language of choice in many network management and TMN areas. We have concluded the chapter by taking a look at JMAPI from the perspective of its use in TMN.

Integrated Network Management V, Integrated Management in a Virtual World, Proceedings of the Fifth IFIP/IEEE International Symposium on Integrated Network Management, has a number of very good articles on the CORBA, Java, and Web implementations in TMN. References to some of the important articles are furnished in the next section.

11.12 References

11.1. Soukouti, N. and U. Hollberg, *Joint Inter Domain Management: CORBA, CMIP and SNMP.* Integrated Network Management V, Integrated Management in a Virtual World, Proceedings of the Fifth IFIP/IEEE International Symposium on Integrated Network Management, San Diego, CA, May 12—16, 1997, Lazar, A., Saracco, R., and Stadler, R. (eds.), London: Chapman & Hall, pp. 153—164, 1997.

11.2. Chadha, R. and S. Wuu, *Incorporating Manageability into Distributed Software.* Integrated Network Management V, Integrated Management in a Virtual World, Proceedings of the Fifth IFIP/IEEE International Symposium on Integrated Network Management, San Diego, CA, May 12—16, 1997, Lazar, A., Saracco, R., and Stadler, R. (eds.), London: Chapman & Hall, pp. 489—502, 1997.

11.3. Whitner, R. B., *Designing Scalable Applications Using CORBA.* Integrated Network Management V, Integrated Management in a Virtual World, Proceedings of the Fifth IFIP/IEEE International Symposium on Integrated Network Management, San Diego, CA, May 12—16, 1997, Lazar, A., Saracco, R., and Stadler, R. (eds.), London: Chapman & Hall, pp. 503—514, 1997.

11.4. Feldkhun, L., M. Marini, and S. Borioni, *Integrated Customer-Focused Network Management: Architectural Perspectives.* Integrated Network Management V, Integrated Management in a Virtual World, Proceedings of the Fifth IFIP/IEEE International Symposium on Integrated Network Management, San Diego, CA, May 12—16, 1997, Lazar, A., Saracco, R., and Stadler, R. (eds.), London: Chapman & Hall, pp. 17—30, 1997.

11.5. ITU-T Recommendation X.703, Information Technology—Open Distributed Management Architecture, 1997.

11.6. ITU-T Recommendation X.901, Information Technology—Open Distributed Processing—Reference Model, Part 1: Overview and Guide to Use, 1997.

11.7. ITU-T Recommendation X.902, Information Technology—Open Distributed Processing—Reference Model: Foundations, 1995.

11.8. ITU-T Recommendation X.903, Information Technology—Open Distributed Processing—Reference Model: Architecture, 1995.

11.9. ITU-T Recommendation X.904, Information Technology—Open Distributed Processing—Reference Model: Architectural Semantics, 1997.

11.10. Revision 2.2, *The Common Object Request Broker: Architecture and Specification*, Framingham, MA: Object Management Group, 1998.

11.11. Updated Version, *CORBA Services: Common Object Services Specification*, Framingham, MA: Object Management Group, 1997.

11.12. Harssema, M., *Integrating TMN and CORBA*, Computer Science Masters Thesis, Enschede, The Netherlands: University of Twente, 1996.

11.13. Raud, R., *OSI and CORBA, Alternatives or Complementary.* Paper in Sonet Interoperability Forum (SIF), 1998.

11.14. Fielding, R., J. Gettys, J. C. Mogul, L. Masinter, P. Leach, H. Frystyk, T. Berners-Lee, N. Freed, and N. Borenstein, *Multipurpose Internet Mail Extensions (MIME) Part One: Format of Internet Message Bodies*, RFC 2045, 1996.

11.15. Freed N., and N. Borenstein, *Multipurpose Internet Mail Extensions (MIME) Part Two: Media Types*, RFC 2046, 1996.

11.16. Moore, K., *MIME (Multipurpose Internet Mail Extensions) Part Three: Message Header Extensions for Non-ASCII Text*, RFC 2047, 1996.

11.17. Franks, J., P. Hallam-Baker, J. Hostetler, P. Leach, A. Luotonen, E. Sink, and L. Stewart, *An Extension to HTTP: Digest Access Authentication*, RFC 2069, 1997.

11.13 Further Reading

Web-Based Enterprise Management Initiative Web Page, http://wbem .freerange.com.

Accessing TMN Through Web-Based Enterprise Management, Vertel White Paper, 1997.

Web-Based Enterprise Management, Microsoft Web page, 1996.

Won-Ki Hong, J., J.-Y. Kong, T.-H. Yun, and S.-S. Kim, "Web-Based Intranet Services and Network Management," *IEEE Communications Magazine*, vol. 35, no. 10, pp. 100—110, 1997.

Mapping of IDL to Java. JavaSoft, 1996.

Weiss, M., A. Johnson, and J. Kiniry, *Distributed Computing, Java, CORBA and DCE*, 1996.

Raman, L., Information Modeling and Its Role in Network Management. In *Telecommunications Network Management*, Aidarous, S. and Plevyak, T. (eds.), New York: The Institute of Electrical and Electronics Engineers, Inc., pp. 1—62, 1998.

CHAPTER **12**

Software Management Frameworks, TMN Challenges, and Trends

12.1 Introduction

In this chapter, we discuss object-oriented software management frameworks. Many vendors are already providing different TMN solutions including software management frameworks based on object-oriented paradigms. Therefore, it is essential to take a look into the basic principles involved in these management frameworks.

Basically, these software management frameworks assist in developing a variety of management applications such as managers and agents. It is better to procure these management frameworks to develop TMN solutions instead of developing TMN solutions from scratch. A rule of thumb is: If you can procure a TMN solution that meets your needs at a competitive price, do so. As an extension to this rule, only if you cannot get the TMN solution you want on the market at a competitive price should you opt for developing network management solutions.

Intense competition in the telecommunications industry is playing a key role in the services provided and in improvements in technology. Every telecommunications service provider and vendor wants to expand its array of services and is trying to offer more and better services than its rivals. As a result, new technologies to cater to new customer requirements are being developed at a fast rate. These new technologies need network management. Also, in many cases, new services are built on existing network infrastructure. The network management solutions for these new services have to coexist with the legacy network management solutions.

In addition, TMN is evolving with many gray areas and a large number of unresolved issues. We need to take a close look at the most important of these issues in order to help designers and implementers to recognize the problems they may encounter while providing TMN solutions.

At the same time, it is absolutely essential to be aware of the trends in TMN. This will aid in providing solutions from a long-range perspective. These solutions, which take note of the future migration issues, will have fewer problems in migrating to the future TMN solutions. Such solutions will require minimal changes to accommodate new technologies. The unresolved issues and future trends in network management are also explained in Reference 12.1.

12.2 Management Frameworks

TMN information models and management protocols are based on object-oriented principles. Some of the major advantages of using object-oriented paradigms are:

- The code written for a particular object class can be reused to satisfy additional requirements by making minor changes.

- Extensibility means that new object classes can be easily derived using inheritance and polymorphism. This permits easy and elegant extensions to object class definitions.

- It is easy to model and map the real systems and resources to object class and objects. The definitions of object classes make sense because they relate to real systems.

- Encapsulation permits hiding of internal details including data. This enables data integrity, as only operations to be performed on an object are visible at the boundary of the object.

The trend in TMN is to use object-oriented management frameworks. These can be used to develop MIBs, managers, agents, and network management applications. The management frameworks provide very generic functionality. The generic managers, agents, or applications have to be modified to meet specific requirements.

Object-oriented methodologies are also used for the design and development of management frameworks. Some of the popular methodologies are based on Paradigm and Unified Modeling Language (UML).

The earlier practice was to use proprietary languages in the development of network management systems. This is slowly giving way to the use of generic programming languages such as C++ and Java. As it is easy to map object-oriented methodologies to C++, it is one of the most popular development languages.

Figure 12-1 gives an overview of the structure of a software management framework. However, each vendor incorporates slight variations in the actual implementations to distinguish its product offerings. Individual components are discussed in the following text.

12.2.1 Communication Infrastructure

The basic function of the communication infrastructure is to provide a communication stack on computer platforms to enable the transfer of

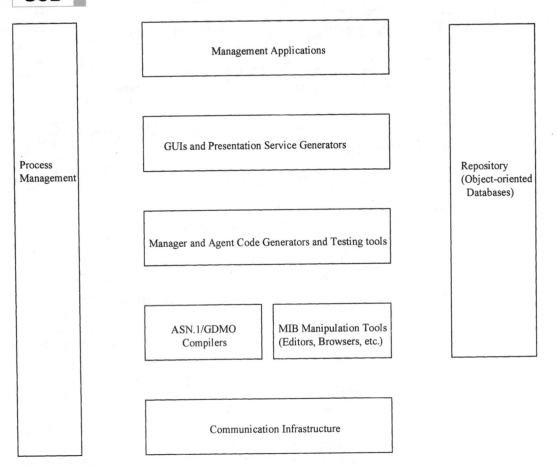

Figure 12-1
Software management framework components (© 1994 IEEE).

management information between managers and agents. This concept can also be extended to provide communication between other TMN layers such as NML, SML, BML, and network elements.

However, many computer platforms provide a variety of communication stacks such as ACSE/presentation layer stacks. There are software packages available for computer platforms to provide a Q3 interface along with the communication stacks. Some use TCP/IP or CORBA IIOP. Some of the computer platforms provide RFC 1006 to run CMIP over TCP/IP. These ready-to-use communication stacks are not enough to convey management information. In management frameworks, communication adapter object classes have to be provided to integrate these ready-to-use communication stacks with the manager or agents.

12.2.2 MIB Manipulation Tools

Most of the management frameworks provide a variety of tools for the creation, editing, and updating of MIBs. There are tools to store the MIBs in a persistent storage. This persistent storage can be an object-oriented database or any of the popular relational databases. Some vendors support most of the popular databases.

GDMO/ASN.1 editors are a common feature used to develop the GDMO/ASN.1 definitions for the managed object classes. These editors have easy-to-use GUIs that assist in developing GDMO and ASN.1 definitions of object classes. Syntax checking is done while the object class definitions are being inputted through the GUI, and there are prompts for errors if wrong entries are made. After syntax checking, these managed object class definitions can be stored in a persistent storage with unique names. The set of object classes in persistent storage is also known as an *object class repository.*

GDMO/ASN.1 editors can also retrieve the object class definitions from persistent storage, update the definitions, and store them again in persistent storage. These GDMO/ASN.1 definitions become input to the GDMO/ASN.1 compilers. If the framework components are purchased from the same vendor, different components are properly integrated. Otherwise, if the framework components are from different vendors, there may not be tight integration of products. As a simple example, if the editors and compilers use different naming syntaxes for files in the repository, there can be problems.

GDMO browsers are another important feature. After error-free object class definitions are compiled, GDMO browsers display the object class inheritance hierarchy and containment hierarchy. These browsers have flexible capabilities to display the object class hierarchies with zoom in, zoom out, and partial displays. There are also capabilities for printing in different formats.

Note that in the preceding explanations, different vendors can use different functionalities in their editors and browsers. We have made the distinction between editors and browsers based on use. Browsers are used after the correct compilation of the GDMO and ASN.1 definitions to view and print the hierarchies, whereas editors are used to make changes to the GDMO and ASN.1 definitions.

12.2.3 GDMO and ASN.1 Compilers

Usually, TMN development frameworks have ASN.1 and GDMO compilers. These compilers accept GDMO/ASN.1 definitions, do the syntax checking, and produce header files and data structures and store them in repositories. These header files and data structures are used for developing managers and agents. Framework libraries also provide support for object filtering, scoping, persistence, object creation, and object deletion services.

The GDMO/ASN.1 definitions are normally stored in files in repositories: They are retrieved from the repositories and then compiled. The normal practice in GDMO and ASN.1 compilers is to prompt for an error, then invoke the GDMO or ASN.1 editors and point to the line/place where the error has occurred. The supporting ASN.1 definitions must be compiled first, using ASN.1 compilers, and then GDMO definitions are compiled. Once these GDMO/ASN.1 definitions are correctly compiled, browsers can be used to display the inheritance and containment hierarchies.

Most of the TMN frameworks are based on standard MIBs such as X.721 and M.3100. This dependency on the standard MIBs places restrictions on deriving new managed object classes, as the new managed object classes are inherited from the object classes defined in X.721 and M.3100.

12.2.4 Manager and Agent Code Generators

Once the GDMO and ASN.1 definitions are correctly compiled, code generators can be used to generate the manager and agent codes. These code generators produce C++ headers and implementation codes for managers and agents. The implementation codes are customized for manager and agent operations by adding further code for association, accessing and searching directories, and communication of management information.

Let us look into the issue of management association a bit further. As we saw in Chapter 7, an association has to be formed between a manager and an agent before any management information can be transmitted using CMIP. For this, the manager has to know the location of the agent. A manager needs the assistance of directory services to locate the agents. These directory services can be X.500 based. These directories have AE-titles or distinguished names used to form associations, so the manager has to have code to go to the directory and search for either the AE-title or the distinguished name of the agent. Here we have made the assumption that the manager is initiating the association. However, there is no such restriction; agents can also initiate an association.

Usually, the implementation codes generated by code generators have markers indicating where the specific customized codes are to be added.

Figure 12-2 shows the flow for generating manager and agent codes. There are return paths to the beginning of the ASN.1 definitions and GDMO definitions from the manager code generator and agent code generator, the manager code, and the agent code. In many cases it is necessary to go back to the original ASN.1 and GDMO definitions and correct them, then go through the cycle again as shown in the figure.

The ASN.1 and GDMO compilers and manager and agent code generators can have enhancements so that they only recompile or generate the codes for the changes made and incorporate them appropriately in the compiled code or generated code.

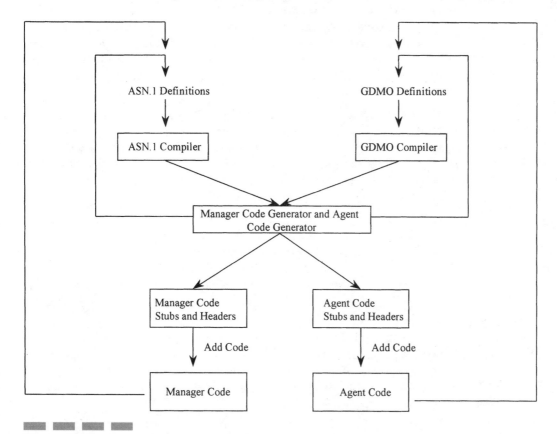

Figure 12-2
Generating manager and agent codes.

In addition to the code generators, many management frameworks provide tools for testing managers and agents in stand-alone environments. As an example, a tool for testing a manager provides for association and simulates the environment for an agent. The manager test tool also simulates different CMIP commands. For easy interface, GUIs are provided. These tools can be used to perform initial predeployment testing of managers and agents.

12.2.5 GUI and Presentation Service Generators

Usually, GUIs insulate the user from the complexities of implementations and present simple menu bars or icon objects to access the manager applications, ASN.1 and GDMO compilers, and code generators. The parameters are entered through dialog boxes. In GUIs, when erroneous data are entered, the user is prompted to correct the errors with appropriate and meaningful messages. Also, help is generally available to explain the steps involved in correctly entering the data and using operations by clicking buttons. Usually in GUIs different colors and different audio and video effects are included to depict different states.

There are many commercially available tools on the market to aid in rapid development of GUIs. The wisest practice is to develop these GUIs in the early stages and listen to customer feedback. In software development, GUI development is complex and very subjective. As everyone has a strong opinion on how a GUI should look, major problems can occur at a later date if customer buy-in does not occur early on.

12.2.6 Persistent Storage

MIBs are normally stored in persistent storage. The persistent storage can be object-oriented databases or relational databases. Object-oriented databases are best suited for storing MIB data structures, as the structures used in these databases are similar to the structures of object classes. When relational databases are used, conversions from the relational record structure to the object class structures are required while storing and retrieving MIB object classes. These conversions can affect the performance of management systems.

Logging of different types of data, including security audit trails, also necessitates storing data in persistent storage. These data can be stored in flat files or in databases as log records. The flat file approach is simple to implement and provides faster logs without size limitations, whereas database logs can have limitations of size and require more time to process each record. The data stored in databases are easier to manipulate as some of the database operations are provided by database tools.

There are many vendors that provide object-oriented databases, and it is becoming a popular trend to use these databases in TMN for providing persistence.

12.2.7 Process Management

Communication between different components of a network management system is accomplished with the help of *processes.* Some of the examples of processes are manager processes, agent processes, client/server processes, and so on. Most of these are cooperative processes in the sense that they have to be well coordinated. Processes have to be maintained properly so that there is no failure in the computer platforms where they reside and execute. In addition, processes have major impact on performance and storage space utilization. Multithreading is an example of how processes can be used to improve performance. The designer of any management platform has to carefully examine the performance and storage space allocations of the end products generated by processes.

12.2.8 Management Applications

The development of managers and agents is a small part of the TMN development cycle. These days, there are many applications, such as fault, performance, and performing service-level activities such as telephone number administration and billing. New applications are frequently being developed to meet customer requirements.

The primary objective of network management application tools is to automate as much as possible the code generation phase for these applications. However, these management applications will have to be customized by adding—and sometimes changing—application code to meet specific requirements.

There are also management application platforms that provide libraries of object classes for implementing systems management functions such as event management, scheduling, software management, alarm management, and so on. As an example, let us take the case of alarm management. This application provides the ability to collect alarms, display the alarms in different order, display the alarm history, filter the alarms based on certain criteria, retire the alarms, and so on.

It is becoming a normal practice to buy different application packages to enhance management systems. Trouble ticket systems, which track problems from inception to closure, constitute one such package. Trouble tickets can be used to coordinate different activities such as managing field resources, providing customer-related reports, generating statistical reports, and so on. Trouble ticket applications can involve different levels of complexity and automation. As an example, when a problem is reported, an e-mail or paging system can notify the proper repair personnel to attend to the problem.

There are two possible scenarios in the development of management applications. In the first, the design has the tools on hand to generate management applications. The other case is that of packaged management software applications. These applications can be bought as separate pieces and integrated into network management applications; an example is the integration of trouble ticketing and fault management.

Application platforms invariably come with easy-to-use GUIs. These GUIs enable the use of the applications without requiring a high level of computer literacy and are designed to avoid the learning curve involved in becoming well-versed in the use of a tool.

12.2.9 Implementation Notes

Many factors must be considered in the selection of management frameworks to generate managers, agents, and management applications. Some of these are:

- The managers and agents generated are dependent upon the information model used in the management frameworks. As an example, if the management framework is based on the M.3100 information model, the generated managers and agents will work only with managed object classes derived from M.3100-based object classes.

- There should be support for multithreading. This is required for enhanced performance, especially when processing linked replies.

- A fast GUI development tool is required to do initial prototyping. This is essential because feedback provides direction on how to improve the GUIs to meet internal and customer requirements. Prototyping is also important to garner support for a project.

- A good GUI interface is required for debugging. Debugging is an important, time-consuming activity during the development process; easy GUI interfaces can facilitate quicker development.

■ Database support is required for providing persistence. This database support has to be available in the platform on which EMs and NEs are deployed. As an example, if the generated code is dependent on *X* object-oriented databases, then *X* object-oriented database support should be available on the development computer platform and the production platform. By *production platform,* we mean the computer platform on which NEs and EMs are deployed. *X* object-oriented database support is also required if the EMs and NEs are to be ported to other platforms; otherwise the porting itself may involve a major rewrite and thus retesting the code.

■ There is a need to consider computer platform incompatibilities. Management frameworks and management applications are normally developed in one computer platform and then ported to different computer platforms. Incompatibilities between computer platforms can pose major problems when porting to different platforms. Many computer platforms have apparent (and sometimes none-too-apparent) differences in their support for data models.

■ Just as there are platform incompatibilities, there are software incompatibilities. As an example, Orbix implementations on Sun Solaris and Windows NT are slightly different.

Interested readers may also consult the chapter on management platforms in Reference 12.2.

12.3 Unresolved Issues and Challenges in TMN

Although from many standpoints TMN is in a fairly advanced stage, there are still many challenges to be faced. Let us examine some of these.

12.3.1 Integration of Legacy Systems and Standard TMN Solutions

Many telecommunications service providers are still clinging to the old proprietary systems. To complicate this problem further, some of the TMN solutions have been on legacy computer platforms and different forms of databases. These disparate TMN solutions have grown independently over time. In addition, telecommunications service providers have made huge investments in proprietary solutions.

Competitive pressures compel these service providers to update their technology. Some service providers see this as an opportunity to change over to the latest technologies and standard solutions. However, due to the large investments of money, time, and personnel, transformation from proprietary legacy TMN solutions to standard solutions will be evolutionary.

Migrating data from old to new systems presents a major challenge in introducing new TMN solutions. As an example, some databases may be proprietary, but the latest trend in TMN is to use object-oriented databases. This variance in the formats of the databases can create a major migration nightmare.

12.3.2 Impact of Changes in Regulatory Environments

Many nations are instituting new regulations designed to increase competition. As an example, in the United States a customer can choose to use any local or interstate and international carrier. Historically, a telephone number has been assumed to be the property of the service provider; now, however, the customer is more and more being considered the owner of the telephone number.

As a first step, local telephone number portability is being implemented across the United States. This means a customer can use any local telephone service provider. This regulatory change has an impact on telephone number administration; in the years ahead, it will extend to the international scene. Such regulatory changes will have their own impact on TMN solutions.

12.3.3 Integration of TMN Solutions for Different Technologies

A large telecommunications network can be a combination of many different telecommunications and data communication networks with different technologies. As an example, one network may be using GSM in one portion, ATM in another portion, and SDH in still another portion. For seamless end-to-end data flow, management of these disparate networks must be integrated. In addition, network management solutions for the different technologies have to be integrated to meet customer requirements for quality service at a reasonable price. To cater to increasing customer requirements, advances in technology will continue to provide more features and better services.

12.3.4 Automation

Automation is a very loosely used term. For some, it means replacing manual TMN work by some form of automatic process without any manual intervention. As an example, sometimes it is necessary to download the latest versions of software for a piece of equipment such as a switch. This can be done by manually loading the latest software using a tape or CD-ROM; however, the software can also be downloaded to the switch from a processor at a designated time.

Many telecommunications service providers and vendors use different levels of automation to provide customer services and to generate reports on telephone numbers, system availability, repairs, and billing. Many times these data are maintained in different systems operated by different people. For many services, there is a need for synchronization of data. Even in those cases where trouble ticketing is used for tracking the repairs, the degree of automation varies. Automation at the service management layer has the potential to provide significant savings to telecommunications service providers.

12.3.5 Information Model Differences

There are differences between different data models. For example, CORBA uses IDL to define the interface data model, compared to TMN, which uses GDMO and ASN.1. On top of this, there are proprietary data models. Every vendor claims that its solutions are the standard ones. However, these data models and language environments are incompatible with one another. These differences in data models create many problems when migrating from one data model to another, and when different TMN systems are to co-exist.

12.3.6 Protocol Differences

Other problems are presented when different management protocols have to interact. This is one of the major hurdles when different management solutions are to interoperate with one another. As an example, SNMP and CMIP protocols are different. Many major telecommunications service providers have a mix of management protocols, such as SNMP, CMIP, and even proprietary management protocols, within the company.

Now imagine the problem of protocol differences if computer and telecommunications networks are to be integrated on a global level. The computer networks have their own variety of management protocols and applications developed just for network maintenance. These management protocol differences can be a major problem in providing an integrated network management solution.

12.3.7 Language Independence

There are subtle programming language differences. Compilers and linkers have some dependence on the computer platforms. Also, some computer platforms may not support all the features of a programming language. This close tie between programming languages and computer platforms makes TMN solutions both language and platform dependent.

Java is expected to be platform independent, which may solve some of the platform dependency problems of TMN.

12.3.8 Platform Independence

Despite all the talk of standardization of management and transport protocols, TMN solutions are in fact based on computer platforms. In the early days, UNIX was claimed to be platform independent; as time went by, however, we saw different flavors of incompatible UNIX systems. So platform independence in the sense that a TMN solution in one platform must be able to work seamlessly on another platform is still a long way off.

There are major differences especially in the communication stacks of different computer platforms. Many UNIX systems have ACSE/Presentation OSI-based stacks; however, these may not be available in non-UNIX platforms. So the communication stack itself can become a major hurdle in porting applications from UNIX to non-UNIX environments. Similarly, object-oriented databases are platform dependent in many cases, making provision of management solutions in a platform-independent manner problematic. As an example, if an object-oriented database vendor supports only some platforms, it may be difficult to port management solutions from one platform to another.

12.3.9 Presentation Services/GUI

The user presentation services through which a network operator interfaces with the management applications should have a uniform look and feel. However, there are not many standards from a GUI point of view. Personal experience shows that GUIs are the most controversial aspect in software development. There is a need to focus on the standardization of presentation services and GUIs.

12.3.10 Standards Lag Behind Solutions

When new equipment is integrated into networks, network management becomes a major issue. Also, the size of networks makes manual intervention and repair difficult. At the same time, customer requirements for better and more reliable service at a cheaper price are continuously increasing. TMN will play a major role in satisfying these requirements.

However, TMN solutions have to be worked out in parallel with the development of equipment. Because of the complex, heterogeneous nature of the networks and the spread of networks over international borders, the solutions have to be open. Proprietary solutions, which were acceptable earlier, can no longer be tolerated in the fast-changing telecommunications industry. Here standards and standardization become critical requirements. The multiplicity of standards bodies and the overlapping work of these bodies are major impediments to speedy implementation of TMN solutions.

Also, in many cases, standards take a long time. They get bogged down in different levels of politics. In addition, the keen competition between different computer and telecommunications vendors also prevents uniform acceptance of standards. These factors impede the quick launch of products and the implementations of TMN solutions, especially when the technology is changing at a fast rate. Also, most telecommunications standards are based on ITU-T standards. However, due to the large size of ITU-T and the number of players involved in the standardization effort, sometimes ITU-T standards lag behind the TMN solutions required. To overcome the lacuna, ITU-T standardization efforts will have to keep pace with technological advances.

12.3.11 TMN Solutions Are Not Open

It is a common practice to claim that a given TMN solution is open. Despite a good amount of standardization in the TMN arena, seamless communication, interaction and management function between open systems is still not a reality. For various reasons, such as standards not being available for all the resources that have to be managed, proprietary solutions become part of the open system solutions to some degree. In some cases proprietary solutions are deliberately introduced for intellectual property and competitive reasons. Therefore it is necessary to be aware of the proprietary hooks in network management systems when evaluating TMN solutions.

12.3.12 Integrated Network Management for Computers, Telecommunications, and Televisions

As we have mentioned many times, the role of telecommunications is expanding; it is no longer limited just to POTS. Television is another common medium that has invaded a large number of homes worldwide, having penetrated more areas than telephony. Therefore cable operators see the opportunity to provide telephone-related services.

In addition to telecommunications and cable TV, there are many LAN-based computer networks that are expanding their spheres of influence. Service providers with data communication networks want to provide Internet telephone services. At the same time, many telecommunications service providers are already providing Internet services. Each sector is competing for services to provide to customers. As a result, new services are being offered to customers by a variety of service providers. These changes have a large impact in service provisioning, network architecture, and pricing (Reference 12.3). This will be a major challenge to some telecommunications service providers and vendors.

The demarcations or lines of separation between computers, cable TV, and telecommunications are becoming blurred. As a matter fact, they are slowly beginning to overlap with respect to services provided. Internet service is an example of this overlapping of the services provided by the computer, television and telecommunications industries. Internet service providers want to provide telephone service as well, and in some cases cable TV service providers want to provide Internet services. Each sector is introducing new services; to cater to these new services, new types of equipment—Web TV, for instance—are introduced.

New equipment in this mixed scenario is being introduced at a fast rate, and this equipment needs network management. In some cases, the control of service providers can span a wide geographical and customer base. Under these circumstances, the role of network management covering a wide variety of equipment can be a very daunting task.

12.4 Future Trends

We need to look into the crystal ball and envision the future of TMN. This is essential for TMN practitioners: If we don't have much of an idea of the future, our TMN implementations will be incomplete when we have to accommodate future solutions. The forecast for TMN industry participants is very rosy in terms of revenue generation. At the same time, the future will be very challenging, with a need to keep pace with fast-changing technologies. From this angle, let us examine where the TMN industry is heading.

12.4.1 Focus on Standardization

Technological improvements in TMN are occurring at a fast rate. To keep pace with these developments, increasing effort is being directed toward TMN. Because of globalization and privatization, standardization is also becoming very important.

12.4.2 Distributed Network Management

In the distributed network management, one of the challenges is figuring out how legacy systems will co-exist with new systems built on the basis of new technologies such as CORBA. Another problem is determining how managers will interface with one another. The coordination of many distributed managers will be a daunting task. Yet another problem is deciding how backup will be activated when one of the managers is down. The issues of data synchronization and consistency will have to be taken into account in these cases.

CORBA will take an increasingly important role in distributed network management. Therefore TMN has to accommodate CORBA.

12.4.3 TMN Solutions on Windows-Based Platforms

Because of the high cost of UNIX-based platforms, Windows 95/98 and Windows NT are finding favor as preferred network management development and production platforms. Java is also becoming a popular programming language.

12.4.4 Increased Use of Object-Oriented Paradigms

Object-oriented methodology has gained acceptance in the design and development of TMN solutions. As a corollary, the use of object-oriented databases for providing persistence is also becoming the norm. These trends have been accelerated by the availability of object-oriented design and development tools on different popular computer platforms. There are also many vendors providing good object-oriented databases and database tools.

12.4.5 Integration of the Web and TMN

The use of Web technology for providing customer service is gaining popularity. A Web browser can also be used as an interface to enable customers to communicate about problems. A customer must be able to enter information about the problems he or she encounters, and this must be enough to ensure that the problems will be acted on. Billing is another area where Web browsers can be used. The trend for customers to receive and pay the bills and resolve billing problems using Web browsers will be growing at an enormous pace.

12.5 Summary

In this chapter we have discussed object-oriented software management frameworks and how they can be used to provide TMN solutions. TMN faces many challenges and opportunities ahead in the struggle to make an impact on telephone services. This is particularly true at a time when "telephone" services include many types of services such as Internet service, wireless, and so on, and when distinctions between local and long-distance services are becoming fuzzy. We have discussed the unresolved issues and challenges confronting TMN solutions. The chapter ends with a discussion of future trends in TMN solutions.

12.6 References

12.1. Udupa, D. K., *Network Management Systems Essentials*, New York: McGraw-Hill, 1996.

12.2. Pauthner, G. and J. Power, Management Platforms. In *The Telecommunications Network Management, Technologies, and Implementations*, Aidarous, S. and Plevyak, T. (eds.), New York: The Institute of Electrical and Electronics Engineers, Inc., pp. 111—149, 1998.

12.3. Ejiri, M., The Paradigm Shift in Telecommunications Services and Networks. In *Integrated Network Management IV*, Sethi, A. S., Raynaud, Y., and Faure-Vincent, F. (eds.), Cornwall, UK: Chapman & Hall, pp. 688—699, 1995.

APPENDIX A

How to Keep Up to Date and Procure
the Latest TMN Standards

A.1 Symposiums and Conferences

Integrated management (IM) and network operations and management symposium (NOMS) conferences are held alternately; IM conferences convene in odd-numbered years, and NOMS conferences convene in even-numbered years. These conferences are organized by the International Federation for Information Processing (IFIP) Working Group (WG) 6.6 on Network Management for Communication Networks and the Institute of Electrical and Electronics Engineers Communications Society's (COM-SOC) Committee on Network Operations and Management (CNOM). The conferences have the latest papers and discussions on network management. They also publish the proceedings of the conferences/symposiums. Attending these conferences or reading the symposium proceedings are good sources for keeping up to date on TMN.

A.2 The World Wide Web (WWW)

One of the easiest ways to access information on any topic—including TMN—is to use the World Wide Web. Large amounts of material are available on many specific topics on TMN. However, care has to be exercised regarding information gathered from the WWW. The material contained in the WWW is not always authentic. Some Web sites contain individual opinions—as contrasted to confirmed facts—so one has to be cautious about gathering information. Still, by and large, the information retrieved from the standards bodies, consortiums, and well-established vendors can be treated as authentic.

Many organizations associated with TMN activities have Web sites. Details of some of the important ones follow. Note that Web pages change frequently, so URLs may change.

The SimpleWeb

The SimpleWeb provides links and information on network management. The primary focus of this Web site is Internet management. The SimpleWeb is a good Web site, and one can find a wealth of information related to network management. The SimpleWeb is maintained by the Telematics Systems and Services management group (TSS) of the University of Twente (the Netherlands), in collaboration with Jürgen Schönwälder of TU Braunschweig (Germany).

The URL of the SimpleWeb is http://wwwsnmp.cs.utwente.nl/.

The URL of the standards page in The SimpleWeb is http://wwwsnmp.cs.utwente.nl/standard/.

NetMan

The University of Buffalo's NetMan is also a good repository of information on network management. The URL of NetMan is http://netman.cit.buffalo.edu/.

International Telecommunications Union— Telecommunications (ITU-T)

ITU-T standards are available only through subscription to the ITU-T. You need a user ID and password to access the ITU-T documents. Most of the vendors have access to the ITU-T standards—so check inside your company to learn whether access to the standards is available there. You can also individually purchase ITU-T documents. The URL for the ITU-T home page is http://www.itu.ch/.

International Standardization Organization (ISO)

ISO documents can be purchased from vendors. Visit the ISO home page for information on how to procure ISO documents. The ISO's home page URL is http://www.iso.ch/.

Internet RFCs

RFCs of the Internet Engineering Task Force are available on the WWW, and they can easily be downloaded. Be sure to check the standard track of an RFC before implementing it.

ATM Forum

Most of the network management forum technical specifications are available on the WWW. The URL of ATM Forum is http://www.atmforum .com/.

TeleManagement Forum

The name Network Management Forum (NMF) has been changed to Tele-Management Forum. TeleManagement Forum documents are available only for subscribers. The URL of TeleManagement Forum is http://www .tmforum.org/.

APPENDIX B

Important TMN and Network Management Standards

Because the material on TMN and network management standards is voluminous, we are listing only some of the important network management documents by ITU-T, ISO, Internet network management—related RFCs, ETSI, and ANSI. For details on how to procure documents from other organizations, refer to Appendix C. Documents marked with asterisks are being revised.

B.1 ITU-T

Note that many ITU-T documents are paired with ISO.

G Series Documents

1. G.774, Synchronous Digital Hierarchy (SDH) Management Information Model for the Network Element View, 1992.

2. G.784, Synchronous Digital Hierarchy (SDH) Management, 1994.

3. G.803, Architectures of Transport Networks Based on the Synchronous Digital Hierarchy (SDH), 1993.

4. G.805, Generic Functional Architecture of Transport Networks, 1995.

5. G.831, Management Capabilities of Transport Networks based on the Synchronous Digital Hierarchy (SDH), 1996.

I Series Documents

6. I.321, B-ISDN Protocol Reference Model and its Application, 1991.

7. I.610, B-ISDN Operation and Maintenance Principles and Functions, 1995.

8. I.751, Asynchronous Transfer Mode Management of the Network Element View, 1996.

Q Series Documents

9. Q811, Lower Layer Protocol Profiles for the Q3 and X Interfaces, 1997.

10. Q812, Upper Layer Protocol Profiles for the Q3 and X Interfaces, 1997.

11. Q821, Stage 2 and Stage 3 Description for the Q3 Interface—Alarm Surveillance, 1993.

12. Q822, Stage 1, Stage 2, Stage 3 Description for the Q3 Interface—Performance Management, 1994.

13. Q823, Stage 2 and Stage 3 Functional Specifications for Traffic Management, 1996.

14. Q824.0, Stage 2 and 3 Description for Q3 Interface, Customer Administration—Common Information, 1995.

M Series Documents

15. M.3010, Principles for a Telecommunications Management Network, 1996.

16. M.3020, TMN Interface Specification Methodology, 1995.

17. M.3100, Generic Network Information Model, 1995.

18. M.3101, Managed Object Conformance Statements for the Generic Network Information Model, 1995.

19. M.3180, Catalogue of TMN Management Information, 1992.

20. M.3200, TMN Management Services and Telecommunications Managed Areas: Overview, 1997.

21. M.3300, TMN Management Capabilities Presented at the F Interface, 1992.

22. M.3320, Management Requirements Framework for the TMN X Interface, 1997.

23. M.3400, TMN Management Functions, 1997.

X Series and ISO Documents

24. X.160, Architecture for Customer Network Management Service for Public Data Networks, 1996.

25. X.161, Definition of Customer Network Management Services for Public Data Networks, 1997.

26. X.162, Definition of Management Information for Customer Network Management Service for Public Data Networks to Be Used With CNMc Interface, 1997.

27. X.163, Definition of Management Information for Customer Network Management Services for Public Data Networks to Be Used With CNMe Interface, 1995.

28. X.200 (ISO/IEC 7498-1), Basic Reference Model: Basic Model, 1994.

29. X.207 (ISO/IEC 9545), Application Layer Structure, 1993.

30. X.208 (ISO/IEC 8824), Specification of Abstract Syntax Notation One (ASN.1), 1988.

31. X.209 (ISO/IEC 8825), Specification Basic Encoding Rules for Abstract Syntax Notation (ASN.1), 1988.

32. X.210 (ISO/IEC 10731), Basic Reference Model: Conventions for the Definition of OSI Services, 1993.

33. X.217 (ISO/IEC 8649), Service Definition for the Association Control Service Element, 1995.

34. X.217 Amendment 1 (ISO/IEC 8649 AM 1), Service Definition for the Association Control Service Element, Amendment 1: Support of Authentication Mechanisms for the Connectionless Mode, 1996.

35. X.218 (ISO/IEC 9066-1), Reliable Transfer: Model and Service Definition, 1993.

36. X.219 (ISO/IEC 9072-1), Remote Operations: Model, Notation, and Service Definition, 1988.

37. X.226 (ISO/IEC 8823-1), Connection-Oriented Presentation Protocol: Protocol Specification, 1994.

38. X.227 (ISO/IEC 8650-1), Connection-Oriented Protocol for the Association Control Service Element: Protocol Specification, 1995.

39. X.227 Amendment 1 (ISO/IEC 8650-1 AM 1), Connection-Oriented Protocol for the Association Control Service Element: Protocol Specification, Amendment 1: Incorporation of Extensibility Markers, 1996.

40. X.228 (ISO/IEC 9066-2), Reliable Transfer: Protocol Specification, Remote Operations: Protocol Specification, 1988.

41. X.229 (ISO/IEC 9072-2), Connection-Mode Protocol Specifications, 1988.

42. X.237 (ISO/IEC 10035-1), Connectionless Protocol for the Association Control Service Element: Protocol Specification, 1995.

43. X.237 Amendment 1 (ISO/IEC 10035-1 Amd. 1), Connectionless Protocol for the Association Control Service Element: Protocol Specification, Amendment 1: Incorporation of Extensibility Markers and Authentication Parameters, 1996.

44. X.500 (ISO/IEC 9594-1), The Directory: Overviews of Concepts, Models and Services, 1993.

45. X.650 (ISO/IEC 7498-3), Basic Reference Model, Naming and Addressing, 1996.

46. X.660 (ISO/IEC 9834-1), Procedures for the Operation of OSI Registration Authorities, General Procedures, 1992.

47. X.660, Amendment 1 (ISO/IEC 9834-1), Procedures for the Operation of OSI Registration Authorities, General Procedures, Amendment 1: Incorporation of Object Identifiers Components, 1996.

48. X.680 (ISO/IEC 8824-1), Abstract Syntax Notation One (ASN.1), Specification of Basic Notation, 1994.*

49. X.680 Amendment 1 (ISO/IEC 8824-1), Abstract Syntax Notation One (ASN.1), Specification of Basic Notation, Amendment 1: Rules of Extensibility, 1995.

50. X.681 (ISO/IEC 8824-2), Abstract Syntax Notation One (ASN.1), Information Object Specification, 1994.*

51. X.682 (ISO/IEC 8824-3), Abstract Syntax Notation One (ASN.1), Constraint Specification, 1994.

52. X.683 (ISO/IEC 8824-4), Abstract Syntax Notation One (ASN.1), Parameterization of ASN.1 Specifications, 1994.

53. X.690 (ISO/IEC 8825-1), ASN.1 Encoding Rules, Specification of Basic Encoding Rules (BER), Canonical Encoding Rules (CER), and Distinguished Encoding Rules (DER), 1994.*

54. X.691 (ISO/IEC 8825-2), ASN.1 Encoding Rules, Specification of Packed Encoding Rules (PER), 1995.*

55. X.700, Management Framework for Open Systems Interconnection (OSI) for CCITT Applications, 1992.

56. X.701 (ISO/IEC 10040)—Systems Management Overview, 1992.

57. X.710 (ISO/IEC 9595), Common Management Information Service Definition for CCITT Applications. 1991.*

58. X.711 (ISO/IEC 9596), Common Management Information Protocol Specification for CCITT Applications, 1991.*

59. X.720 (ISO/IEC 10165-1), Management Information Model, 1992.

60. X.721 (ISO/IEC 10165-2), Definition of Management Information, 1992.

61. X.722 (ISO/IEC 10165-4), Guidelines for the Definition of Managed Objects, 1992.

62. X.723 (ISO/IEC 10165-5), Generic Management Information, 1993.

63. X.724 (ISO/IEC 10165-6), Requirements and Guidelines for Implementation Conformance Statement Proformas Associated with OSI Management, 1996.

64. X.725 (ISO/IEC 10165-7), General Relationship Model, 1995.

65. X.730 (ISO/IEC 10164-1), Object Management Function, 1992.

66. X.731 (ISO/IEC 10164-2), State Management Function, 1992.

67. X.732 (ISO/IEC 10164-3), Attributes for Representing Relationships, 1992.

68. X.733 (ISO/IEC 10164-4), Alarm Reporting Function, 1992.

69. X.734 (ISO/IEC 10164-5), Event Report Management Function, 1992.

70. X.735 (ISO/IEC 10164-6), Log Control Function, 1992.

71. X.736 (ISO/IEC 10164-7), Security Alarm Reporting Function, 1992.

72. X.737 (ISO/IEC 10164-14), Confidence and Diagnostic Test Categories, 1995.

73. X.738 (ISO/IEC 10164-13), Summarization Function, 1993.

74. X.739 (ISO/IEC 10164-11), Metric Objects and Attributes, 1993.

75. X.740 (ISO/IEC 10164-8), Security Audit Trail Function, 1992.

76. X.741 (ISO/IEC 10164-9), Objects and Attributes for Access Control, 1995.

77. X.742 (ISO/IEC 10164-10), Usage Metering Function for Accounting Purposes, 1995.

78. X.743. (ISO/IEC 10164-20), Time Management Function.*

79. X.744 (ISO/IEC 10164-18), Software Management Function, 1996.

80. X.745 (ISO/IEC 10164-12), Test Management Function, 1993.

81. X.746 (ISO/IEC 10164-15), Scheduling Function, 1995.

82. X.750 (ISO/IEC 10164-16), Management Knowledge Management Function, 1996.

83. X.751 (ISO/IEC 10164-17), Change Over Function, 1995.

84. X.790, Trouble Management Function for ITU-T Applications, 1995.

85. X.791, Profile for Trouble Management Function for ITU-T Applications, 1996.

86. X.800 (ISO/IEC 7498-2), Security Architecture for Open Systems Interconnection for CCITT Applications, 1991.

87. ISO/IEC 13244, ITU-T Recommendation X.703, Information Technology—Open Distributed Management Architecture, 1997.

88. ISO/IEC 10746-1, ITU-T Recommendation X.901, Information Technology—Open Distributed Processing—Reference Model, Part 1: Overview and Guide to Use, 1997.

89. ISO/IEC 10746-2, ITU-T Recommendation X.902, Information Technology—Open Distributed Processing—Reference Model: Foundations, 1995.

90. ISO/IEC 10746-3, ITU-T Recommendation X.903, Information Technology—Open Distributed Processing—Reference Model: Architecture, 1995.

91. ISO/IEC 10746-4, ITU-T Recommendation X.904, Information Technology—Open Distributed Processing—Reference Model: Architectural Semantics, 1997.

92. ISO/IEC 7498-4, Basic Reference Model—Part 4: Management Framework, 1989.

93. X.749 ISO/IEC 10164-19, Management Domain and Management Policy Management Functions.

94. ISO/IEC 10646-1, Universal Multiple-Octet Coded Character Set (UCS): Architecture and Basic Multilingual Plane, 1993.

B.2 Internet RFCs

Here, we are listing only important TMN/Network Management RFCs.

1. RFC 1155, Structure and Identification of Management Information for TCP/IP-Based Internets, 1990.

2. RFC 1157, Simple Network Management Protocol, 1990.

3. RFC 1212, Concise MIB Definitions, 1991.

4. RFC 1213, Management Information Base for Network Management of TCP/IP-Based Internets: MIB-II, 1991.

5. RFC 1595, Definitions of Managed Objects for the SONET/SDH Interface Types, 1994.

6. RFC 1695, Definitions of Managed Objects for ATM Management Version 8.0 using SMIv2, 1994.

7. RFC 1901, Introduction to Community-Based SNMPv2, *SNMPv2 experimental,* 1996.

8. RFC 1902, Structure of Management Information for Version 2 of the Simple Network Management Protocol (SNMPv2), 1996.

9. RFC 1903, Textual Conventions for Version 2 of the Simple Network Management Protocol (SNMPv2), 1996.

10. RFC 1904, Conformance Statements for Version 2 of the Simple Network Management Protocol (SNMPv2), 1996.

11. RFC 1905, Protocol Operations for Version 2 of the Simple Network Management Protocol (SNMPv2), 1996.

12. RFC 1906, Transport Mappings for Version 2 of the Simple Network Management Protocol (SNMPv2), 1996.

13. RFC 1907, Management Information Base for Version 2 of the Simple Network Management Protocol (SNMPv2), 1996.

14. RFC 1908, Coexistence between Version 1 and Version 2 of the Internet-Standard Network Management Framework, 1996.

15. RFC 1909, An Administrative Infrastructure for SNMPv2, *SNMPv2u experimental,* 1996.

16. RFC 1910, User-based Security Model for SNMPv2, *SNMPv2u experimental,* 1996.

17. RFC 2089, Mapping SNMPv2 onto SNMPv1 within a Bilingual SNMP Agent, *SNMPv2 informational,* 1997.

18. RFC 2271, An Architecture for Describing SNMP Management Frameworks, 1998.

19. RFC 2272, Message Processing and Dispatching for the Simple Network Management Protocol (SNMP), 1998.

20. RFC 2273, SNMPv3 Applications, 1998.

21. RFC 2274, User-Based Security Model (USM) for Version 3 of the Simple Network Management Protocol (SNMPv3), 1998.

22. RFC 2275, View-Based Access Control Model (VACM) for the Simple Network Management Protocol (SNMP), 1998.

B.3 ETSI Standards

1. EN 301 251 (GSM 12.11 Version 4.2.0 Draft), Fault Management of the Base Station System (BSS), 1998.

2. ETS 300 612-1 (GSM 12.00), Part 1: Objectives and Structure of Network Management, 1996.

3. ETS 300 612-2 (GSM 12.01), Part 2: Common Aspects of GSM/DCS 1800 Network Management, 1996.

4. ETS 300 612-3 (GSM 12.07), Part 3: Operations and Performance Management. (This is a draft document at the time of writing.)

5. ETS 300 613 (GSM 12.02), Subscriber, Mobile Equipment (ME) and Services Data Administration, 1996.

6. ETS 300 614 (GSM 12.03), Security Management, 1996.

7. ETS 300 615 (GSM 12.04), Performance Data Measurements, 1996.

8. ETS 300 616 (GSM 12.05 Version 4.3.1), Event and Call Data, 1998.

9. ETS 300 617 (GSM 12.06), GSM Network Configuration Management, 1996.

10. ETS 300 622 (GSM 12.20), Base Station System (BSS) Management Information, 1996.

11. ETS 300 623 (GSM 12.21), Network Management (NM) Procedures and Messages A-bis Interface, 1996.

12. ETS 300 624 (GSM 12.22), Interworking of GSM Network Management (NM) Procedures and Messages at the Base Station Control, 1996.

13. ETS 300 627 (GSM 12.08 Version 4.5.1), Subscriber and Equipment Trace, 1998.

14. ETR 128 (GSM 12.30), ETSI Object Identifier Tree, Common Domain, Mobile Domain, Operation and Maintenance (O&M), Managed Object Registration Definition, Edition 2, 1995.

B.4 ANSI Standards

1. T1-TR34 Technical Report: Network Capabilities, Architectures and Interfaces for Personal Communications, 1994.

2. T1.210-1993, Operations, Administration, Maintenance, and Provisioning (OAM&P)—Principles of Functions, Architectures, and Pro-

tocols for Telecommunications Management Network (TMN) Interfaces. 1993.

3. T1.227-1995, Operations, Administration, Maintenance, and Provisioning (OAM&P)—Extension to Generic Network Model for Interfaces between Operations Systems across Jurisdictional Boundaries to Support Fault Management—Trouble Administration, 1995.

4. T.228-1995, Operations, Administration, Maintenance, and Provisioning (OAM&P)—Services for Interfaces Between Operations Systems across Jurisdictional Boundaries to Support Fault Management—Trouble Administration, 1995.

5. T1.229a-1995, Operations, Administration, and Provisioning (OAM&P)—Performance Management Area Service for Interfaces, 1995.

6. T1.232-1996, Operations, Administration, and Provisioning (OAM&P)—G Interface Specification for Use with the Telecommunications Management (TMN), 1996.

7. T1.233-1993, Operations, Administration, and Provisioning (OAM&P)—Security Framework for Telecommunications Management Network (TMN) Interfaces, 1993.

8. T1.240-1996, Operations, Administration, and Provisioning (OAM&P)—Generic Network Information Model for Interfaces between Operations Systems and Network Elements, 1996.

9. T1.244-1995, Operations, Administration, and Provisioning (OAM&P)—Interface Standards for Personal Communication Services, 1995.

10. T1.245-1997, Directory Services for Telecommunications Management Network (TMN) and Synchronous Optical Network (SONET), 1997.

11. T1.247-1995, Operations, Administration, and Provisioning (OAM&P)—Performance Management Functional Area Service and Information Model, 1995.

12. T1.252-1996, Operations, Administration, and Provisioning (OAM&P)—Security for the Telecommunications Management Network (TMN) Directory, 1996.

13. T1.257-1997, Operations, Administration, and Provisioning (OAM&P)—Traffic Management Services and Information Model for Interfaces between Operations Systems and Network Elements, 1997.

14. T1.651-1996, Mobility Management Application Protocol (MMAP), 1996.

15. T1.651a-1996, Mobility Management Application Protocol (MMAP)—Extensions, 1996.

APPENDIX C

Suggested Exercises

Chapter 1

1.1 Why is TMN needed?

1.2 Define what TMN is.

1.3 Explain the key differences between data communication network management and telecommunications network management.

1.4 Give the details of different standard bodies in the TMN arena. Include in this list the important consortiums that affect TMN.

1.5 Describe different TMN management layers.

1.6 Furnish details of the five systems management functional areas (SMFAs).

1.7 Explain the concepts of a manager and agent.

1.8 Research software tools available for implementing the SMFAs and make comparisons of the functionality provided.

Chapter 2

2.1 Explain the salient points of TMN functional architecture.

2.2 What is a TMN function block?

2.3 Define different TMN function blocks.

2.4 How are TMN functional components related to TMN function blocks? Provide the functional components in the OSF function block.

2.5 Provide the functional components in a WSF function block.

2.6 What is a reference point, and what is the relationship between reference points and interfaces?

2.7 Define TMN physical architecture and the different components of physical architecture.

2.8 List and describe different TMN interfaces.

2.9 Explain X interface, using examples.

2.10 Explain TMN information architecture.

2.11 Describe shared management knowledge, using an example.

2.12 What is OAM&P? Explain different OAM&P categories.

2.13 What is CNM?

2.14 Describe CNM functional and physical architectures.

2.15 What are CNMc and CNMe interfaces? Where are these interfaces used?

2.16 Map the SMFA and CNM capabilities.

Chapter 3

3.1 What is a TMN MS? How is it related to TMN management functions?

3.2 What is a TMN management function set group? Map SMFAs and different TMN management function set groups.

3.3 Define provisioning function set group.

3.4 Design a traffic management application. Use M.3400 and Q.823. Provide use cases in the design.

3.5 Design an alarm surveillance application. Use M.3400 and Q.821 for designing the application. Use any object-oriented design technique of your choice.

Chapter 4

4.1 What are service providers and service users?

4.2 State the differences between connection-oriented and connectionless communications.

4.3 What is a primitive?

4.4 What is a management information model?

4.5 What is a registration hierarchy?

4.6 Define containment hierarchy. What are the differences between registration and containment hierarchies?

4.7 What is meant by management information tree?

4.8 Explain the concept of scoping.

4.9 What is filtering? Where are scoping and filtering used?

4.10 Describe the concepts of polymorphism and allomorphism.

4.11 What is the idea behind synchronization? Can we do without this function?

4.12 Explain different generic state attributes.

4.13 Describe different status attributes.

4.14 What is an intelligent agent? Where is it used?

Chapter 5

5.1 Why is abstract syntax required?

5.2 Explain different structure types.

5.3 Why are tagged types used? Explain each of the tagged types.

5.4 Why are subtypes required? Describe different subtypes.

5.5 Why is BER required?

5.6 Explain the ILC fields.

5.7 Describe definite and indefinite length forms, using examples.

5.8 Discuss the issues involved in the design of an encoder/decoder.

5.9 What enhancements are made in X.680 over X.208?

5.10 Discuss the areas where the use of ASN.1 and BER may not be required. Discuss the areas where they are absolutely required.

5.11 List the requirements for an ASN.1 compiler.

5.12 From the list of requirements in the previous exercise, provide a high-level design for an ASN.1 compiler. State the assumptions you have made.

Chapter 6

6.1 Why do we need managed object class definitions?

6.2 What are the important issues involved in the definition of a managed object class?

6.3 Where are attribute groups used?

6.4 Why should the naming of a managed object class be unique?

6.5 What are the similarities between definitions of managed object classes used in ITU-T recommendations and managed object classes defined in object-oriented languages? What are the differences?

6.6 Write GDMO and ASN.1 definitions for a performance management—related object class. Use a scanner managed object class (defined in X.739) to a derive the managed object class. State the assumptions clearly.

6.7 For the performance management—related object class used in the previous exercise, provide the name binding. Here also furnish all the related GDMO and ASN.1 definitions.

6.8 Discuss the strategy to instantiate the performance management—related object class defined in exercises 6.6 and 6.7 such that efficient use of the performance management—related objects can be made.

6.9 Provide the list of requirements for a GDMO compiler. State the assumptions clearly.

6.10 From the list of requirements in the previous exercise, provide a high-level design for a GDMO compiler.

6.11 Make a comparative study of GDMO and ASN.1 compilers available from two important vendors. State the strengths and deficiencies of these compilers.

Chapter 7

7.1 Why are ACSE services required?

7.2 Explain different ACSE services.

7.3 List and explain each of the CMISE services.

7.4 State the error processing cases involved in each of the CMISE services.

7.5 State the advantages and disadvantages of using CMIP.

7.6 Explain why CMIP implementations have been slow to come by in the market.

7.7 Provide a high-level design for a manager and an agent using ACSE, ROSE, and CMISE services.

Chapter 8

8.1 State the important principles in Internet network management.

8.2 Explain the rationale for using UDP for SNMPv1.

8.3 Describe the SNMPv1 protocol messages, including their shortcomings.

8.4 Why are proxies required?

8.5 What is MIB-II? Explain the main object group classifications of MIB-II.

8.6 What are the differences between SNMPv1 and SNMPv2?

8.7 Describe SNMPv2 protocol messages.

8.8 State the extensions made to SMI in SNMPv2.

8.9 What are the differences between SNMPv2 and SNMPv3?

8.10 Which RFCs constitute SNMPv3? State the key features of SNMPv3.

8.11 Describe the salient points of SNMPv3 architecture, using RFC 2271.

8.12 Explain managers and agents as defined in SNMPv3 architecture.

8.13 Describe the primitives provided by dispatcher, message-processing subsystem, and security subsystem.

8.14 Explain the security features of SNMPv3, using RFC 2274 and RFC 2275.

8.15 Briefly describe the Internet standardization process.

8.16 Compare SNMP with CMIP protocols. State where each protocol is useful.

8.17 What are the advantages and limitations of SNMP protocols?

8.18 Download the SNMP implementation code from the WWW and study the code. List strengths and shortcomings in the code. Use the SNMP version of your choice.

8.19 Run the code downloaded in the previous exercise. Write the manager and agent code to run the downloaded SNMP code.

Chapter 9

9.1 What are the important issues involved in network management for mobile communications?

9.2 List some of the important requirements for PCS network management. Consult ANSI T1.244-1995 for answering this question.

9.3 List the protocols used in the protocol stack for PCS network management. Consult ANSI T1.244-1995.

9.4 Describe the ETSI-based OAM for PLMN.

9.5 Describe the PLMN information model and define MOCs.

9.6 List the cases where FTAM can be used in network management for mobile communications.

9.7 Describe different FTAM scenarios.

9.8 Explain the different protocol layers used in PLMN.

Chapter 10

10.1 Explain the different layers in the B-ISDN reference model.

10.2 What are the important requirements of SDH network management?

10.3 Explain the concepts of SMN and SMS.

10.4 List SDH-specific parameters for which alarm conditions are raised.

10.5 State SDH-specific management functions.

10.6 Describe the primary groups in Internet-based SONET/SDH MIB.

10.7 Explain SDH OAM. (Note that this explanation is to be based on I.610.)

10.8 List and explain different ATM Forum network management interfaces.

10.9 Describe ATM Forum CNM.

10.10 What is ILMI? Describe the primary object groups in ILMI.

10.11 Describe the primary managed object groups in Internet-based ATM MIB.

10.12 Explain the key issues involved in broadband network management.

Chapter 11

11.1 Explain the differences between distributed and centralized network management.

11.2 Why is distributed network management needed?

11.3 Explain different distributed network management architectures. Make a comparison highlighting the strengths and weaknesses of different architectures.

11.4 List and explain the requirements of distributed network management systems.

11.5 What are the different viewpoints in ODP?

11.6 List the different distribution transparencies.

11.7 List the ODP functions.

11.8 What is ODMA? Explain how different viewpoints defined in RM-ODP are handled in ODMA.

11.9 How can CORBA be used in TMN?

11.10 Compare different CORBA implementations, and pick one of the vendors for your needs.

11.11 Describe important CORBA services required for a TMN application.

11.12 List the TMN applications that can be used by Web browsers.

11.13 What is WBEM? Explain how it can be used in TMN.

11.14 How can you use Java in TMN?

11.15 What are the limitations of IDL to Java mapping?

Chapter 12

12.1 Explain the principles behind TMN management frameworks.

12.2 Compare two widely used management frameworks. Describe their strengths and weaknesses.

12.3 Provide the requirements for an object-oriented TMN management framework.

12.4 Provide a high-level design for the object-oriented based TMN management framework. Develop a high-level design from the list of requirements in the previous example.

12.5 Research different object-oriented database implementations available and compare the implementations.

12.6 What are the challenges facing TMN?

12.7 Highlight the important trends in TMN.

12.8 Explain the impact on TMN of integrating the cable, telecommunications, and computing industries.

LIST OF ACRONYMS

AA	Application Association
AAL	ATM Adaptation Layer
AARE	A-ASSOCIATE-RESPONSE, ACSE PDU
AARQ	A-ASSOCIATE-REQUEST, ACSE PDU
ABRT	A-ABORT, ACSE PDU
AC	Application Context
ACSE	Association Control Service Element
ADC	Administration Center
AE	Application Entity
AIN	Advanced Intelligent Network
ANSI	American National Standards Institute
AP	Application Process
APDU	Application Protocol Data Unit
API	Application Programming Interface
APS	Automatic Protection Switching
ASE	Application Service Element
ASN.1	Abstract Syntax Notation One
ATM	Asynchronous Transfer Mode
AUC	Authentication Center
AUDT	A-UNIT-DATA APDU
AVM	Admin View Model
AWT	Abstract Window Toolkit
BER	Basic Encoding Rules
BER	Bit Error Rate
BICI	Broadband Inter Carrier Interface
B-ISDN	Broadband Integrated Services Digital Network
BISSI	Broadband Inter Switching System Interface
BML	Business Management Layer
bps	Bits per Second
BSC	Base Station Controller

BSS	Base Station System
BTS	Base Transceiver Station
CDMA	Code Division Multiple Access
CER	Canonical Encoding Rules
CF	Control Function
CGI	Common Gateway Interface
CIM	Common Information Model
CLTS	Connectionless-mode Transport Service
CMIP	Common Management Information Protocol
CMIPM	Common Management Information Protocol Machine
CMIS	Common Management Information Service
CMISE	Common Management Information Service Element
CNM	Customer Network Management
CNMc	Customer Network Management using CMIP
CNMe	Customer Network Management using EDI/MHS
CONM	Committee on Network Operations and Management
CONS	Connection-mode Network Service
COM	Component Object Model
CORBA	Common Object Request Broker Architecture
CPDU	CMIP Protocol Data Units
CRC	Cyclic Redundancy Check
CSPDN	Circuit Switched Public Data Network
CV	Coding Violation
DAF	Directory Access Function
DCC	Data Communications Channel
DCF	Data Communication Function
DCN	Data Communication Network
DCOM	Distributed Component Object Model
DCS	Digital Cellular System
DER	Distinguished Encoding Rules
DIB	Directory Information Base
DII	Dynamic Invocation Interface
DISMAN	Distributed Management (Internet Network Management)

DMI	Desktop Management Interface
DMTF	Desktop Management Task Force
DN	Distinguished Name
DS3	Digital Signal 3
DSF	Directory System Function
DSL	Digital Subscriber Line
DSOM	Distributed System Object Model
ECC	Embedded Control Channel
EDI	Electronic Data Interchange
EFD	Event Forwarding Discriminator
EIA	Electronic Industry Association
EIR	Equipment Identity Register
EM	Element Management
EML	Element Management Layer
EOC	Embedded Operations Channel
ES	Errored Second
ETS	European Telecommunication Standard
ETSI	European Telecommunications Standards Institute
FSM	Finite State Machine
FTAM	File Transfer Access and Management
FTIF	File Transfer Initiator Function
FTRF	File Transfer Responder Function
GDMO	Guidelines for the Definition of Managed Objects
GIOP	General Inter-ORB Protocol
GNE	Gateway Network Element
GRM	General Relationship Model
GSM	Global System for Mobile Communications
GTP	Group Termination Point
GUI	Graphical User Interface
HEC	Header Error Control
HLR	Home Location Register
HMMP	HyperMedia Management Protocol
HMMS	HyperMedia Management Schema

HMOM	HyperMedia Object Manager
HTML	HyperText Markup Language
HTTP	HyperText Transfer Protocol
IAB	Internet Activities Board
ICF	Information Conversion Function
IDL	Interface Definition Language
IEC	International Electrotechnical Commission
IEEE	Institute of Electrical and Electronics Engineers
IESG	Internet Engineering Steering Group
IETF	Internet Engineering Task Force
IFIP	International Federation for Information Processing
IIOP	Internet Inter-ORB Protocol
ILC	Identifier, Length, and Contents
ILCE	Identifier, Length, Contents, and End-of-Contents
ILMI	Integrated Local Management Interface
IM	Integrated Management
IME	Interface Management Entity
IN	Intelligent Network
IP	Internet Protocol
IPX	Internet Package Exchange
ISDN	Integrated Services Digital Network
ISO	International Organization for Standardization
ITU-T	International Telecommunications Union-Telecommunications.
JIDM	Joint InterDomain Management
JMAPI	Java Management API.
kbps	Kilo bits per second (10^3 bps)
LAN	Local Area Network
LAPD	Link Access Protocol on D Channel
LATA	Local Access and Transport Area
LCN	Local Communications Network
LLA	Logical Layered Architecture
LOF	Loss of Frame
LOS	Loss of Signal

MAF	Management Application Function
MAPDU	Management Application Protocol Data Unit
MCF	Message Communication Function
MD	Mediation Device
ME	Mobile Equipment
MF	Mediation Function
MF-MAF	Mediation Function-Management Application Function
MHS	Message Handling System
MIB	Management Information Base
MIME	Multipurpose Internet Mail Extensions
MIT	Management Information Tree
MMAP	Mobility Management Application Protocol
MML	Man Machine Language
MO	Managed Object
MOC	Managed Object Class
MOF	Managed Object Format
MS	Mobile Station
MS	Management Services
MSC	Mobile Services Switching Center
NE	Network Element
NEF	Network Element Function
NEF-MAF	Network Element Function-Management Application Function
NM	Network Management
NMF	Network Management Forum
NML	Network Management Layer
NMS	Network Management Station
NNE	Non-SDH Network Element
NOC	Network Operations Center
NOMS	Network Operations and Management Symposium
NPC	Network Parameter Control
NSAP	Network Service Access Point
OAM	Operation, Administration, and Maintenance
OAM	Operation and Maintenance (ITU-T)

OAM&P	Operation, Administration, Maintenance, and Provisioning
ODMA	Open Distributed Management Architecture
ODP	Open Distributed Processing
OID	Object Identifier
OMC	Operations and Maintenance Center
OMG	Object Management Group
OMT	Object Modeling Technique
OOB	Out of Band
ORB	Object Request Broker
OS	Operations Systems
OSF	Operations Systems Function
OSF-MAF	Operations Systems Function-Management Application Function
OSI	Open Systems Interconnection
OSS	Operation Support System
PBX	Private Branch Exchange
PCI	Protocol Control Information
PCS	Personal Communication System
PDN	Public Data Network
PDU	Protocol Data Unit
PDV	Presentation Data Value
PER	Packed Encoding Rules
PICS	Protocol Implementation Conformance Statement
PLCP	Physical Layer Convergence Protocol
PLMN	Public Land Mobile Network
PM	Performance Monitoring
POTS	Plain Old Telephone Service
PMC	Personal Mobility Controller
PMD	Personal Mobility Datastore
PPDU	Presentation Protocol Data Unit
PRM	Protocol Reference Model
PSAP	Presentation Service Access Point
PSC	PCS Switching Center
PSTN	Public Switched Telephone Network

PVC	Permanent Virtual Circuit
QA	Q Adaptor
QAF	Q Adaptor Function
QAF-MAF	Q Adaptor Function-Management Application Function
QOS	Quality of Service
RAS	Reliability, Availability, and Survivability
RASC	Radio Access System Controller
RDN	Relative Distinguished Name
RFC	Request For Comments
RLRE	A-RELEASE-RESPONSE, ACSE PDU
RLRQ	A-RELEASE-REQUEST, ACSE PDU
RM-ODP	Reference Model—Open Distributed Processing
RMI	Remote Method Invocation
RMON	Remote Network Monitoring
ROER	Remote Operation Error, ROSE APDU
ROIV	Remote Operation Invoke, ROSE APDU
RORJ	Remote Operation Reject, ROSE APDU
RORS	Remote Operation Result, ROSE APDU
ROS	Remote Operations
ROSE	Remote Operation Service Element
RPC	Radio Port Controller
SAP	Service Access Point
SDH	Synchronous Digital Hierarchy
SDU	Service Data Unit
SEFS	Severely Errored Framing Second
SES	Severely Errored Second
SF	Security Function
SIF	SONET Interoperability Forum
SM	Systems Management
SMFA	Systems Management Functional Area
SMI	Structure of Management Information
SMK	Shared Management Knowledge
SML	Service Management Layer

SNMP	Simple Network Management Protocol
SNMPv1	Simple Network Management Protocol Version 1
SNMPv2	Simple Network Management Protocol Version 2
SNMPv3	Simple Network Management Protocol Version 3
SMAE	Systems Management Application Entity
SMASE	Systems Management Application Service Entity
SMI	Structure of Management Information
SMN	SDH Management Network
SMS	SDH Management Sub-Network
SOM	System Object Model
SONET	Synchronous Optical Network
SPDU	Session Protocol Data Unit
SSAP	Session Service Access Point
SS No. 7	Signaling System No. 7
SVC	Switched Virtual Circuit
TC	Transmission Convergence
TCP	Transmission Control Protocol
TDMA	Time Division Multiple Access
TIA	Telecommunications Industry Association
TINA	Telecommunications Information Network Architecture
TL1	Transaction Language 1
TMC	Terminal Mobility Controller
TMD	Terminal Mobility Datastore
TMN	Telecommunications Management Network
TP	Termination Point
TPDU	Transport Protocol Data Unit
TR	Technical Report
UAS	Unavailable Second
UCS	Universal Multiple-octet Coded Character Set
UDP	User Datagram Protocol
UNI	User Network Interface
UPC	User Parameter Control
URL	Uniform Resource Locator

USM	User-based Security Model
UTC	Coordinated Universal Time
VACM	View-based Access Control Model
VCC	Virtual Channel Connection
VCI	Virtual Channel Identifier
VCL	Virtual Channel Link
VLR	Visitor Location Register
VPC	Virtual Path Connection
VPI	Virtual Path Identifier
VPL	Virtual Path Link
WAN	Wide Area Network
WBEM	Web-Based Enterprise Management
WSF	WorkStation Function
WSSF	WorkStation Support Function
WWW	World Wide Web

LIST OF TRADEMARKS

AppleTalk	Apple Computer, Inc.
IBM	International Business Machines Corp.
IPX/SPX	Novell, Inc.
Java	Sun Microsystems, Inc.
Netware	Novell, Inc.
Windows 95/98	Microsoft Corporation
Windows NT	Microsoft Corporation

INDEX

A

A-ABORT, 187—188
  CMISE use of, 194
A-ASSOCIATE services, 181—186
  normal mode parameters, 184
  X.410-1984 mode parameters, 183
Abstract service interfaces in
  SNMPv3, 250—252
Abstract syntax, 110
  encoding and decoding, 133
Abstract Syntax Notation One (see
  ASN.1)
Access Control, 194
Access control models:
  in SNMPv3 subsystem, 248
  view-based, 255
Accounting management, 12, 64—66
  in CNM, 42, 44
Acronyms, list of, 401—409
ACSE services, 180—189
  A-ASSOCIATE, 182—186
  application protocol data units,
    182
  connectionless, 188—189
  connection-oriented, 181—182
  modes, 181
Action operations, 204
Action template, 149, 154—155
Administration, 37
  of DCS, 279
Administrative domain, 87
Administrative state, 101
Advanced intelligent network (AIN),
  6
Agents, 15—19
  code generators for, 364—366
  functions of, 212
  intelligent, 105—106
  intermediary, 86
  managing type, 106
  proxy, 229—230
  service type, 106
  in SNMPv3, 246

Agents (Cont.):
  (See also Manager-agent associa-
    tions)
Alarms, 58
Alarm status attribute, 101
Alarm surveillance, 43, 57—58,
  167—168
  for PCS, 276
  versus performance monitoring,
    55
  in SDH, 296
Allomorph attribute, for managed
  object class, 147
Allomorphism, 99
American National Standards Insti-
  tute (ANSI), 8
ANSI standards, 390—391
  for wireless communication, 272,
    274—276
ANY, 125—126, 129
ANY DEFINED BY, 129
A-P-ABORT, 188
Application association (AA), 177
Application context (AC), 178
Application context name, 178
Application context negotiation
  functional unit, 181—182
Application entities (AEs), 176—177
  aborting associations, 187—188
  associations between, 181—186
  ending associations, 186
Application layer, concepts of,
  176—178
Application process (AP), 176
Application protocol data units
  (APDUs), 178
  in ACSE, 182
Application service elements (ASEs),
  177
Architecture, TMN:
  functional, 26—31
  information, 35—36
  physical, 31—33
A-RELEASE, 186
ASE invocations, 178

ASN.1, 110—125
  and CORBA, interoperability of,
    341—342
  current (see X.680)
  disadvantages of, 142
  example managed object class def-
    initions, 168—171
  module definitions, 122—123
  rules of, 111—112
  simple types, 112—114
  structured types, 115—117
  subtypes, 123—125
  tagged types, 117—122
Association, 83
  (See also Manager-agent associa-
    tions)
Association control service element
  (ACSE), 177
ATM (asynchronous transfer mode),
  4
  ATM Forum network manage-
    ment, 307—318
  B-ISDN use of, 290
  configuration management,
    310—312
  fault management, 312
  integrated local management
    interface, 313—315
  managed object class ensembles of,
    306—307
  MIBs, 315—318
  performance management, 312
  security management, 312—313
ATM Forum, 10
  network management, 307—318
  Web access to, 381
AtNotation, 132
Atomicity, 179
Attribute groups:
  state, 103
  template for, 149, 153—154
Attributes:
  allowed value and permitted sets,
    153
  of managed object classes, 150

Attributes (*Cont.*):
  of managed objects, 13
  operations on, 157—158, 203—204
  pass-through services on, 205
  property lists of, 157
  role, 104
  systems management operations
    on, 203—204
Attribute template, 149, 151—153
A-UNIT-DATA service, 189
Authentication:
  in HTTP, 345
  of SNMP messages, 215, 225—226
  (*See also* Security management)
Authentication functional unit, 181
AUTOMATIC TAGS, 127
Automation, 6, 371
Availability status attribute, 102

B

Base object, and scoping, 94
Basic encoding rules (BER), 110,
  132—142
  disadvantage of, 142
Behavior:
  of managed object classes, 15
  of managed objects, 13
BEHAVIOR, 152—153
Behavior template, 149, 155
Bellcore, 10
  SONET interface development, 292
  wireless communications stan-
    dards, 272
Billing management, 12, 51—52
B-ISDN, protocol reference model of,
  290—292
Bit error rate (BER) testing, 72
BIT STRING value, encoding of,
  138—139
BMPString, 128
BOOLEAN values:
  CER and DER for, 141
  encoding of, 137
Bottlenecks, 19, 72
Bottom-up approach to modeling,
  70
Broadband communications, 290
Broadband-integrated services digital
  network (B-ISDN) architec-
  ture, 290—292
Broadband networks:
  B-ISDN protocol reference model,
    290—292
  management issues, 319
  SDH network management,
    292—298

Broadband networks (*Cont.*):
  SONET network management,
    298—306
B trees, 105
Business management layer (BML),
  20

C

C++, mapping IDL to, 334
Cancel Get functional unit, 201
Canonical encoding rules (CER), 133,
  141
Cardinal variables, in ASN.1, 113
Cascaded environments, 18
Centralized network management,
  328—329
  with SNMP, 260
CHARACTERIZED BY, 157, 160
Character String types, 114
ChoiceValue, 126—127
Code division multiple access
  (CDMA), 272
Code generators, 364—366
Collections and finance, 65—66
Command generators, 249
Command responders, 249—250
Common Information Model
  (CIM), for WBEM, 349—350
Common management functions,
  for DCS, 282—283
Common management information
  protocol machine (CMIPM),
  CMIS primitive conversion in,
  202
Common management information
  protocols (CMIP), 17, 179,
  202—203
  and CORBA, message flows of,
    339
  for managed object classes, 167
  for mobile network management,
    274
  and SNMP, coexistence of,
    262—263
Common management information
  service (CMIS), 50
  SMASE use of, 179
Common management information
  service element (CMISE), 177,
  193—200
  A-ABORT, use of, 194
  for bulk data transfer, 282
  functional units of, 200—201
  services and parameters, 195
Common object request broker
  architecture (*see* CORBA)

Communication:
  connection and connectionless
    modes of, 83—84
  fixed and mobile, 272
  infrastructure for, 361—363
  requirements for, 73—74
  wired and wireless, 272
Communication stacks, 18—19
Community, 214—215
Community name, 215
Compilers for managed object class
  definitions, 160
Component Object Model/Distrib-
  uted Component Object
  Model (COM/DCOM), 325
Component values, canonical encoding of, 141
CONDITIONAL PACKAGES, 157,
  158, 160
Configuration management, 11—12,
  60—63
  of ATM networks, 310—312
  of CNM, 42
  for PCS, 276
  for SDH, 297
Confirmation, 84—85
conflictDetector, 88
Conformance, 44
  in SNMPv2, 236—237
Connection, 83
  in HTTP, 345
  persistent, 344—345
Connectionless mode, 83—84
  ACSE for, 188—189
Connection mode, 83—84
  service primitives of, 84
Consistency, 179
Constructed forms, encoding with,
  139—140
Containment, 92
  and naming, 92—93
  and recovery, 67—68
Containment hierarchy, 89, 92
  of GSM object classes, 280—281
contextEngineID, 245—246
Control functions (CFs), 178
Control status attribute, 102
CORBA, 260—261, 324, 325, 331—344
  applications of, 334
  architecture of, 331—332
  GDMO/ASN.1, interoperability
    with, 341—342
  implementation notes on,
    343—344
  importance of, 375
  joint interdomain management,
    340—342
  and OSI and SNMP, coexistence of,
    340—342

CORBA (*Cont.*):
  services of, 332—333
  and TMN, integration of, 335—340
Corrective maintenance, 38
Create operations, 98, 204
Customer administration, 51
Customer interface, 6
Customer network management
    (CNM), 24, 38—44
  ANSI-based, 42—44
  functional architecture of, 39—40
  management services of, 41—42
  physical architecture of, 40—41
  supporting services, 42

D

Databases:
  of DCS, 277
  for MIB storage, 366
  for storage, 367, 369
Data communication network
    (DCN), 31
Data contents field, 136—142
  octets of, 138
Data elements, constructed, 134
Data types, 110
Data values, 110
Dates, data type and tags for,
    121—122
DCS (digital cellular system):
  common management functions
    of, 282—283
  databases of, 277
  and GSM architecture, 276—277
  GSM standards for, 276—285
  information model for, 280—282
  interfaces of, 277
  operation, administration, and
    maintenance of, 279—280
  PLMN, management of, 278—279
  protocol layers and standards,
    283—285
Debugging, 368
De facto industry standards, 7—8
Delete operations, 204
  limiting of, 159
Deregulation, in telecommunica-
    tions industry, 5
DERIVED FROM, 159
Desktop Management Interface
    (DMI), 351
Desktop Management Task Force
    (DMTF), 10, 351
Detection, 67
Development cycle for network
    management solutions, 70

Digital Cellular System 1800 (DCS
    1800), 272
Dispatcher in SNMPv3, 247
DisplayString, 223
Distinguished encoding rules (DER),
    133, 141—142
Distinguished name (DN), 93
Distributed network management,
    19, 75, 105—106, 328—329, 375
  and broadband network manage-
    ment, 319
  with CORBA, 260
  for SDH management, 293
Distributed processing, 324—325
  distribution transparency, 327
  ODP function groups, 328
  requirements of, 326
  standardization of, 326—327
Distributed trees, 105
domainCoordinator, 88
Durability, 179

E

Editors, for managed object class def-
    initions, 160
Elastic processes, 106
Electronic data exchange (EDI),
    CNMe use of, 41
Electronic Industry Association
    (EIA), 9
Element manager, 21
Encoders and decoders, use of, 142
Encoding, 133
  ILC and ILCE, 133—136
  packed, 142
  primitive versus constructed, 134,
    141
  (*See also* Basic encoding rules)
Enterprise control, 66
Enterprise management, Web-based,
    347—353
Entities, 81
  peers, 83
Entity relationship (E-R) diagrams, 71
Equality test, 96
Error codes, in X.680, 129—130
Errors:
  A-ABORT services for, 187—188
  handling, in SNMPv1, 224,
    226—228
  in remote operations, 190, 192—193
European Telecommunications Stan-
    dard (ETS), 278
  (*See also* Global System for Mobile
    Communications (GSM) stan-
    dards)

European Telecommunications Stan-
    dards Institute (ETSI), 8—9, 272
  standards of, 390
Event forwarding discriminators
    (EFDs), 156
Event information, 103
Event reply, 103
EVENT-REPORT attributes, 161
Event reporting, 17, 86
  in SNMPv3, 259
Events, 58
  notification of, 155—156
Event type, 103
Extended service functional unit,
    201
EXTERNAL, encoding of, 141

F

Fabric, 293
Fault correction, 59
Fault localization, 58—59
  for PCS, 276
Fault management, 12, 57—60
  for ATM networks, 312
  in CNM, 42—44
  in SDH, 295—296
FieldName, 129
File transfer access and management
    (*see* FTAM)
Filter functional unit, 201
Filtering, 95—97
  of managed object classes, 152
Finite state machines (FSMs), 44
F interface, 35
Formal languages, for managed
    object class descriptions, 15
Formal standards, 8
Fragments, 166
FTAM, 35, 177
  for bulk data transfer, in DCS,
    282—284
  for managed object classes, 167
  for message exchanges, 50
  for SONET, 299
Functional architecture, 26—31
  of CNM, 39—40
  functional components, 27—31
  function blocks, 26—27
  reference points, 31
Functional components, 27—31
Functional groups, control and
    transport, 292
Functional layers, 19—21
Functional units, 179—180, 200—201
  for connection-oriented ACSE ser-
    vice, 181—182

Functional units (*Cont.*):
negotiated release, 182
Function blocks, 26—29
of CNM, 39—40
Function sets, 48

G

Gateway network element (GNE), 31
GDMO, 14, 146, 148—160
and CORBA, interoperability of, 341—342
example definitions, 168—170
limitations and constraints of, 160
GDMO/ASN.1 compilers, 364, 365
GDMO/ASN.1 editors, 363
GDMO browsers, 363
General Relationship Model, 104—105
Generic Information Model, 15
Generic state attributes, 99—101
GetBulkRequest, 232
GetRequest, 227
G interface, 35
Globalization of telecommunications industry, 5
Global System for Mobile Communications (GSM) standards, 9, 272
architecture of, 276—277
managed object class definition, 280—282
01 through 12 series standards, 70, 278
Graphical User Interface (GUI) generators, 366, 368
Guidelines for the definition of managed objects (*see* GDMO)
GUIs:
for debugging, 368
of management applications, 368
uniformity of, 373

H

Heartbeats, 86
HMMP (HyperMedia Management Protocol), 348—351
HMOM (HyperMedia Object Manager), 348, 349
HMTP (HyperMedia Transport Protocol), 350
HTTP (Hypertext Transfer Protocol), 344—345

I

IAB Official Protocol Standards, 264
Identifier:
in ASN.1, 111—112
for managed object classes, 147
Identifier, length, and contents (ILC), 133
Identifier field, 133—135
Indefinite form, encoding with, 139
INDEX clause, 221—222
Indication, 84—85
Information architecture, 35—36
Information models, 15, 70—71
differences in, 371
Information module, 233
InformRequest, 232
Inheritance, 89, 146
multiple, 91
Inheritance hierarchy, 89, 91, 160
of GSM object classes, 280—281
Initialization, of managed objects, 102
Initial value managed object (IVMO) values, 157
Instance identification, for Internet objects, 220—222
InstanceOfType, 131
Instantiation, 15
INTEGER value, encoding of, 137
Integrated local management interface (ILMI), 313—315
Integrated management conferences, 379
Intelligent agents, 105—106
Interface definition language (IDL):
for CORBA object classes, 334
GDMO/ASN.1, mapping to, 336
Java mappings to and from, 353—354
Interfaces, 33—35
of CNM, 40—41
International Electrotechnical Commission (IEC), 8
International Organization for Standardization (*see* ISO)
International Telecommunications Union (ITU), 8
International Telecommunications Union-Telephony (*see* ITU-T recommendations)
International Telephone and Telegraph Consultative Committee (CCITT), 8
Internet:
management of, 11, 210
standards for, 9, 265—266
Internet Activities Board (IAB), 9, 264

Internet Assigned Numbers Authority, 219, 220
Internet Engineering Steering Group (IESG), 265
Internet Engineering Task Force (IETF), 9, 265
Internet objects, 215—218
aggregate, 261
ASN.1 data types, 215
defining and standardizing, 223, 261
instance identification, 220—222
partitioning of, 262
registration of, 219—220
syntax of, 216—217
types of, 217
Internet registration hierarchy, 219—220
Interoperability:
and conformance, 44
and information model differences, 371
and language independence, 372
and protocol differences, 371—372
and protocol independence, 372—373
Invocations, for remote operations, 191—192
Invoke-ID, 196
ISO, 7—8
documents of, 380, 384—385
ISO 9735, Electronic Data Interchange for Administration, Commerce, and Transport (EDIFACT), 41
ISO 10164-19, Management Domain and Management Policy Management Functions, 87—88
Isolation, 179
ITU-T recommendations, 6, 8
and CNM, 38
G series documents, 383
I series documents, 383
M series documents, 384
on open distributed processing, 325
Q series documents, 384
for SDH, 292—293
and TCP/IP, interoperability with, 263—264
Web access to, 380
X series and ISO documents, 384—385
ITU-T Recommendation M.3400, 54
ITU-T Recommendation Q822, 74
ITU-T Recommendation X.720, Management Information Model, 146—147

ITU-T Recommendation X.800, 66
ITU-T Recommendation Z300, 16

J

Java, 324
  Abstract Window Toolkit, 353
  platform independence of, 372
  and TMN, 353—354
  for updating network manage-
    ment applications, 347
JavaManagement API (JMAPI),
  354—355
Joint Inter-Domain Management
  (JIDM), 340—342
JTC1, 8

K

Kernel functional units, 181, 200

L

Language independence, 372
Legacy systems, 5
  and distributed network manage-
    ment, 329
  integration of, 6, 369—370
Length field, 135—136
Lexicographic ordering, 221
Logistics management, 52—53

M

MACRO notation, 126
M-ACTION, 199
Mailboxes, 41
Maintenance, 37—38
  of DCS, 280
Maintenance management, 52
Managed nodes, 212
Managed objects (MOs), 12—14
  attribute values, changing, 199
  creation of, 199—200
  deletion of, 200
  filtering, 95—97
  naming, 92—94
  notification from, 17
  pass-through services, 205
  relationships among, 89—93, 104
  retrieving values from, 196—197

Managed objects (MOs) (*Cont.*):
  scoping, 94—95
  state of, 99
  systems management operations
    on, 203—204
Managed object boundary, 13—14
Managed object class (MOC), 14—15,
  73—74
  ATM ensembles of, 306—307
  definition of, 146—160
  fragments, 166
  GDMO for, 148—160
  generic, 161
  for management domains, 88
  in M.3100, 164—167
  for PLMNs, 281—282
  polymorphism of, 98—99
  relationships among, 89—93
  of SDH, 297—298
  specializing, 167
Managed Object Class parameter, 196
Managed object class templates, 148,
  159—160
Managed object instance, 13
Managed relationship classes, 104
Managed relationships, 104
Managed systems, 18
Management:
  by delegation, 106
  out-of-band and point-to-point,
    214
Management applications, 367—368
Management domains, 19, 86—89,
  260
  action types, 88
  management operations for, 88
  unresolved issues of, 89
Management frameworks, 361—369
  communications infrastructure,
    361—363
  compilers, 364
  GUI and presentation generators,
    366
  implementation notes, 368—369
  management applications,
    367—368
  manager and agent code genera-
    tors, 364—366
  MIB manipulation tools, 363
  object-oriented, 361
  persistent storage, 366—367
  process management, 367
Management information:
  CMISE for, 193—200
  exchange of, 16—19, 35—36, 71,
    361—363
  structure of, 146—147, 161—166
Management information base (*see*
  MIB)

Management information model, 14,
  15, 71—72
Management information tree
  (MIT), 105
Management knowledge, 36
Management layers, 19—21
Management mobility application
  protocol (MMAP), 274
managementPolicy, 88
Management protocols, 17
Management state, reporting
  changes in, 103
Management state attributes, 99—103
Manager-agent associations, 85—86,
  364—365
  ACSE services for, 180—189
  initiation of, 189
Managers, 15—19
  code generators for, 364—366
  in SNMPv3, 246
  test tools for, 366
Managing systems, 18
  and resources, information
    exchange between, 71
Man Machine Language (MML), 16
MATCHES FOR, 152
Matching rules, in filtering, 95—97
M-CANCEL-GET, 196, 198
M-CREATE, 199—200
M-DELETE, 200
Mediation device (MD), 32
Message handling service (MHS), 41
Message processing subsystem in
  SNMPv3, 247—248
M-Event-Report, 103, 104, 196
M-GET, 196—197
MIB, 105, 210
  for ATM networks, 309—310,
    315—318
  extensions to, 260—262
  for integrated local management
    interface, 313—315
  manipulation tools for, 363
  for mobile communications, 273
  persistent storage of, 366—367
  in SNMPv2, 240—242
  in SNMPv3, 255—260
  SONET/SDH, 299—303
MIB-I, 218
MIB-II, 218—223
  extension of, 231
  RFCs related to, 218—219
MIB view, 255
M interface, 35
Mobile networks:
  billing and routing for, 273
  DCS, 276—285
  management of, 273—274
  operational stress of, 273

Mobile networks (*Cont.*):
  PCS, 275—276
  provisioning of, 273—274
  QOS parameters for, 273
  topology changes in, 273
MODE CONFIRMED, 155
Modeling, 70
Module definitions, for ASN.1,
  122—123
Module name, in ASN.1, 111
M-SET, 199
M3 and M4 interfaces, 308—312
M.3000-series documents, 48
M.3100, Generic Network Informa-
  tion Model, 146, 164—167
Multiple object selection functional
  unit, 200—201
Multiple reply functional unit, 201
Multithreading, 367, 368

N

Name binding, 93
Name binding attribute, 147
Name binding template, 149,
  158—159
NamedType, 126
Naming, 92—94
  in CORBA, 333
  global versus local, 94
Naming hierarchy, 89
  in SNMPv2, 234
Naming tree, 93, 94
Narrowband communications, 290
NetMan site, 380
Network element (NE), 33, 211
  and OSs, data transfers between,
    49—50, 75
  of SDH, 293—295
Network element layer (NEL), 21
Network element management layer
  (NEML), 21
Network layer, in SNMPv1, 214
Network management, 11, 210
  of ATM, 306—318
  centralized versus distributed,
    260
  integrated, for computers, telecom-
    munications, and television,
    374—375
  of mobile communications,
    273—274
  standardization of applications,
    262
  Web sites on, 380
  (*See also* Distributed network man-
    agement)

Network management applications,
  69
  enhancements to, 69—70
Network Management Forum
  (NMF), 9
  Web access to, 381
Network management layer (NML),
  20—21
Network management solutions,
  69—70
  (*See also* TMN solutions)
Network management stations
  (NMSs), 211
  centralized management func-
    tions of, 212
Network operations and manage-
  ment symposium (NOMS)
  conferences, 379
Network operations center (NOC),
  214
Network performance administra-
  tions, 52
Network planning and engineering,
  60—61
Network provisioning management,
  51
Network-to-network management
  (NNM) interface, 41
Non-null set intersection test, 97
Normal mode, 181
  A-ASSOCIATE parameters for, 184
Notification originator, 250
Notification receiver, 250
Notifications, 13
  pass-through services for, 205
Notification template, 149, 155—156
NULL value:
  encoding of, 139
  use of, 93—94

O

OAM (operation, administration,
  and maintenance), 24
  components of, 279—280
  information flows of, 304—305
  for SONET, 303—306
OAM&P (operations, administration, maintenance and provisioning), 37—38
  by TMN-MSs, 48
Object classes, defining, 71
ObjectClassFieldType, 128—129
ObjectDescriptor, encoding of, 141
Object identifiers, 120—121
  for BER, CER, and DER, 140—142
  formation of, 90

Object identifiers (*Cont.*):
  for Internet objects, 219—221
Object instances, 72—73
  allomorphism of, 99
  hierarchical arrangement of, 105
Object Management Group (OMG),
  9—10
Object modeling, 70
Object Modeling Technique (OMT),
  330
Object-oriented paradigms:
  advantages of, 361
  and TMN solutions, 376
Objects:
  aggregate, 230
  (*See also* Internet objects; Managed
    objects)
OCTET STRING value, 139
Open distributed management
  architecture (ODMA), 324,
  329—330
Open distributed processing,
  325—328
Open systems, information exchange
  between, 202
Open Systems Interconnection (*see*
  OSI)
Operation, 13, 37
  of DCS, 279
Operational state, 100
OperationErrorSet, 130
Operations systems (OSs), 25, 31
  and NEs, 49—50, 75
  requirements for, 75
Orbix, 334, 343
OrbixWeb, 347
OSI:
  and CORBA and SNMP, coexis-
    tence of, 340—342
  normal mode ACSE services use
    of, 181
  service primitives of, 82
  service providers of, 81—82
  service users, 81—82
  seven-layer architecture of, 80
  systems management functions,
    11—12, 42—44
OSI 10165-4, 149

P

Package attribute, 147
Packages, conditional and manda-
  tory, 160
Package template, 148, 157—158
Packed Encoding Rules (PER), 142
PARAMETER, 153

Parameterization, in X.680, 132
Parameter template, 149, 156
Pass-through services, 204—205
Password verification, 181
PCS (personal communications system):
    ANSI standards for, 274—276
    functional elements of, 275
    network management principles, 275—276
Peer entities, 83
Performance:
    analysis of, 56—57
    bottlenecks in, 19, 72
    and process management, 367
Performance management, 12, 54—57
    for ATM networks, 312
    attribute types for, 161
    of CNM, 42, 43
    development of, 74—75
    managed object classes of, 168
    of SDH, 296—297
Performance management control, 56
Performance monitoring (PM), 43, 55—56
    for DCS, 279
    for PCS, 276
Performance quality assurance, 55
Persistent storage, 366—367
Personal communications services (PCS), 272
PhyAddress, 223
Physical architecture, 31—33
    of CNM, 40—41
    of TMN, 29—31, 275, 305
Plain old telephone service (POTS), 4
Platform independence, 372—373
Polling, 85—86
    in SNMPv1, 225
Polymorphism, 98—99, 261
PossibleTypes, 131—132
PowerBroker, 334
Presentation services, uniformity of, 373
Present test, 97
Preventive maintenance, 38, 67
Pricing, 64—65
Primitives:
    for ROSE, 189, 190
    service, 84—85
    for SNMPv3, 251—252
Principal, in SNMPv3, 246
Procedural status attribute, 102
Process management, 367
Productions, in ASN.1, 113
Programming languages, independence from, 372
Protocol conversion, 340—342
    with proxy agents, 229—230

Protocol data units (PDUs), 85, 178
Protocols, differences in, 371—372
Protocol specification, 81—82
Prototype standards, 265
Provisioning, 38, 62—63
    in mobile networks, 273—274
    (See also OAM&P)
Proxy agents, 229—230
    for migration to SNMPv2, 242
Proxy forwarder, 250
Public land mobile network (PLMN), 278
    information model of, 280—282
    network management of, 278—279
    services and business areas of, 278—279
P-UNIT-DATA, 189

Q

Q Adaptor (QA), 33
Q821, Alarm Surveillance, 167—168
Q822, Performance Management, 167, 168
Q823, 54, 165
Q interface, 33—34
Quality of service administration, 52, 54
    for mobile networks, 273

R

RAS quality assurance, 57
RealType, 127
REAL values, encoding of, 138
Reference model, 82
Reference points, 26, 31
REGISTERED AS, 151, 155, 158, 160
Registration hierarchy, 89, 90
    Internet, 219—220
Relative distinguished name (RDN), 93, 158
Relays, 31
Reliable transfer service element (RTSE), 177
Remote management, 6
Remote network monitoring (RMON), 260
Remote operations, 189
    invocations for, 191—192
Remote operations service element (ROSE), 177, 189—193
Remote procedure calls (RPCs), 189—190

Requests, confirmed and unconfirmed, 84
Responses, 84—85
Resources, 6
    logical, 166
    management of, 13
    physical, 166
    provisioning of, 7, 38 (see also Provisioning)
RFCINDEX, 264
RFCs (requests for comments), 211
    implementation of, 264
    for Internet, 388—389
    standards and nonstandard, 264—265
    Web access to, 381
RFC 1006, 263—264
RFC 1155, Structure and Identification of Management Information for TCP/IP-based Internets, 218
RFC 1212, Concise MIB Definitions, 218
RFC 1213, MIB-II for Network Management of TCP/IP-based Internets: MIB-II, 218
RFC 1902, 231, 232, 238, 239
RFC 1903, 232, 233
RFC 1904, 232, 236
RFC 1905, 235, 237
RFC 1906, 239
RFC 1907, 240
RFC 1908, 231, 240
RFC 2271, 243, 244, 246
RFC 2272, 246, 247
RFC 2273, 249, 259
RFC 2274, 252, 255
RFC 2275, 243, 255
RM-ODP (reference model for open distributed processing), 325
Roaming, support of, 273
RO-ERROR, 192
RO-INVOKE, 191—192
Role attribute, 104
RO-REJECT, 192—193
RO-RESULT, 192
Routing and digit analysis administration, 52

S

Scalar objects, 220
Scheduling, of data collection, 75
Scoping, 94—95
SDH (synchronous digital hierarchy), 4
    B-ISDN use of, 290, 292

SDH (synchronous digital hierarchy)
(*Cont.*):
configuration management, 297
fault management, 295—296
managed object classes of,
297—298
network management, 292—298
performance management,
296—297
protocol stack, 298
Security:
of DCS, 279
of SNMPv2, 231
of SNMPv3, 248
Security management, 12, 52,
66—69
for ATM networks, 312—313
CNM, 42, 44
SEQUENCE and SEQUENCE OF
values, encoding of, 140
Service access point (SAP), 81
Service data unit (SDU), 178
Service definition, 82
Service establishment, 42
Service information, 42
Service management, 106
Service management layer (SML),
20
Service planning and negotiation,
62
Service primitives, 84—85
Service providers, competition
among, 5, 374
Service provisioning, 7, 38
(*See also* OAM&P; Provisioning)
Service reconfiguration, 42
SET and SET OF values, encoding of,
139—141
Shared management knowledge
(SMK), 36
Simple gateway monitoring protocol
(SGMP), 210
Simple network management proto-
col (*see* SNMP)
SimpleWeb, 380
SNMP, 210—213
advantages of, 260
agents, 246
application entities, 211
and CMIP, coexistence of, 263
context, 245
and CORBA and OSI, coexistence
of, 340—342
over different protocols, 230
engines, 244, 246—248
entities, 244
manager, 246
messages, 215
MIB, 214

SNMP (*Cont.*):
for mobile network management,
274
notes on, 260—262
snmpMIBConformance group, 242
snmpSetGroup, 241—242
snmpTrap group, 241
snmpTraps group, 241
SNMPv1, 14, 19, 213—215, 223—229
PDUs of, 223—229
and SNMPv2, coexistence with,
231—232, 242—243
SNMPv2, 14, 19, 231—243
conformance statements of,
236—237
MIB, 240—242
naming hierarchy, 234
new terms of, 233—234
PDUs of, 232, 237—239
protocol messages, 237—239
RFCs related to, 231
and SNMPv1, coexistence with,
231—232, 242—243
structure of management information, 232—236
textual conventions, 235—236
transport mapping, 239—240
SNMPv3, 243—260
abstract service interfaces and
primitives of, 250—252
access control model, 255
applications of, 249—250
architecture of, 244—246
engine, 246—248
MIB, 255—259
RFCs related to, 243—244
security in, 248, 254—255
textual conventions, 252—254
Software management, 7
SOM/DSOM (System Object
Model/Distributed System
Object Model), 325
SONET (Synchronous Optical Network), 4, 298—306
architecture of, 298—303
B-ISDN use of, 290, 292
SONET Interoperability Forum
(SIF), 299
SONET/SDH MIB, 299—303
Specific information model, 15
Standardization, importance of, 375
Standards, TMN, 8, 383—391
implementation of, 80
implementation time of, 373
symposiums and conferences on,
379
types of, 7—8
Web access to, 379—381
Standards bodies, 7—10

Standby status attribute, 102—103
State, 99
State attribute group, 103
Status and control, 63
Status attributes, 99—103
Structured types, 119
Structure of management informa-
tion (SMI), 14, 210, 213
of SNMPv2, 232—236
Subdomains, 88
Subnetworks, 21
Subset of test, 97
Substring test, 97
Subtypes, of ASN.1, 123—125
Superdomains, 88
Superset of test, 97
Synchronization, 97—98
Synchronous digital hierarchy (*see*
SDH)
Synchronous optical network (*see*
SONET)
systemID, 93
Systems managed objects, 93—94
(*See also* Managed objects)
Systems management, 11
Systems management application
entities (SMAEs), 178—180
Systems management application
service element (SMASE),
177—179
Systems management functional
areas (SMFAs), 11—12
versus OAM, 37, 279
and TMN management function
set groups, 53
Systems management operations,
203—204
systemTitle, 93—94

T

Table constraints, 130
Tables, MIB-II, 222—223
Tags, 117—121
in BER, 134—135
canonical order of, 141
for date and time, 121—122
in X.680, 127
Tariff, charging, and accounting
administration, 51—52, 64—65
TCP/IP, and ITU-T/OSI, interoperability, 263—264
Telecommunications industry:
categorization of, 21—22
deregulation of, 5
Telecommunications Industry Association (TIA), 9

Telecommunications Information
Technology Networking
Architecture Consortium
(TINA-C), 10, 329
Telecommunications management
network (see TMN)
Telecommunications network:
components of, 6—7
and TMN, 24—25
Telecommunications service
providers, 22
Telecommunications switches, 5
Telecommunications Technical
Committee, 9
Telecommunications Technology
Council, 9
Telecommunications vendors, 22
TeleManagement Forum, 380
Templates, for managed object class
definition, 148—150
Testing, 43—44, 59—60, 97
bit error rate, 72
for conformance, 44
during development, 70
of managers, 366
of PCS, 276
TIA/EIA/IS-136, 272
Time, data type and tags for, 121—122
Time division multiple access
(TDMA), 272
Timeliness check, in SNMPv3, 255
TMN, 4
automation in, 371
challenges to, 369—375
and CORBA, integration of,
338—339
CORBA-based, 335—338
evolution of, 4—5
functions of, 6—7
future trends in, 375—376
integration of different technologies, 370—371
and Java, 353—354
regulatory changes and, 370
and telecommunications networks, 24—25
Web-based, 344—347
and Web-based Enterprise Management, 351—353
and Web technology, integration
of, 376
TMN architecture, 25—36
functional, 26—31
information, 35—36
interfaces of, 33—35
physical, 31—33
TMN information model, 166—168

TMN management function sets,
54—59
and SMFAs, 53
TMN-MSs (TMN management services), 48—53
TMN SM (TMN systems management) services, 49—50
TMN solutions:
development cycle for, 70
language dependence of, 372
platform dependence of, 372—373
proprietary nature of, 374
standards for, pace of, 373
from vendors, 360
on Windows-based platforms, 376
Top-down approach to modeling, 70
top managed object class, 91, 159—160
Traffic management, 52, 54, 56
Traffic measurement and analysis,
43, 52
Transaction Language 1 (TL1), 16
Transaction processing (TP), 179
Transactions, properties, 179
Transfer syntax, 110
Transport layer, in SNMPv1, 213
Transport mapping, in SNMPv2,
239—240
Traps, 211—212
in SNMPv1, 224—226, 228—229
in SNMPv2, 241
Trouble administration, 44, 60
Trouble tickets, 12, 52, 368
Types, 110, 111
of ASN.1, 111—122
in X.680, 126—132

U

UDP, connectionless, 212, 214
Unified Modeling Language (UML),
361
UniversalString, 127—128
Usage measurement, 64
Usage state, 101
User-based security model (USM),
254—255
User needs, 70

V

Value assignment, in ASN.1, 112
Values, 110, 111
in X.680, 126—132

Variables, 210
(*See also* Objects)
View-based access control model
(VACM), 255
Virtual channel connection (VCC),
303
Virtual path connection (VPC),
303
VisiBroker, 334

W

Web-Based Enterprise Management
(WBEM), 347—353
Web-based TMN, 344—347
Web browsers, 344
information requests of, 346
TMN applications, viewing and
changing with, 346—347
Web technology, 324
and TMN, integration of, 376
Windows-based platforms:
agents on, 18—19
managers on, 18—19
TMN solutions on, 376
WITH INFORMATION SYNTAX,
155
WITH REPLY SYNTAX, 155
WITH SYNTAX, 129
Workforce management, 51
Workstation (WS), 32—33
World Wide Web, TMN information
on, 379—381

X

X interface, 34—35
X.208 (*see* ASN.1)
X 217, 180
X.410-1984 mode, 181
A-ASSOCIATE parameters for,
183
X.680, 111
versus X.208, 125—132
X 710, 202—203
X 711, 203
X 720, 146, 156
X.721, 147, 161—163
X.722, 147
X.723, 147, 161
X.724, 147
X.734, 161

About the Author

Divakara K. Udupa has been working in the network management area for about 10 years. He has worked for IBM and ISR Global Telecom; currently, he is working in the TMN Solutions group in Siemens Telecom Networks. He has a wide range of experience as a designer and developer with networking protocols, network management protocols, and TMN.

Mr. Udupa is the author of the successful book *Network Management Systems Essentials*, published by McGraw-Hill. He owns one patent and has published many articles.

Mr. Udupa has an MS in computer science from Rensselaer Polytechnic Institute and ME in mechanical engineering from Calcutta University, and a BS in mechanical engineering from Banaras Hindu University. He is a member of the Association of Computing Machinery (ACM) and a senior member of the American Institute of Industrial Engineers (AIIE).